Wace

Le Roman de Brut:
The French Book of Brutus

Medieval and Renaissance
Texts and Studies

Volume 279

WACE

Le Roman de Brut: The French Book of Brutus

Translated by

Arthur Wayne Glowka

Arizona Center for Medieval and Renaissance Studies
Tempe, Arizona
2005

Library of Congress Cataloging-in-Publication Data

Wace, ca. 1100-ca 1175.
[Roman de Brut. English]
Le Roman de Brut : the French book of Brutus / Wace ; translated by Arthur Wayne Glowka.
p. cm. — (Medieval and Renaissance texts and studies ; v. 279)
Includes bibliographical references and index.
ISBN-13: 978-0-86698-322-8 (alk. paper)
1. Arthurian romances. 2. Romances — Translations into English.
I. Glowka, Arthur Wayne. II. Title. III. Series.

PQ1545.W2A613 2005
841'.1 — dc22

2005021089

∞
This book is made to last.
It is set in Adobe's Caslon Pro,
smyth-sewn and printed on acid-free paper
to library specifications.

Printed in the United States of America

Table of Contents

A Note About the Cover

Special thanks go to my brother, Texas Hill Country landscape painter Greg Glowka, for his splendid cover art depicting Stonehenge II, a central Texas landmark, and to Todd Halvorsen of ACMRS for his eye-catching cover layout and design.

Acknowledgments

I could not have completed this translation without the help of a number of colleagues and friends. Roger Noël supported the project in many ways and gave me invaluable help with matters of Old French lexicography and syntax. I especially thank him for pointing me to Algirdas Julien Greimas' *Dictionnaire de l'ancien français*, which made this work much easier. Keith Busby helped me locate a page missing from my copy of Wace. Mary Jones of the Ina Dillard Russell Library of Georgia College & State University secured many articles and books for me through the efficiency of her interlibrary loan office. Elizabeth Bryan, Steven K. Brehe, James Wilhelm, and Mario di Cesare read part of an early draft and generously encouraged my involvement with the project; Brehe later read the whole manuscript and made some valuable suggestions for revisions. Norris Lacy also gave me helpful suggestions concerning diction. Dean Kenneth Jones and the Faculty Research Committee of Georgia College & State University gave me a grant to collect the materials I needed to work on the project. Dean Jones, Dean Bernie Patterson, Associate Vice President Andrea Hardin, and R. B. Jenkins, all of Georgia College & State University, dipped into their budgets to support my trip to the Third International Conference on Laȝamon's *Brut* at the University of New Brunswick-St. John, where James Noble allowed me to read a selection to receptive conference participants. Ultimately, however, the source of much of this funding was the Georgia College & State University Foundation. I owe a lot to the work of graduate assistants: Steve Johnson dug through years of MLA bibliographies before the electronic version was available to us; Anders Butler, Jr., proofread a draft of the manuscript and pointed out sections that were hard to read; and Brenda K. Lester did some fast library work for me while I hastened to finish the manuscript. Two anonymous readers for MRTS also provided me with a number of useful suggestions for improvement, and Robert Bjork entertained my impatient e-mails with prompt, helpful replies. In addition, the manuscript was much improved by the thorough copyediting of Leslie MacCoull of MRTS. Roy Rukkila gave quick responses to questions and concerns with the business of getting the manuscript through publication, and colleagues Deborah Vess and David R. Evans urged me to complete revisions when I most seemed most pessimistic. Printing subventions were provided from the institutional budgets of

David R. Evans, Dean Beth Rushing, and Dean Kenneth Jones. To all of these people, I obviously owe a debt of thanks that I cannot possibly ever repay.

I also owe a debt of sorts to my daughter Lena. For most of the first four years of her life, her daddy sat at the kitchen table with a tablet, a collection of pencils, and an Old French dictionary. Instead of watching *Barney* or playing with her on the floor, he sat hunched over his work, lifting up every now and then to read aloud. Without fail, she told him to be quiet. She offered him many distractions and became a source of guilt, but she imitated him and learned to write her name and other words at an early age. Her daddy hopes that her precocious literacy will compensate her for his devotion to medieval literature.

Introduction

Wace's *Roman de Brut* is a wonderful introduction to the medieval world, a world of kings and feudal loyalty, of castles and siege machines, of battles and invasions, of moral and immoral love, of famines and storms, and of sin and salvation. Wace turned the details of his Latin sources into Norman French verse for royals and nobles who were men and women of their times. Since these men and women were not scholars or historians, Wace told his tale in terms that they would understand. Consequently, when we read Wace, we get an understanding of what he and his audience valued and held important. Under the guise of chronicle history, he succeeds in writing a living legend that describes a heroic past in the romantic terms of his age.

The author of the *Roman de Brut* is generally known as *Wace*. However, his name also appears variously in works ascribed to him as *Guace*, *Gace*, and even *Grace* and *Baqua*. Hans-Erich Keller notes that the name may be related to forms of *Walter* and *Walt*. Further, as Keller says, *Wace* is a first name, and the practice of naming the poet as *Robert Wace* is a long-standing error.[1] Wace's biography is based on the meager details provided in his works, especially the *Roman de Rou*, his history of the Norman kings. He says that he was born on the island of Jersey (3.5305), but does not specify the date. Charles Foulon guessed that Wace was born "probably about 1100,"[2] but since Wace probably lived until at least 1174[3] and says that he saw three Henrys (3.178; 3.11431–11432), it is certainly fair to say that he was born in the early decades of the twelfth century. At an early age, he was taken to Caen, where he began his education (3.5306–7). He says too that he spent some time in France, meaning Paris and its environs (3.5308). When he returned to Caen, he set himself to writing in his native language; in his estimation, he wrote a fair amount (3.5310–12). At some time or other, he went to the Forest of Brocéliande to see the magical places and fairies, but he was disappointed and

[1] "Le mirage Robert Wace," in *Zeitschrift für Romanische Philologie* 106 (1990): 465–66.

[2] Charles Foulon, "Wace," *Arthurian Literature in the Middle Ages*, ed. Roger Sherman Loomis (Oxford: Clarendon Press, 1959), 94–103, esp. 95

[3] S. P. Tatlock, *The Legendary History of Britain: Geoffrey of Monmouth's* Historiae Regum Britanniae *and Its Early Vernacular Versions* (Berkeley: University of California Press, 1950), 463–64, here 464.

confessed to being a fool in the endeavor (3.6393–98). Noting the better situations of Horace and Virgil, Wace complains (perhaps a bit too much) about money and lack of support from his benefactor Henry II (1.1–23; 3.11419–30), but thanks God and Henry for a prebend at Bayeux, which he apparently enjoyed from 1160 to 1170, and for other gifts (3.171–76; 3.5313–18). Dates in his life are generally open to speculation, but Wace notes in his *Roman de Brut* that he completed this work in 1155 (line 14865) and notes in his *Roman de Rou* that he began this latter work in 1160 (1.1). At the end of the *Roman de Rou*, Wace announces that his work will be continued by "Maistre Beneeit," otherwise known as Benoît de Sainte Maure. With some resignation, Wace says that he should be quiet because the king's favor has gone elsewhere. Wace acknowledges that the king once gave him many things and promised him even more. Had the promises come true, things would have been better, Wace says (3.11419–30).[4]

Wace often calls himself "Maistre," a title indicating that he was a teacher. He also calls himself a *clerc lisant*, a title open to various interpretations. According to Jean-Guy Gouttebroze, a certain unanimity can be drawn out of the arguments about its meaning. The title refers to a minor ecclesiastical function and appears to be at the lower end of the hierarchy priest, monk, canon, *clerc lisant*. Given the meanings of the verb *lire* (generally "to read"), it can be argued that a *clerc lisant* was someone who studied and documented texts and declaimed them in a loud voice before the public.[5]

---

[4] For some lively speculation on Wace's intellectual life in Paris and on his involvement with the Norman aristocracy as a self-conscious modern author, see H.-E. Keller, "The Intellectual Journey of Wace," *Fifteenth-Century Studies* 17 (1980): 185–207. Other summaries of Wace's life may be found in Tatlock, *The Legendary History,* 463–64; William W. Kibler, "Wace," in *The New Arthurian Encyclopedia*, ed. Norris J. Lacy (New York: Garland, 1996), 501; James J. Wilhelm, "Wace: *Roman de Brut* (Merlin Episodes and 'The Birth and Rise of Arthur')," in *The Romance of Arthur II*, ed. idem (New York: Garland, 1986), 5–17, esp. 5–6; Ivor Arnold, *Le Roman de Brut de Wace*, 2 vols. (Paris: Société des Anciens Textes Français, 1938–1940), 1: lxxiv–lxxix; Elizabeth Francis, ed., *La vie de Sainte Marguerite* (Paris: Champion, 1932), iv; Mary Sinclair Crawford, ed., *Life of St. Nicholas* (Philadelphia: University of Pennsylvania Press, 1923), 18–21; Foulon, "Wace," 95; Jean Blacker, *Faces of Time: Portrayal of the Past in Old French and Latin Historical Narrative of the Anglo-Norman* Regnum (Austin: University of Texas Press, 1994), 41–42; H.-E. Keller, "Wace," in *Medieval France: An Encyclopedia*, ed. William W. Kibler et al. (New York: Garland, 1995), 969–70; Elizabeth van Houts, "Wace as Historian," in *Family Trees and the Roots of Politics: The Prosopography of Britain and France from the Tenth to the Twelfth Century*, ed. K. S. B. Keats-Rohan (Woodbridge: Boydell & Brewer, 1997), 103–32, esp. 103–6; and Judith Weiss, *Wace's Roman de Brut* (Exeter: University of Exeter Press, 1999), xi–xiii. See also Françoise Le Saux, "Wace's *Roman de Brut*," in *The Arthur of the English*, ed. W. R. J. Barron (Cardiff: University of Wales Press, 1999), 18–22.

[5] "Henry II Plantagenêt: Patron des historiographes Anglo-Normands de Langue d'Oil," in *La littérature angévine médiévale* (Paris: Champion, 1981), 91–105, here 95–96.

This speculation about the duties of a *clerc lisant* fits well with what we know about the conditions under which Wace worked as a professional writer. Tatlock emphasizes that Wace, unlike many medieval writers, named himself and included comments about himself probably because he was worried about his reputation and his advancement. Wace tells us that he wrote translations, *romans,* "narrative poems in French", and *serventeis*, "duty-poems of unknown character but perhaps short and broadly lyric in nature" (Tatlock, *Legendary History of Britain*, 464). Wace wrote most of his surviving works for "particular prominent people, and doubtless was repaid by them. . . . though [he] deprecat[ed] the smallness of his recompense" (464–65).

Wace's surviving minor poems are religious in nature. There is no way to date them,[6] but they often have the roughness of early works and do not have the scope of his datable major works. These minor works include a fanciful life of Mary the Mother of Jesus (*La conception Nostre Dame*);[7] a traditional rendering of the life of St. Margaret the virgin martyr who endured torture, defeated demons, and suffered beheading rather than give up her faith and her chastity (*La vie de Sainte Marguerite*); and the entertaining life and posthumous miracles of St. Nicholas of Myra (*La vie de Saint Nicholas / Life of St. Nicholas*).[8] Tatlock judges these works to be "uninspired, unoriginal and unreal, Wace being cramped by a pious fidelity to a traditional manner formed by the saints' legends of the fourth century" (*Legendary History of Britain*, 465). Others would beg to differ. Elizabeth A. Francis, editor of *La vie de Sainte Marguerite*, sees Wace's reworking of his source as "a work of an artist, having intellectual rather than sentimental preoccupations" (ix [my translation]). Edward Montgomery takes the same work seriously enough to say that

> . . . the *Vie de Sainte Marguerite* draws upon medieval man's fundamental sensitivity for traditional symbolism and his innate sense of proportion and thereby becomes an enduring narrative monument to the inevitable and unending conflict between Good and Evil, between the reality of Temptation and the promise of Resurrection.[9]

---

[6] For some speculation on order of composition and possible dating, see H.-E. Keller, "Vers une nouvelle édition de la 'Vie de Sainte Marguerite' de Wace," *Critique et édition de textes* 9 (1986): 85–97.

[7] See also S. Panunzio, "Una redazione del *Trespassement Nostre Dame* di Wace e altri testi inediti da un codice in antico francese della Biblioteca Nazionale di Torino," *Studi mediolatini e volgari* 21 (1973): 39–85.

[8] See Ruth J. Dean, "*La Conception Nostre Dame*," "The *Life* of St. Margaret," "The *Life* and *Miracles* of St. Nicholas," in eadem, *Anglo-Norman Literature: A Guide to Texts and Manuscripts* (London: Anglo-Norman Text Society, 1999), 269–70, 315, 297–98.

[9] "Structure and Symbol in Wace's 'Vie de Sainte Marguerite'," *Kentucky Romance Quarterly* 24 (1977): 301–9, here 308.

More recently, Laurie Postlewate has argued that Wace uses his version of the life of St. Margaret to introduce his lay audience to new trends in spiritual devotion: "This spirituality, seen most clearly in the works of Anselm and Bernard of Clairvaux, emphasized the humanity of Christ and the union of God and Man through divine love."[10] Mary Sinclair Crawford, editor of *Life of Saint Nicholas*, claims that "the skillful author adopts a style in keeping with his audience. Interest is . . . sustained by the rapidity of narration, by the vividness of direct, instead of indirect quotation" (39). Wace's "nuns and robbers, merchants, prisoners and money-lenders, clercs and their rich patrons all come in turn to offer a realistic picture of twelfth-century life" (41). In summary, Crawford says that "Wace thus shows in this, probably his first long poem, that he has the art of seizing upon the salient points of the story" (43). Gerald Carr argues that the *exhortatio* of the introduction to the same work "has a basic symmetrical structure" and that Wace employed "direct repetitions and antitheses according to a definite plan of composition; the frequent use of triads can hardly be fortuitous."[11] Whatever their ultimate value, the minor works indicate that Wace was an author conscious of his audience.

The most important audience of Wace's literary career was Henry II, who in 1154 came to the throne of England, Normandy, and large sections of modern France. Wace apparently wrote his history of the Anglo-Norman state, *Le Roman de Rou*, to please Henry. Wace began this versified history in 1160 but stopped working on it in 1174. The work treats the succession of Norman lords from Rollo, who died in 927, to Henry I (1106). During the time he worked on the *Roman de Rou*, Wace enjoyed his prebend at Bayeux, but in 1174 he abandoned his work and turned the project over to Benoît de Sainte Maure, who mentions Wace (Tatlock, *Legendary History of Britain*, 465). Disagreeing with earlier scholars who suggest that Wace was replaced because of his old-fashioned style or because of his allegiance to Henry's estranged wife Eleanor of Aquitaine, Gouttebroze agrees with Ivor Arnold's speculation that Henry lost patience with Wace's inability to finish the work in a timely manner ("Henry II," 98). Others see Henry's motives as serious and political. Matthew Bennett has noted that "As a version of the Conquest it represents the Norman, baronial view, stressing the value of tradition against what were seen as the alarming innovations of Henry II's government."[12] Jean Blacker-Knight has argued that Wace failed to maintain the Norman party line in three ways: by not relating the blessing of Edward on William

---

[10] "Vernacular Hagiography and Lay Piety: Two Old French Adaptations of the Life of Saint Margaret of Antioch," in *Saints: Studies in Hagiography*, ed. S. Sticca, MRTS 141 (Binghamton: MRTS, 1996), 115–30, here 117.

[11] "The Prologue to Wace's *Vie de Saint Nicholas*: A Structural Analysis," *Philological Quarterly* 47 (1968): 1–7, here 7.

[12] "Poetry as History? The 'Roman de Rou' of Wace as a Source for the Norman Conquest," in *Proceedings of the Battle Conference 1982*, ed. R. Allen Brown (Woodbridge: Boydell Press, 1983), 21–39, here 38.

through the agency of Harold; by offering Henry I (grandfather of Henry II) as the usurper of first-born Robert's throne; and by failing to fill in details by often claiming a lack of knowledge of the facts.[13] In a later article, the same scholar adds the problem of Wace's numerous remarks about his personal problems and the state of patronage. She notes that Benoît de Sainte Maure later lost his patronage too for prolixity and failure to concentrate on what Henry wanted.[14] More recently, Gouttebroze has argued that Wace was replaced by Benoît de Sainte Maure because Wace did not overtly support Henry II's desires to meddle in the affairs of the church and failed to sanctify the predecessors of Henry II as Wace's sources often do.[15] However Wace's work may have been regarded by Henry, a modern historian, according to Elizabeth van Houts, might find the *Roman de Rou* valuable for its "combination . . . of oral and written family history[,] . . . perhaps Wace's most important contribution to the historiography of the Norman conquest of England" ("Wace as Historian," 116).

Whatever favor Wace gained or lost in the last decades of his life followed the success of his *Roman de Brut*, which he finished in 1155. This success may be measured in several ways. One, the book had a royal audience. Wace's first English translator, the early thirteenth-century priest Lawman,[16] notes in the introduction to his much-expanded version of Wace that the *Roman de Brut* was presented to the Queen herself:

---

[13] "Wace's Craft and His Audience: Historical Truth, Bias, and Patronage in the *Roman de Rou*," *Kentucky Romance Quarterly* 31 (1984): 355–62. Blacker later notes that Wace in the *Roman de Rou* was determined "to appear nonevaluative and to remain as distant as possible from his material" and that his "chief aim was to write a relatively judgment-free, non-propagandistic history of the Normans from a military perspective, excluding both social and administrative topics and motivations and individuality": *Faces of Time*, 119.

[14] Jean Blacker, "'La geste est grande, longue et grieve a translater': History for Henry II," *Romance Quarterly* 37 (1990): 387–96.

[15] "Pourquoi congédier un historiographe: Henri II Plantagenêt et Wace," *Romania* 112 (1991): 289–311. In a 1996 dissertation ("Authorial Interventions in Wace's *Roman de Rou*"), Ilkyung Chung Lim argues that Wace's narrative interventions in the *Roman de Rou* "do not always mesh with his patron's need for a history of his ancestors" (*Dissertation Abstracts International* 57.7 [Jan. 1997]: 3012–A). In the same year, Dolores Buttry, "Contempt or Empathy? Master Wace's Depiction of a Peasant Revolt," *Romance Notes* 37 (1996): 31–38, reads sympathy for the peasants into Wace's treatment of the peasant revolt in the *Roman de Rou* (3.815ff.). See also Laurence Mathey, "De l'*Historia Regum Britanniae* de Geoffrey de Monmouth au *Roman de Brut* de Wace: Étude d'un écart à valeur idéologique," in *Et c'est la fin pour quoy sommes ensemble: Hommage à Jean Dufournet*, ed. J.-C. Aubailly et al., 3 vols. (Paris: Champion, 1993), 2: 941–48, on Wace's attitudes toward peasants.

[16] *Lawman* is one of the modernized forms of the names *Laȝamon* and *Laweman*, the name of the author as recorded in the two manuscripts containing his work; the other commonly used modernized form is *Layamon*, a concession to the typewriter and modern printing fonts. At a recent meeting of the International Laȝamon's *Brut* Society, an attendee recorded over a dozen pronunciations of the author's name.

A book he took as third source, and set by this his whole course:
A French cleric composed it,
Wace was what they called him, and very well he wrote it,
And he gave it to her highness, Eleanor of Aquitania;
She was the queen of Henry, the king of such high fame.
(trans. Allen, lines 19–23)

The truth of this claim gives some authority to Lawman's work, but we do not know if Wace presented the work or merely sent it. Given the dates generally ascribed to Lawman (early to mid thirteenth-century), the English author would probably have known about the presentation only at second hand.

A second claim to success, however, is that Wace's poem directly influenced later works in both Middle English and Old French. In his Prologue, Lawman claimed that he used Wace and other sources, but he generally followed Wace closely.[17] Wace's *Roman de Brut* was also the source of the first half of Robert Mannyng's fourteenth-century *Chronicle of England*. As Idelle Sullens points out in the introduction to an MRTS edition of Mannyng, the Middle English writer follows Wace closely until line 13400, adding only occasional details from Geoffrey; thereafter, departures from Wace occur more frequently, but Mannyng "generally rewrites the story without entirely abandoning the outline of events as given by Wace."[18] The fourteenth-century *History of the Kings of Britain* (College of Arms Arundel 22) also follows Wace closely from after the time Corineus wrestles Gogmagog until Cadwalader (*Chadwalader* in this translation) is exiled in Brittany with the Saxons in control of England (Kennedy, *Chronicles*, 2628).[19]

---

[17] Françoise H. M. Le Saux has published the most detailed study of Lawman's use of sources. Le Saux's chapter "From Wace to Laȝamon" in *Laȝamon's Brut: The Poem and Its Sources* (Cambridge: D. S. Brewer, 1989), 24–58, gives a detailed look at the differences between the two authors.

[18] Robert Mannyng of Brunne, *The Chronicle*, ed. Idelle Sullens, MRTS 153 (Binghamton: MRTS, 1996), 57; see also E. D. Kennedy, *Chronicles and Other Historical Writing* (New Haven: Connecticut Academy of Arts and Sciences, 1989), 2625; A. Gransden, *Historical Writing in England c. 550 to 1307* (Ithaca: Cornell University Press, 1979), 477; and T. Summerfield, *The Matter of Kings' Lives* (Amsterdam and Atlanta: Rodopi, 1998), 1–2.

[19] The Arthurian section of this manuscript has recently been edited as a Ph. D. dissertation by Laura Gabiger, who does not believe that the manuscript's departures from its sources are necessarily an "innovation on the part of the translator" ("The Middle English 'History of the Kings of Britain' in College of Arms Manuscript Arundel 22" [Ph. D. Diss., University of North Carolina-Chapel Hill, 1993], xlvi). Wace is also a minor source for Thomas Bek of Castelford's *Chronicle of England*: Kennedy, *Chronicles*, 2624.

While the Middle English writers mined Wace as a source to be closely followed in translation, Old French writers adopted Wace's attitudes toward courtliness and social manners. As William Kibler succinctly claims in *The New Arthurian Encyclopedia*, Wace "had enormous influence on subsequent French authors of Arthurian materials: on Chrétien de Troyes and Marie de France, as well as on the anonymous authors of the Vulgate *Merlin*, the *Mort Artu*, the Didot-*Perceval*, the *Suite du Merlin*, and the *Livre d'Artus*" (501)—a claim that follows the conclusions of the classic study of Wace's influence on the development of romance by Margaret Pelan.[20] To this list of Old French authors and works, Peter Noble adds Renaut de Beaujeu, who drew on Wace for certain details in *Le Bel Inconnu*.[21] In short, Wace prepared the way for the romance writers.[22]

Another piece of evidence for the claim of Wace's success is that his *Roman de Brut* survives in a number of manuscripts in an age when books were copied by hand. The manuscripts range in date from the thirteenth to the fifteenth century and appear in Anglo-Norman, Northern French, Champenois,[23] and Ile de France forms. In 1938, Ivor Arnold, the editor of the text of Wace used for the present translation, reported in the first volume of his edition that he knew of twenty-four manuscripts containing all or parts of the *Roman de Brut*. He used nineteen manuscripts containing more or less whole copies of the text to establish his edition. He had seen seven fragments of the text as they were contained in three manuscripts, but he did not use them to establish his text. He also had information about two other manuscripts containing three fragments that he had not seen (vii–xiv). In an appendix to the second volume in 1940, he lists the variants of an additional whole copy he saw in a Vatican manuscript (*Roman de Brut*, ed. Arnold, 2: 786–90). In 1959, Edith Brayer described the Vatican manuscript seen by Arnold and an additional fragmentary one. In 1964, Elspeth Yeo described another fragment; and in 1977, Muhamed Nezirovic reported the discovery of two pages of a Wace manuscript in the cathedral of St. Anastasia of

---

[20] *L'influence du* Brut *de Wace sur les romanciers français de son temps* (Paris: Droz, 1931), 170.

[21] "Wace and Renaut de Beaujeu," *French Studies* 47 (1933): 1–5.

[22] See Jean Marx, "Wace et la matière de Bretagne," in *Mélanges de langue et de littérature de moyen âge et de la renaissance offerts à Jean Frappier*, 2 vols. (Geneva: Droz, 1970), 2: 771–74. For further discussion of influence, see Foulon, "Wace," 102–3; J. B. H. Box and A. D. Deyermond note that the Portuguese *Livro de Josep Abarimatia* mentions Wace's French translation of the Latin story of the Britains, a mention indicating that Wace had a reputation on the Iberian peninsula in the fourteenth century: "Mestre Baqua and the Grail Story," *Revue de Littérature Comparée* 51 (1997): 366–70.

[23] For a grammatical examination of a Champenois version (partly edited by Arnold and Pelan [Wace, *La partie*]), see B. Woledge, "Un scribe champenois devant un texte normand: Guiot copiste de Wace," in *Mélanges Jean Frappier*, 2: 1139–54.

Zadar in (the former) Yugoslavia.[24] Also, in 1999 Judith Weiss reported on two further fragments.[25]

So what is this popular and influential French work of the twelfth century? In simplest terms, it is a vernacular verse chronicle. A chronicle, in whatever language, is basically a history book that reports events in chronological order, sometimes as entries for a year. The most authoritative kind of chronicle for a medieval person would have been one written in Latin, the language of the church and of the educated. Latin literacy was not universal, but there were many medieval people with little or no facility in Latin who had an interest in historical events. For these people, the vernacular chronicles filled an important educational function as popularized versions of more

---

[24] Counting the number of manuscripts and fragments can be a confusing proposition. In the first volume of his edition of the *Roman de Brut*, Arnold lists a total of nineteen complete manuscripts used to establish his text. Three other manuscripts he had seen (with seven fragments) and the two that he had heard about (with three fragments) bring the total number of manuscripts known to Arnold at the time of the publication of the first volume (1938) to twenty-four (with twenty-nine whole or fragmentary examples of the text). In an appendix to the second volume (1940), Arnold lists the variant readings of a Vatican manuscript containing a whole text, bringing the total number of manuscripts known to Arnold to twenty-five (and examples of the text to thirty). In 1959, Edith Brayer described this Vatican manuscript and an additional fragment, bringing the total of known manuscripts to twenty-six (and examples of the text to thirty-one): "Deux manuscrits du *Roman de Brut* de Wace," in *Studi in onore di Angelo Monteverdi*, ed. Giuseppina Gerardi Marcuzzo, 2 vols. (Modena: Società Tipografica Editrice Modenese, 1959), 1: 100–8. In 1964, Elspeth Yeo adds one more fragment to the count to make twenty-seven manuscripts (and thirty-two examples of the text): "Wace's *Roman de Brut*: A Newly Discovered Fragment," *Manuscripta* 7 (1964): 101–4; and in 1977 M. Nezirovic adds two pages—countable as an additional manuscript, bringing the total number of manuscripts to twenty-eight (with thirty-three examples of the text): "Les fragments de Zadar du *Roman de Brut* de Wace," *Romania* 98 (1977): 379–89. By Jean Blacker's count in 1994, however, there are "twenty complete manuscripts and twelve fragments" (*Faces of Time*, 36) or "twenty complete manuscripts and eight manuscripts containing twelve fragments" (177). Weiss reports that "the text of the *Brut* survives in approximately thirty-two manuscripts and fragments of manuscripts" (*Wace's Roman de Brut*, xxv) but says that "enumeration of Wace's manuscripts varies" (xxvii). Weiss conveniently lists nineteen "Complete or nearly Complete" manuscripts and names twelve "Fragments" (xxviii–xxix). However, fragment X has "four fragments from two separate MSS," the Zadar (Croatia) fragment may be countable as two fragments, and the Westminster Abbey has two fragments "apparently both from the same MS" (xxix). No matter how one counts the whole and fragmentary texts, the initial claim still stands: Wace's work was valuable enough in the Middle Ages to be copied a number of times in a number of places.

[25] Judith Weiss, "Two Fragments from a Newly Discovered Manuscript of Wace's *Brut*," *Medium Ævum* 68 (1999): 268–77.

serious Latin chronicles. Since vernacular chronicles were read aloud, it should come as no surprise that these chronicles were often written in verse. Rhyme and meter intensified the emotion of performance and made what might otherwise seem distant, alive. In a study of French verse histories from the twelfth century (those by Gaimar, Wace, and Benoît de Sainte Maure) and Latin histories of the same century (those by William of Malmesbury, Orderic Vitalis, and Geoffrey of Monmouth), Blacker concludes that "the Old French texts stand in relation to the Latin texts as summaries of great works of literature do to the works themselves" (*Faces of Time*, 134). The reader of the Old French works can get the names of the characters and the outline of events without the complications of the original texts. The Old French texts simply had different purposes. The Latin texts defended legal claims, followed ecclesiastical history, and indicated the need for future research. Jane Zatta nonetheless argues that Wace, like other writers of vernacular versions of Geoffrey, rejected Geoffrey's notion "that participation in the national destiny" required "submission to institutional authority as the means to achieving that end . . . stress[ed] the role of vassals in the success of the nation[,] . . . challeng[ed] the devaluation of the individual . . . and promot[ed] an ideal of personal merit as the quality on which the legitimacy of lordship depend[ed]."[26]

Instead of technical details, as Thea Summerfield explains, verse chronicles "present a linear, genealogical and chronological survey of kings from Brutus onwards, in which some episodes are fleshed out by narrative episodes in varying lengths, relating the actions of a particular king in more detail." Summerfield notes that "verse chronicles do not offer the reader intricate structures or interesting psychological developments" but offer instead "[d]escriptions of the reigns of kings" with a general focus on "the martial activities of the king concerned."[27] The verse chronicles rely on both historiographical and literary conventions. Conventions include time references made to "milestone occurrences of the past," etymologies of place names, serious attention to prophecies and prophets, and the explanation of events "in terms of sinfulness and divine retribution" (6).

Many of these impulses are easy to identify in Wace's *Roman de Brut*. Since Wace was a Norman and not a Briton, he tells the story as an outsider for an audience of Normans curious in a superior way about the land and people that their immediate ancestors had conquered.[28] Since Wace is concerned about factual truth,

---

[26] "Translating the *Historia*: The Ideological Transformation of the *Historia Regum Britanniae* in Twelfth-Century Vernacular Chronicles," *Arthuriana* 8 (1998): 148–61, here 158.

[27] *The Matter of Kings' Lives*, 6.

[28] "Wace wrote for a Norman public which had a strong interest in the history and legends of their adopted country" (Weiss, *Wace's Roman de Brut*, xiii). Weiss also gives an overview of Norman chronicles of England (xiii–xiv) and of earlier British chronicles (xiv–xvi).

he often admits to not knowing details and refuses to relate tales that he considers fabulous and untruthful (Blacker, *Faces of Time*, 34–36). But this reticence and honesty do not prevent him from telling a good story. As Wace popularizes scholarly materials, he does his best to animate the story with his invitations to his audience to witness the events that he relates. His best stories are those of Brutus, Leir, Belin and Brennes, Caesar, Vortigern, Aurelius, Uther, Arthur, St. Augustine of Canterbury, and Brian.

The common understanding is that Wace got the broad outlines of his work from Geoffrey of Monmouth's very popular *Historia Regum Britanniae*, which was completed some time in the 1130s.[29] But scholars have disputed over exactly what text or texts Wace may have actually used. In her comprehensive account of Wace's sources in 1941, Margaret Houck apparently had access only to what is now called the Vulgate version of Geoffrey. Nonetheless, Houck concluded that Wace was a very conscious artist in his reworking of Geoffrey, claiming that Wace "maintained consistently a tone and manner of expression which is markedly different from Geoffrey's" and showed "himself an independent and apparently self-conscious artist, working in his own fashion with the plastic material of character and event from which the *Historia* supplied to him."[30] Allowing for Wace's individuality as a narrative artist, however, Houck notes that Wace replaces Geoffrey's outmoded names and practices with current ones that his audience would recognize (*Sources*, 213–14); adds geographical details that he may have known from hearsay or actual travel; and includes details from Virgil's *Aeneid*, the *Historia Romana* of Landolfus Sagax, the *Vita Beati Nicolai Episcopi* of Johannes Diaconus, the Bible, common knowledge, the oral tradition of England (259–60), and other possible sources (286–87). Following the publication of an edition of the Variant Version of Geoffrey, Robert Caldwell argued in 1954 and 1956 that this version of Geoffrey was Wace's source since it generally accounts for the additions to Geoffrey that Houck ascribed to Landolfus Sagax and other sources.[31] Pierre Gallais, in 1966, painstakingly examines

---

[29] A useful translation of Geoffrey's work is that of Lewis Thorpe (Harmondsworth: Penguin, 1979). The major editions of the Latin versions of Geoffrey's work are listed in the works cited. Weiss gives a useful short summary of Geoffrey's contributions to the development of the legendary history of Britain (*Wace's Roman de Brut*, xvi–xvii). See also W. R. J. Barron, "Geoffrey of Monmouth's *Historia Regum Britanniae*," in *The Arthur of the English*, ed. idem, 11–18.

[30] *Sources of the* Roman de Brut *of Wace* (Berkeley: University of California Press, 1941), 165–66.

[31] R. Caldwell, "Wace's *Brut* and the *Variant Version* of Geoffrey of Monmouth's *Historia Regum Britanniae*," *Bibliographical Bulletin of the International Arthurian Society* 6 (1954): 109; idem, "Wace's *Roman de Brut* and the *Variant Version* of Geoffrey of Monmouth's *Historia Regum Britanniae*," *Speculum* 31 (1956): 675–82.

the Arthurian sections of the Vulgate and Variant versions and Wace's *Brut* and concludes that Wace based his text on the Vulgate and that the Variant is a composite of Wace and the Vulgate. According to Gallais, the Variant Version thus comes after Wace.[32] Hans-Erich Keller takes up the issue again in 1977 and argues that Pierre Gallais is wrong to claim that the Variant Version is at the end of the chain of sources leading from the Vulgate version. Supporting Caldwell, Keller says that Wace used the Variant Version up to the prophecies of Merlin and then used a composite text for the rest. Keller substantiates these views with a study of names.[33] Neil Wright reviews the arguments concerning the question of precedence in regard to the Vulgate and Variant versions and concludes:

> The Variant version was not Geoffrey's source nor was it written by Geoffrey himself; it is a redaction of the vulgate text made by an unknown contemporary of Geoffrey at some time between 1138, the probable publication date of the *Historia*, and the early 1150s—certainly no later than 1155, since the Variant version was used extensively in Wace's *Roman de Brut*, which was completed in that year.[34]

Blacker names Wace's sources as both the Vulgate and First Variant versions without comment.[35] Weiss supports Wright's conclusions (*Wace's Roman de Brut*, xvii), and Françoise Le Saux states simply that "Wace used both" versions but explains that "he appears to have had access only to the Variant for most of his project[;] then, approximately half-way through the composition of his work, he seems to have come across Geoffrey's original version" and "regularly merges the two Latin accounts, not consistently corresponding to either" ("Wace's *Roman de Brut*," 19).

Whatever Wace's source may have been exactly, the *clerc lisant* emerges from the process of textual comparison as a poet in his own right. Indeed, scholars have generally had a high regard for Wace's talent as an imaginative translator, storyteller,

---

[32] P. Gallais, "La *Variant Version* de l'*Historia Regum Britanniae* et le *Brut* de Wace," *Romania* 87 (1966): 1–32.

[33] "Wace et Geoffrey de Monmouth: Problème de la chronologie des sources," *Romania* 98 (1977): 1–14. Geoffrey of Monmouth cites the *Britannici sermonis liber vetustissimus* by the putative archdeacon Walter of Oxford as the source of the *Historia*; Kibler, "Wace," seems to cite this yet undiscovered work as Wace's source. See Barron, "Geoffrey of Monmouth's *Historia Regum Britanniae*," 15 with n. 11 (on p. 271).

[34] Introduction to Geoffrey of Monmouth, *The* Historia Regum Britanniae *of Geoffrey of Monmouth II: The First Variant Version* (Cambridge: D. S. Brewer, 1988), lxx.

[35] "Where Wace Feared to Tread: Latin Commentaries on Merlin's Prophecies in the Reign of Henry II," *Arthuriana* 6 (1996): 36–52.

and historian. In 1931, Pelan pronounces that "it is time to recognize Wace not as a simple translator of the *Historia*, but as an original writer who was the literary model of the romance writers of his time" (*L'influence*, 166 [my translation here and below]). Accepting her pronouncement, Arnold notes Wace's "talent for color and narrative" and his success "in recreating the details of an event and in enhancing them" (*Roman de Brut*, 1:lxxxvii). Arnold thinks that no one "can find a better technician in the art of description among the authors of his age" and compares Wace favorably with Benoît, Chrétien de Troyes, "and others" (lxxx–vii). Arnold concludes that Wace "is a writer of romance rather than a historian" (lxxxvii). However, Arnold sees that Wace is securely attached to the real world of events and is not given to exaggeration and the other faults generally ascribed to medieval writers (lxxxix–xc). Like Arnold, Houck rates Wace highly as a writer and makes much of Wace as a narrative poet of considerable skill. Among other things, she notes "his development of dramatic settings for events" and "his tendency to enter sympathetically into the situation he is presenting" (*Sources*, 167). Even a scholar as gloomy and discriminating as Tatlock could praise Wace for a certain amount of talent. Tatlock sees Wace as "a favorable specimen of the Norman literary man of the mid-twelfth century, though unaffected by some of its fresh intellectual momentum and some of its emotional interests" (*Legendary History of Britain*, 465).[36] Tatlock's evaluation of Wace the man sounds like a confidential letter of recommendation:

> He shows himself well-informed, enquiring, critical, honest and refined, in short an able, energetic and civilized man; but not an intellectual, not learned or notably well-read. (465)

Tatlock's evaluation of the style of the *Roman de Brut*, however, is similarly restrained but nonetheless appreciative. Tatlock grants Wace "literary imagination," a talent for "description and incident," and a tolerable presentation of "gnomic 'sentence'" (416).[37] Tatlock concludes that Wace's poem is "well fitted to be read aloud to people who were intelligent but not highly cultivated, and wished to

---

[36] Keller, however, sees examples of *fin'amour* in the Arthurian sections ("De l'amour dans le *Roman de Brut*," in *Continuations: Essays on Medieval French Literature and Language in Honor of John L. Grigsby*, ed. Norris J. Lacy and Gloria Torrini-Robbin [Birmingham: Summa, 1989], 63–81) and argues that Wace shares Abelard's concerns for the individual ("The Intellectual Journey of Wace," *Fifteenth-Century Studies* 17 [1990]: 185–207).

[37] For a full look at Wace's use of proverbs see L. Brosnahan, "Wace's Use of Proverbs," *Speculum* 39 (1964): 444–73.

feel that they were getting history and not romance" (466).[38] Foulon observes, however, that Wace's expansion of Geoffrey "was due largely to the fact that one author posed as a sober historian, while the other felt free to exercise some of the privileges of a story-teller and poet, replacing the dry, colourless narrative with descriptive scenes" ("Wace," 96).[39] Foulon sees the poem as midway between history and romance (101).[40] However, in an essay that compares Wace to Lawman, C. S. Lewis is careful to point out that Wace "certainly did not regard himself as a writer of what we should call romance."[41] Lewis goes on to claim that Lawman's "*Brut* is more archaic and unsophisticated than the *Geste* [Wace's *Roman de Brut*]" and that "Wace was familiar with real, contemporary courts and camps" (25). Readers familiar with only the Arthurian section of both works may think that Lawman's work is crueler than Wace's, but Lewis argues that the opposite is true if the works are considered as wholes: "In general the *Brut* is a kinder work than the *Geste*. It is both fiercer and more tender. The Norman courtesy can be callous, the Norman lightness can be cynical; the *Brut* is, at bottom, more sensitive" (27).[42]

---

[38] These mid-century scholars seem to be in disagreement about whether Wace's intentions were to produce history or romance, but the same division can be read into the manuscript collections containing the *Roman de Brut*. Jean Blacker has pointed out in a paper read at the annual meeting of the MLA that the British manuscripts of the *Roman de Brut* are bound with historical works but the French manuscripts are bound with romances ("History or Romance? Wace's *Roman de Brut* in Insular and Continental Manuscripts"); this information also appears in Blacker, *Faces of Time*, 177, 232 n. 230.

[39] Foulon also comments on Wace's omission of passages devoted to religious history or displaying savagery, cruelty, or exaggerated sentiment ("Wace," 96). See also M.-C. Blanchet, "Arthur chez Wace et Lawman," *Bibliographical Bulletin of the International Arthurian Society* 6 (1954): 108, and Le Saux, "Wace's *Roman de Brut*," 20–22; also eadem, "Laȝamon's *Brut*," in *The Arthur of the English*, ed. Barron, 22–32, esp. 24–27, 30–31.

[40] Foulon also notes Wace's appeal to the imagination and clever use of repetition and antithesis and names Wace as the first French poet of the sea ("Wace," 101–2). Gwyn Jones's introduction to Eugene Mason, trans., *Wace and Layamon* (London: Dent, 1962) echoes many of the sentiments and observations of the critics discussed above (viii). See also Norris J. Lacy et al., "Early Arthurian Literature," in *Arthurian Handbook*, 2nd ed. (New York: Garland, 1997), 57–135, here 61–62.

[41] "The Genesis of a Medieval Book," in idem, *Studies in Medieval and Renaissance Literature*, ed. W. Hooper (Cambridge: Cambridge University Press, 1966), 18–40, here 20.

[42] Scattered observations on Lawman's additions to Wace can also be found in Derek Brewer, "The Paradox of the Archaic and the Modern in Laȝamon's *Brut*," in *From Anglo-Saxon to Early Middle English: Studies Presented to E. G. Stanley*, ed. M. Godden et al. (Oxford: Clarendon Press, 1994), 188–205. See also Le Saux, "Laȝamon's *Brut*."

Evaluations that are more recent also attempt to elucidate Wace's goals as a historian and as a translator. Although no one in the modern world would turn to Wace for history as it is commonly understood, Martin B. Shichtman hazards the thesis that Wace should be examined with the modern understanding of history as narrative shaped by a teller—what we would normally regard as unscientific history. In this view, the verse chronicles of Wace and Lawman have more value as historical sources than they would ordinarily have. Accordingly, Wace shapes the "emplotment" of Geoffrey to celebrate the view of a conquering people: the Normans with their desire for empire. Lawman has the view of a priest who serves a defeated people: for him, history is a string of tragedies in which everyone loses eventually; people should therefore turn from their ambitions to God. Consequently, Wace's Gawain represents the new order of the twelfth century; he espouses the values of chivalry in his debate with Cador, who represents the old order. Lawman's Gawain is concerned with *contemptus mundi* and becomes involved in a conflict of loyalties: he must turn against his brother Modred to support Arthur.[43] In a similar kind of analysis, Laurence Mathey ("De l'*Historia Regum Britanniae* de Geoffroy de Monmouth au *Roman de Brut* de Wace") argues that Geoffrey still espouses the values of the eleventh century while Wace has adopted the chivalric ideals of the court of Henry II in which society has three rigidly separate classes—knights, clerics, and peasants. Jean Blacker-Knight also sees a connection between Wace's notions of translation and the political purposes of his work. She argues that

> the changes Wace made [to Geoffrey's *HRB*] in characterization, arrangement of material, and, especially, the political import of that material stemmed from a broad view of translation; an opportunity to present the work officially to the court during a period of relative stability; and an audience of non-experts.[44]

Blacker-Knight argues that "Wace presents historical events as if to convey the inevitability of change" ("Transformations of a Theme," 62) and develops a theme about the "shifting of peoples and the changes of languages"—"his original contribution to the legendary histories of the Britons and Normans" (Blacker, *Faces*

[43] M. B. Shichtman, "Gawain in Wace and Laȝamon: A Case of Metahistorical Evolution," in *Medieval Texts & Contemporary Readers*, ed. L. A. Finke and idem (Ithaca: Cornell University Press, 1987), 103–19.

[44] "Transformations of a Theme: The Depoliticization of the Arthurian World in the *Roman de Brut*," in *The Arthurian Tradition: Essays in Convergence*, ed. M. F. Braswell and J. Bugge (Tuscaloosa: University of Alabama Press, 1988), 54–74, here 55.

of Time, 32). Therefore, the "demise of the Britons is of no consequence to Wace" and results in the "depoliticization of Geoffrey's material" (97). Blacker's two studies of Wace's failure to incorporate the prophecies of Merlin from Geoffrey support this notion of depoliticization since Geoffrey's inclusion of the prophecies had an overtly anti-Norman political purpose that Wace was sophisticated enough to understand.[45] Nancy Vine Durling is also concerned with Wace's view of translation and truth, seeing translation as "a vision of truth which allows the author to add or delete material."[46] This view of translation as interpretation leads her to see the *Roman de Brut* as "an innovative, but also a most authoritative text" in its century (31). Édouard Langille sees Wace's avoidance of lies and fictions as a reflection of his being a churchman. Langille argues that Wace followed Geoffrey as a Latin authority,[47] but J. Zatta ("Translating the *Historia*," 158), as noted above, sees a sharp political difference between Geoffrey and Wace. Whatever the authority of Geoffrey might have been, Domenico D'Alessandro insists that the *Roman de Brut* is not a vulgarization, but a work demonstrating literary techniques from a variety of genres: "The child of the encounter between cultivated Latin literature and the voice of the *jongleurs*, this *roman* joins the institutional character of the one to the communicative character of the other."[48] Barbara N. Sargent-Baur notes that Wace "displays a critical historical sense along with an appreciation of the need to convince his readers that his account is reliable" and that his work "is on the side of the wall marked 'truth'."[49]

While it is the hope of the present translator that readers look at the whole of the *Roman de Brut*, much Wace scholarship has focused solely on the Arthurian section. Early comments concern Wace's mention of the Round Table. Laura Hibbard Loomis noted, in 1926, that Arthur's Round Table was introduced into the Arthurian matter by Wace and claimed that it did not come from Celtic sources. Rather, it was derived from a long tradition of representations of the Last Supper,[50]

---

[45] "'Ne vuil sun livre translater': Wace's Omission of Merlin's Prophecies from the *Roman de Brut*," in *Anglo-Norman Anniversary Essays*, ed. I. Short (London: Anglo-Norman Text Society, 1993), 49–59; "Where Wace Feared to Tread."

[46] "Translation and Innovation in the *Roman de Brut*," in *Medieval Translators and Their Craft*, ed. J. Beer (Kalamazoo: Medieval Institute Publications, 1989), 9–39, here 30.

[47] "'Mençunge ou folie?': Commentaire sur la mise en 'romanz' de Wace," *Dalhousie French Studies* 39–40 (1997): 19–32.

[48] "*Historia Regum Britanniae* et *Roman de Brut*: Une comparison formelle," *Medioevo romanzo* 21 (1994): 37–52, here 49.

[49] "'Veraces historiae aut fallaces fabulae'?" in *Text and Intertext in Medieval Arthurian Literature*, ed. Norris J. Lacy (New York: Garland, 1996), 25–39, here 30.

[50] "Arthur's Round Table," *PMLA* 41 (1926): 771–84.

representations with which Wace would have been familiar.[51] Tatlock discusses Wace's refusal to elaborate on the many tales that have been spread about Arthur and notes Wace's skepticism in regard to the "'Briton hope' of Arthur's messianic return one day to help his people" (*Legendary History of Britain*, 471–72). In 1965, Félix Lecoy summarized the arguments made about the nature of the Round Table after Loomis's article and argued that Wace's wording indicates that everyone at the Round Table sits with someone on both sides and that no one sits outside or on an end.[52]

The discussion of the Arthurian section of the *Roman de Brut* covers much broader issues in the last third of the century.[53] David Anthony Light makes the case that Wace is a poet in his own right, a poet who writes history with a moral concern lacking in Geoffrey. Light concludes that the Arthurian section offers a vision of a world ruled by humanistic values.[54] Norris Lacy, in 1977, de-emphasizes Geoffrey's contributions as subordinate to Wace's control as redactor and explores the entrelacement in Arthur's battles with the Saxons, Scots, and Irish and with the Romans. Lacy notes ironies: Constance needs Vortigern; Vortigern needs Hengist. Lacy concludes that "Wace's greatest contribution is without doubt his part in the creation and dissemination of the Arthurian story, but beyond that he indisputably develops and cultivates techniques which belong to the world of imaginative literature" and that "the *Brut* merits serious critical study—perhaps as the first French Arthurian romance, certainly as a finished narrative poem carefully executed by a writer of sensitivity and talent."[55] In a study of the types of love in the *Roman de Brut*, Keller argues that in the magical world of King Arthur *fin'amor* is possible and that Wace has written a romance ("De l'amour dans le *Roman de Brut*"). According to James Noble's 1992 discussion of Geoffrey, Wace, and Lawman,[56] the figure of Arthur in Geoffrey and Wace is consistent with their

[51] Tatlock reviews other studies that speculate on the nature and origin of the Round Table (*Legendary History of Britain*, 472, n. 29); so does Foulon ("Wace," 99–100) and Norris J. Lacy, "Round Tables," in *The New Arthurian Encyclopedia*, ed. idem, 391; also idem, "Round Table," in *Arthurian Handbook*, 2nd ed., 347–48.

[52] F. Lecoy, "*Meain* et *forain* dans *Le Roman de Brut*," *Romania* 86 (1965): 118–22.

[53] See also Ivor Arnold and Margaret Pelan, *La Partie Arthurienne du* Roman de Brut *de Wace* (Paris: Klincksieck, 1962).

[54] "The Arthurian Portion of the *Roman de Brut* of Wace" (Ph. D. Diss., New York University, 1971), 71.

[55] "The Form of the *Brut*'s Arthurian Sequence," in *Jean Misrahi Memorial Volume*, ed. H. R. Runte et al. (Columbia, SC: French Literature Publications Company, 1977), 150–58, here 157.

[56] "Patronage, Politics, and the Figure of Arthur in Geoffrey of Monmouth, Wace, and Layamon," in *Arthurian Yearbook II*, ed. K. Busby (New York: Garland, 1992), 159–78.

concern to curry favor with the Norman court: Geoffrey celebrates Arthur as an empire builder in the style of the Normans; Wace, who populates Arthur's court with a number of Frenchmen, emphasizes the courtliness of Arthur's kingdom as a reference to the courtly interests of Henry II and Eleanor of Aquitaine. Lawman, however, exhibits a spirit of rebellion against the Norman and Angevin regimes, and his cruel and violent Arthur is offered as hope for the Angles (who are separate in Lawman's account from the Saxons). More recently, Dominique Boutet has offered a similar thesis[57] about how various tales of the fall of Arthur's kingdom reflect different philosophies of the causes of human history. Consequently, Arthur's decision to invade France in Wace is inspired by an aesthetic of prowess—fundamentally an ethic. The philosophy of Wace is the philosophy of ostentation and prestige; his ideology is a political ideology in the service of the Plantagenets. The treason of Modred is just an accident and not a part of some cycle or pattern of history. Charlotte A. T. Wulf focuses on Wace's additions to the characters of Modred and Guinevere.[58] Modred is presented as a heroic figure who lacks faith—essentially a feudal flaw. Guinevere is noted at first for her qualities; at the end, she is indecisive and shows what her feelings are. She is a woman in love. Wace puts her into the triangle and makes her part of "the Arthurian orbit, where she remains a key figure" (78). In two articles, Rupert T. Pickens has examined Wace's use of the notion of courtesy. In the first article,[59] Pickens argues that the channel voyage marks the transition from the values of courtesy back to the values of feudal vassalage and war. Upon arrival in Brittany, courteous Arthur and his men are presented with a most discourteous giant. In the second article,[60] Pickens examines how forms of the word *courtoisie* appear in Old French literature and demonstrates how the word takes on the added refinements associated later with *fin'amor* in the Arthurian section of the *Roman de Brut*. Wace thus takes the epic and moves it toward romance, a view supported by Weiss (*Wace's Roman de Brut*, xxiii), who also notes that "Wace is far more interested in human emotions than either Geoffrey of Monmouth or the author of the first Variant Version of the *Historia*" (xxii). Laurie Finke and Martin B. Shichtman examine the incidents concerning the giant of Mont St. Michel in Wace and

---

[57] "La fin des temps arthuriens, du *Roman de Brut* au Lancelot-Graal: critique esthétique et critique historique," in *Lancelot-Lanzelet: hier et aujourd'hui*, ed. D. Buschinger and M. Zink (Greifswald: Reineke, 1995), 39–52, here 41.

[58] "A Comparative Study of Wace's Guenevere in the Twelfth Century," in *Arthurian Romance and Gender*, ed. F. Wolfzettel (Amsterdam: Rodopi, 1995), 66–78.

[59] "Arthur's Channel Crossing," *Arthuriana* 7 (1997): 3–19.

[60] "*Vassalage* épique et courtoisie romanesque dans le *Roman de Brut*," in *De l'aventure épique à l'aventure romanesque: Mélanges offerts à André de Mandach*, ed. Jacques Chocheyras (Bern and New York: Peter Lang, 1997), 165–200.

Lawman as illustrative of twelfth-century concerns over imperialism and the significance of rape as a measure for territorial expansion.[61]

In view of this discussion and my own experience with translating the *Roman de Brut*, I can offer some conclusions about Wace. He was an ambitious man who nonetheless knew his place in society and did not let ambition obscure his interest in truth. He was reasonably well educated, but was not perhaps a savant. He knew how to tell a good story and was worldly enough to tell it in the language of his audience. He was an able versifier and did not let his material take control of him. He had an interest in the history of toponyms that may wear thin with modern readers, but his Norman audience was anxious to hear the stories behind the names of places that its members or their friends or relatives claimed as feudal possessions. A stickler for details could say that Wace is given too much to anachronism, but a student of the Middle Ages might enjoy the incidental details of battles, battle machinery, and seamanship. Someone might complain that all this pseudo-history is a waste of time, but a serious student of literature will see a series of exciting tales concerned with wars and invasions, religion and love, and family harmony and discord. This student will see life through the eyes of a medieval writer concerned with making the truth lively. It is my hope that this translation faithfully conveys Wace's vision and concerns.

[61] "The Mont St. Michel Giant: Sexual Violence and Imperialism in the Chronicles of Wace and Layamon," in *Violence Against Women in Medieval Texts*, ed. Anna Roberts (Gainesville: University Press of Florida, 1998), 56–74.

A Note on the Translation

In 1993, I wanted to order a translation of Wace's *Roman de Brut* in Modern English for use in the classroom and was surprised to learn that no translation of all of Wace's important work was available at that time. A translation of the Arthurian section had been widely available since 1912 in Everyman's *Wace and Layamon: Arthurian Chronicles*,[62] and in 1970, David A. Light's nearly inaccessible New York University dissertation provided a very useful translation of the same section. Since the rest of Wace's poem had lain virtually hidden from everyone in the modern English-speaking world except specialists in Old French, I began the present verse translation of the entire text in 1993. Before I could get the translation to press, however, Everyman re-issued its text in 1997 with a new translation of the Arthurian section of Wace by Judith Weiss, who then also published a prose translation of all of Wace's text in 1999. Weiss has thereby made a major contribution to Wace studies in the English-speaking world. Her book offers a re-edition of Arnold's half-century-old text and provides a facing-page translation in Modern English prose. Her prose is clear, and her translation has been instructive in the revisions given to the translation presented here. Weiss's accurate prose translation will be appreciated by students of the legendary history of Britain, but my own study of metrics leads me to believe that prose translations of works in verse often fail to provide the reader with the poetic experience of the original. Since much of the beauty of Wace's work is derived from his skillful and disciplined handling of rhyme and meter, I humbly offer my verse translation beside Weiss's prose translation as a gesture toward providing the reader with a sense of the poetry of the original—even when the poetry may seem a little redundant and repetitious with its allowance for what may be doublets (like lines 11606-09, 12714-15, and 13617-18).

The present translation closely follows the text of Ivor Arnold's two-volume *Le Roman de Brut*, which was published in Paris by the Société des Anciens Textes Français in 1938 and 1940. After making a comparative study of the surviving

---

62 *The "Arthurian" Portion of the Roman de Brut*, trans. Eugene Mason (Toronto: University of Toronto Press, 1996), is now available online at <http://www.yorku.ca/inpar/Arthurian.html>.

texts of the *Roman de Brut*, Arnold wanted to use MS D (Durham Cathedral C.IV.27.I—an Anglo-Norman text of the thirteenth century) as his base. Since it has a number of omissions, he used P (from the library of Boies Penrose—seen only in photographs made for him by John Manly) up to verse 11999; then he used D for the remaining lines (lxiv-lxvi). Despite a general reliance on Arnold's text, I occasionally (and without notice) adopt a variant reading found in Arnold's footnotes when the reading in the text does not make sense to me. There is generally a one-to-one correspondence here with the lines of Arnold's text (and with his numbering of lines by fours), but sometimes the correspondence is lost for several lines when problems of syntax, clarity, or syllable count dictate otherwise.

Wace's poem is constructed of octosyllabic rhyming couplets, but I chose not to rhyme couplets since the prospect of coming up with some 7,500 Modern English rhymes was more than daunting. I do not want to diminish the accomplishment of Wace in any way, but Wace had a distinct advantage when it came to finding rhymes. As the following excerpt shows, Wace's Old French had a wealth of monosyllabic and disyllabic inflectional and derivational endings to use for rhyme—a wealth that is lacking in Modern English:

Quant Uther li reis fu finez,
A Estanhanges fu portez,
Illuec dedenz fu enterrez
Juste sun frere, lez a lez.
Li evesque s'entremanderent
E li barun s'entr'assemblerent;
Artur, le fiz Uther, manderent,
A Cilcestre le corunerent.
Juvencels esteit de quinze anz,
De sun eage fors e granz.
Les thecches Artur vus dirrai,
Neient ne vus en mentirai. (9005-16)

These opening lines from Arnold's volume two illustrate well the kind of options Wace had for rhymes. Nine of the twelve rhymes use inflectional syllables that are arguably stressed. A good compromise for the translation, it seemed to me, was to render the rhymed octosyllabics into unrhymed iambic tetrameter. I allow for the variations and substitutions normal in the tradition of English verse: trochaic inversions, anapestic substitutions, headless lines, and hypermetric final unaccented syllables. I hope that the result is pleasing and readable. I also hope that the poetic experience of reading my verse is comparable in some way to reading Wace's and that readers will forgive my frequent reliance on American English colloquialisms (like "bad-mouth," "show and tell," and "hollered") as solutions to problems in metrics and will realize that with English spoken in numerous varieties by over a half billion people worldwide the syllables I stress may occasionally differ from those other English speakers may stress.

To break up Wace's continuous text into sections that can be read comfortably in one sitting, I have divided Wace's text into chapters that make narrative sense. Chapter I, "Brutus" (lines 9-1250), treats the career of the founder of Britain, Brutus, who proves to be both a heroic and wise king. Chapter II, "Lesser Men, Lesser Kings" (lines 1251-2312), covers the lives of men like Locrin and Leir who for the most part have some flaw or peculiarity that prevents them from assuming the stature of Brutus. Chapter III, "Belin and Brennës" (lines 2313-3240), presents the exciting and detailed story of two royal brothers who turn from fighting over Britain to conquering Rome. Chapter IV, "Belin's Heirs" (lines 3241-790), returns to a list of minor figures whose portraits are nonetheless interesting in their variety. In Chapter V, "The Coming of the Romans" (lines 3791-5152), an internecine conflict that develops at a victory celebration leads to the ultimate victory of Caesar over the Britons. In Chapter VI, "Life Under Roman Influence" (lines 5153-6320), the Britons finds themselves harassed by the newly arrived Picts and constantly enmeshed in the politics of Rome; in this chapter, however, the Britons are converted to Christianity and later found Brittany, from which great kings and aid will later come. Chapter VII, "The House of Constantine: Vortigern and the Saxons" (lines 6321-7582), presents the most interesting evil character of the entire work: Vortigern the usurper who makes an ungodly alliance with the Saxons. The chapter also introduces Merlin, who becomes more prominent in Chapter VIII, "The House of Constantine: Aurelius Ambrosius" (lines 7583–8284), in which Aurelius, newly arrived from Brittany with his brother Uther, defeats the Saxons and Vortigern and has Stonehenge moved from Ireland by Merlin and Uther. After the treacherous death of Aurelius, Uther Pendragon assumes the throne in Chapter IX, "The House of Constantine: Uther Pendragon" (lines 8285-9004); he has further victories over the Saxons and at a victory celebration woos the beautiful Ygerne upon whom he fathers Arthur by means of a disguise devised by Merlin. After Uther's treacherous death, the young Arthur assumes the throne in Chapter X, "The Rise of Arthur" (lines 9005-10132), which covers Arthur's consolidation of power over Britain, the northern lands, and France. Chapter XI, "Arthur at the Height of Power" (lines 10133-11058), celebrates the civilization of Arthur's empire. When Roman ambassadors come demanding tribute, Arthur can refuse them as the sole power of northwestern Europe. In Chapter XII, "Arthur's Roman Campaign" (lines 11059-13009), Arthur amasses an army, sails to France, defeats the giant of Mont St. Michel, engages the Romans, and begins to lose his best knights to death. Chapter XIII, "The Great Destruction" (lines 13010-13662), focuses on a series of disasters: the destruction of Arthur and his empire through the malevolence of the adulterous Modred and Guenevere, the return of the Saxons, and the ravages of their ally Gurmund, the conqueror from Africa. In the last chapter, Chapter XIV, "The Britons Lose Britain" (lines 13664-14866), St. Augustine converts the Saxons to Christianity, Chadwalein succeeds in his struggles with the Saxons, but famines and plagues drive the last British king Chadwalader to Brittany, where a vision tells him to go to Rome and turn to God, an action that mirrors the image of Diana telling the pagan Brutus to go to Britain. As one can see, the story has a vast scope, and its characters are many.

Preamble

For him who wants to hear and know
About the kings and their descendants,
And who they were and whence they came,
And who first held the land of England,
And how the kings in order came,
And who was first and who was last,
Master Wace translated this
And told the truth in his account.

Notes to the Text

The following notes offer some guidance in the scholarship done on details of the *Roman de Brut*. Since many of the details in Wace can also be found in Geoffrey, students are urged to consult Tatlock's nearly encyclopedic *The Legendary History of Britain* for information about names, places, cultural and religious practices, and general sources. Arnold's notes (which are in French) are helpful for the names of people and places (*Roman de Brut*, 2.791–815). Light's notes ("Arthurian Portion") are also useful for items in the Arthurian section. Weiss's notes to her translation provide many details about the differences between Wace and his sources. For general Arthurian information, however, students might start with *The New Arthurian Encyclopedia* and *The Arthurian Handbook*; for information about medieval France, students are referred to *Medieval France: An Encyclopedia* (see list of works cited under Keller, "Wace"). Another good source of information (in French) is E. Faral, *La légende arthurienne*, 2 vols. (Paris: Champion, 1929; repr. New York: AMS Press, 1973). The numbers below refer to lines of the text.

1–8 According to Langille, "'Mençunge ou folie?'," Wace, a churchman with a devotion to truth, avoided relating what he considered to be fictions and lies and followed Geoffrey as his Latin authority. Blacker points out, however, that Wace never names Geoffrey as the source of *Brut* (*Faces of Time*, 32).

I. Brutus

And so the book relates the story
That when the Greeks had conquered Troy
And had then ravaged the whole land
In vengeance for the acts of Paris,
Who stole Helen from the Greeks,
Duke Eneas, at some cost,
Made an escape from the great slaughter.
He led away a son he had
Who bore the name Ascanius;
He had no other boy or girl.
With relatives, chattels, and slaves,
He loaded up a score of ships.
He wandered on the sea at length—
Many and great the dangers, storms,
And labors that he was to pass.
Later, he came to Italy:
The place was then called Italy,
The land where Rome was later founded.
But there was nothing then at Rome,
Though later it was a great place.
Eneas labored hard and long:

9 Arnold notes that the book is Geoffrey's (*Roman de Brut*, 2.791); but see the discussion in the introduction to this translation about the sources of Wace's text. Arnold also details the differences between Wace and Geoffrey in the early parts of the story and gives references to other sources accounting for those differences (2.791–92)

24 Houck (*Sources*) believes that Wace probably got his details of Roman history from Virgil's *Aeneid*, although he may have derived them from the *Historia Romana* of Landolfus Sagax (259). For an interesting account of medieval knowledge about Virgil, especially in England, see Christopher Baswell, *Virgil in Medieval England* (Cambridge: Cambridge University Press, 1995).

Much did he sail, much did he row;
He sailed across a lot of oceans
And wandered through a lot of lands.
At last, he came to Italian shores,
In a rich place of good and plenty,
There where the Tiber joins the sea,
A place not far from future Rome.
Latinus, the king who ruled that land,
Who held the reign entirely in peace,
A man both rich and powerful,
Was old and past his prime, however.
He greatly honored Duke Eneas;
He granted him a portion of
His land that lay beside the sea.
Despite the wishes of the queen,
He promised him his daughter's hand
With which he'd also get the kingdom.
Since he'd no heir beside the girl,
She'd get it all when he was gone.
The girl was very beautiful,
And she was called Lavine, by name.
But Turnus had a prior claim,
The lord and duke of Tuscany.
Turnus, who lived nearby by chance,
This man of power, learned Latinus
Had given his daughter to Eneas.
He was in pain; he suffered envy—
He'd loved the woman for a while,
And she'd been guaranteed to him.
He launched a war against Eneas;
Man against man set into battle.
Turnus the knight was strong and hardy,
But he was vanquished, killed at last.
Eneas wed the beauty then;
King he was as she was queen.
He found no other to defy him
Or even dare to be against him.
After Eneas took Lavine
And conquered all that land entirely,
He lived and reigned for some four years,
And to a castle that he built,

He gave the name of his dear wife,
And it was called Lavinium.
Four years he held the crown and woman;
The fourth year, when his end arrived,
Lavine, who had conceived a child,
Had not yet brought the child to term;
But come to term it did on time,
And then Lavine produced a son.
Silvius was his proper name;
Postumus was his second name.
In great love was Silvius raised
By the first-born Ascanius,
Who with his father came from Troy;
Creusa was his mother's name,
The daughter of Priam the King;
But in the tumult and confusion,
When leaving from the falling Troy,
Eneas lost her in the crowd.
Ascanius then held the throne
For many days after his father
And had a great city constructed
That had the name of Albalonga;
And to his father's wife he left
The land and also quit his claim
To the castle that Eneas made,
Both of which were gotten by force.
He kept the gods of Troy, however,
Which had been taken by Eneas;
He wanted them to stay in Alba,
But they could not remain there ever:
He never knew just how to move them
So that he could keep them on hand;
They always went back to the temple,
But I don't know at all just how.
He held the land for four and thirty
Years and never fought a war.

104 Lawman, who turns Wace's text into Middle English, says that the devil was responsible for the constant return of the gods of Troy to the temple (line 120).

Ascanius then met his end
And passed the land to Silvius,
Who was the son Lavine had born
After Eneas had left this life.
Ascanius produced a son
Whose name was also Silvius,
(He had the name his uncle had)
But whose life didn't last too long.
For he made love to a pretty girl
In secret, to Lavine's own niece.
He talked with her; and she conceived.
His uncle came to know the case
And called together casters of lots,
And soothsayers, and wise diviners.
Through them, he said, he wished to know
What kind of child the girl would have.
They cast their lots, prognosticating,
And so they found in magic sticks
The male child that the lady'd have
Would kill his mother and his father
And then be harried into exile—
Where afterwards he'd gain great honor.
And so it happened as they said,
And so it came as they had sworn,
For at the time the child was born,
The mother died, the child survived.
She died in labor, giving birth,
And the boy child was safely born
And given Brutus as his name.
At fifteen years and nothing more,
He followed his father to the woods,

115 According to Keller, "De l'amour," the secret love of Silvius is the first example of passionate, disastrous love in the *Roman de Brut*. For a discussion of the varieties of heterosexual eroticism in this story and in the stories of Locrin, Eldol, Vortigern and Rowena, Guinevere and Modred, Merian, Gudlac, Uther and Ygerne, and Aganippus and Cordeille, see Keller, "De l'amour." Keller concludes that the erotic interests of the work qualify it as a romance. We might also note that, in accordance with the theories of celibacy current in Wace's day, Silvius pays for his lack of sexual self-control and thus his lack of manhood by dying ignobly in a hunting accident at the hand of his young son (see Glowka, "Masculinity," 417–20).

118 The uncle of Silvius, son of Ascanius, is Silvius Postumus, son of Lavine and Eneas.

Who led him there at a bad hour.
At a bad hour they went together
To seek a herd of woodland deer.
The father chased them toward the son;
The son was stalking one of them;
He aimed at one within his view—
The arrow never found its mark:
Instead, he shot and killed his father,
But not on purpose or with will.
His relatives became enraged
And banished Brutus from the land.

He crossed the sea and went to Greece
And found some people there from Troy,
All of the line of Helenus,
One of the sons of Priam the King,
And plenty others of the line
Who'd been enslaved despite their births.
They valued much their royalty,
But they were held in slavery.
Brutus thus found some relatives
Of whom in Greece there were a lot:
For they had multiplied indeed
After they found themselves in exile.

Brutus had been there only a while
When he had claimed great fame and praise
For prowess and for hardihood
And for great wisdom and largesse.
His close relations honored him
And so did all the other captives;
Gifts they gave and pledges too
And often they would say enough
That if he could or if he dared
Free them from their servitude,
He'd have a band of many men.
And if they formed a cavalry
That he'd command and put in shape
And lead them into fights and battles,
They would be able easily
To free themselves from slavery.
In all they came to seven thousand
Good and hardy, proven knights—

Plus infantry and servants,
Plus all the women and the children.
And if he wished to lead them all
They'd have him raised up as a duke,
For much they'd suffer many times
To live in peace without enslavement—
And all were in accord in this.
In Greece there was a nobleman;
Assaracus was his name;
He was the son of a rich baron,
One of the best the country had—
But the son too of a Trojan mother.
He was a Greek on his father's side,
A Trojan on his mother's side;
But he was born in loving care.
Denying not paternity,
The father made his son a grant
Of three good castles in his will.
The bastard Assaracus, though,
Had on his father's side a brother,
Who was a lawful spouse's son.
This son would not at all permit
Assaracus to have the castles,
Unless he'd take them—if he could.
Assaracus defended himself
And held the land by force of arms
And to the Trojans turned for aid
Because he was a Trojan too
And they themselves had no defense
In all of Greece except for him.
With his advice and his agreement,
They made young Brutus general;
And for his fame and for their good,
Brutus agreed to be their lord.
He saw the men were great in number
And all the castles were quite strong.
He had the castles reinforced

215–24 D'Alessandro notes that these lines are examples of *amplificatio* with remarkable realism ("*Historia* et *Roman*," 41–42).

And had them set up for a war.
He then assembled all the wretches
And all the captives in the land,
All of the men, women, and infants
And all their beasts and all their servants,
Of which they had a massive host,
And sent them to the woods and mountains;
He next had food and pillage gathered;
He had a letter drafted then.
Saluting the royal king of Greece,
He sent to him these very words:
"Both for the shame and for the insults
Thrust on the noble folk and line
Derived from royal Dardan blood
And held in vile contempt and shame
In servitude for much too long,
Assembled now as one they are,
These captive slaves, who act as one,
As people who by right are one.
They've formed themselves into a troop
And drawn themselves into these woods;
They'd rather live on foraged roots
Like beasts and forest savages,
And by this means be thus set free,
Than live as slaves in relative ease.
It's better to live free and poor
Than be enslaved in luxury.
And if they wish to free themselves,
You should not spite them in this wish
And should not marvel in the least,
If they should prosecute their will.
Each person wishes, as is right,
And has a will to free himself.
And so they ask—so I demand
That freely from the present hence
They all may live there where they are
And go wherever it may please them."
  The king sat listening to the letter;
It seemed a great amazing thing
For Trojans to express themselves
In an appeal for liberty:

"They've taken on a foolish task
And put themselves in foolish work."
He summoned all his princes, dukes,
Barons and all his loyal men—
Both cavalry and infantry.
They rode toward the Trojan forces.
So said the king and so he thought
That he'd besiege the castles then
That Assaracus should have held
But Brutus had prepared for war;
And if he could capture Brutus there,
He could not do what he intended.
But Brutus soon enough was told
The king was coming with an army.
So in a pass that Brutus knew,
Through which the king would have to march,
He set three thousand in a trap.
The king arrived to cross the pass,
And Brutus lay in wait for him
And made of royals many corpses.
The Greeks, who were surprised completely,
Soon turned themselves into a rout;
To Achalon, a mighty river,
A mass of fleeing men went down.
Brutus, who chased them from the back,
Enclosed this number at the river;
He slaughtered some upon the banks
And drowned some more within the river;
Many he drowned and many he killed,
But many he left alive, however.
The king himself, though, fled away
And took his leave of all his host.
Antigonus, the king's own brother,
Looked at the chaos made by Brutus,
Looked at the slain, looked at the drowned,
And rallied his companions then:
Spurred by anger and by ire,

289–93 D'Alessandro notes that Wace uses a repetition of the same verb to create a rhythm whereas Geoffrey uses a variety of verbs ("*Historia* et *Roman*," 47).

He turned around toward the fight.
Then you'd have seen the bitter battle,
Many blows of lance and sword,
Many falling, many slaying,
Many fleeing, many fighting,
Many blows taken and given.
The Trojans broke through enemy ranks,
Many they killed; many they felled;
Many they took with oaths as captives.
Antigonus himself was caught,
The noblest captive of these men.
Brutus took these men with him,
Bound and tied and sworn to submit.
Pandrasus suffered heavy pain
About his brother and the others.
He mustered troops the morning after
And laid his siege on Sparatin.
He thought that Brutus would be there
With all the prisoners that he had,
But he had gone into the woods
Where he had sent the captives too.
The castle held instead his knights—
Six hundred, plus the archers too.
The king laid siege upon the castle,
Setting his barons all around,
Telling each one where he should be
And on which side he should attack.
He ordered catapults and towers;
He often had men brandish and strike.
He ordered the tower to the wall
And ordered the catapults to throw.
The men inside the battlements
Returned attack with arrows and quarrels,
Throwing great stones and flaming torches
And tossing spears and sharpened sticks.
They also had quick engineers
Who soon enough made mangonels
To throw back stones at catapults;
There was no man who dared to stop.
Still others made up flaming balls
That they launched out upon the tower

And turned it all to cinders and ashes.
They did a lot to give resistance!
When the king saw that nothing worked—
That through assault he could not take them
Nor through machines that he could make,
He turned to higher ground for rest.
He had his army all enclosed
With well-dug trenches as defense.
He left but only three ways in,
And these were guarded very well.
He swore, though, that he wouldn't leave
Until he had the castle in hand.
Now those who were besieged inside
Swore that they would not be taken
Before they died of lack of food.
And such they feared, for grain was scarce:
Too many with too little food.
Because they feared their food would fail,
They asked their duke to send them aid,
For if this aid was late in coming,
Their state would be so pressed by hunger
That they could not defend themselves.
Brutus was very anxious then
To find a way to rescue them;
He thought about what he should do,
About some means of helping them.
Indeed, some trick is what he sought;
He could not face a force this large.
He had to use a trick or ruse
To bring his enemy defeat;
And to deliver all his friends,
He'd have to put himself in peril.
Brutus considered all this briefly,
And moving very forcefully,
He took a prisoner by the hair;
Anacletus was his name,
Taken with the king's own brother.
Brutus dragged him roughly toward him,
Holding a naked sword in hand,
Acting as if he'd kill him quick.
"You'll die, you low-grade dog," he said,

"You won't get through this very day,
Not you and not the king's own brother
Unless you save him or yourself.
But you can save him and yourself
And from my prison gain your freedom."
"You'll please yourself, of course," he said,
"But if I can thus free us two,
Tell me how I ought to do it."
Brutus then said, "This I'll show you."
"Tonight," he said, "before the time
That people call the time for bed,
You'll go to those who guard the host.
And to these watchmen you will say
That with a trick and on the sly
You have escaped from my detention.
You've stolen the brother of the king,
But in the woods you've hidden him
And do not dare to lead him forth
Because I've set a forest guard.
They'll come with you to see themselves.
And when they come into that place,
Out from my hiding place I'll come
And strike them down, both one and all."
Anacletus acquiesced
In that which Brutus had described,
And Brutus swore and took an oath
To let him have both life and limb.
That night, when darkness was complete,
And when all men should be asleep,
Brutus got his folk arranged
And put them all into a valley
That he'd surveyed himself before
Inside the woods, close to the exit.
Inside the valley, in the woods,
In three places he set them up.
When Brutus had prepared them all,
Anacletus took his leave.
Running, he came to guards on watch
As if he rushed to them in flight.
The watchmen recognized the man;
Some of them knew him rather well.

They asked him how he ever left
And what the royal brother did.
"From prison, I have led him forth,
But in these woods I've hidden him,
For he dared not to go alone
Before you could come out for him.
He lies in chains and cannot move,
And I can't move him by myself.
Just come with me, and you will see.
I left him close enough from here.
You'll give the king some needed help
When you present him with his brother."
These men believed he spoke the truth,
And who'd have thought that he was lying?
They had no fear that this was treason,
And toward the woods they took their way.
Anacletus led the way,
Going ahead with them behind.
He led them straight into the place
He knew where Brutus lay in wait,
And Brutus, who was well prepared,
Captured them all on every hand.
Not even one escaped or fled,
And no one told the host a thing.
Then Brutus took his army's troops
And split them up in three divisions.
"Barons," he said, "you'll face the foe
In three attacking lines of force;
And I'll attack the royal tent,
With anyone who'll go with me.
But none of you will do a thing,
Not you in front, not you in back,
And none of you will speak a word
Until you hear me blow my horn.
When I have reached Pandrasus' tent,
I'll give my horn an awesome blast;
And when you hear me blow my horn,
You'll have the Greeks like pigs for slaughter:
You'll take their bodies deep in slumber
And chop them up without delay."
The horsemen then did all the things

That Brutus had described for them.
Three forces went among the host
And stopped among the enemy tents.
Brutus did not act slow at all:
Swiftly he came to the tent of the king;
And at the point of going in,
He blew a blast upon his horn.
And when the sound had reached the ears
Of all, the sides of tents were slit.
The Greeks were lying still asleep.
Before they had a chance to fight,
Inside the tents fell blows were given,
And hands and arms and feet were hacked,
And many brains were splattered then,
As well as many a tender belly.
The Greeks were not allowed the time
To take to arms or take to flight,
For Trojans would not let them move,
Coming before and after them,
Disdaining never the chance to slay
Wherever they could reach the Greeks.
And those escaping from their hands,
There where they thought it might be safer,
Cascaded over giant cliffs
And in the river's depths they drowned.
On every hand they found bad luck.
Brutus came to the royal tent
And took the king alive and well.
And when the sun arose at dawn,
He led the king into the castle
And ordered him put under guard.
Then Brutus had the spoils brought forth
And to his men he gave out all,
And by command he had the living
Collect and bury all the dead.
    On the next day he took the wisest
Men of his people privately,
Commanding that they counsel him
On what to do with the Greek king—
To have him killed or have him freed
Or have the score declared resolved.

With their advice he wished to work
So that they wouldn't later blame him.
The men were all of different minds
And offered different counsel to him.
Some advised him to request
A section of the land of Greece
Where all the Trojans could remain
And live in liberty and freedom;
It pleased another group to say
The king should let them leave the country.
They wished to go to other lands
With both their children and their wives.
But while they sat and talked and wondered
Which plan of action they should take,
Membritius cried out to speak,
A man of wisdom, and took the floor:
"And why," he asked, "are you in doubt?
You don't amount to more than spit.
So isn't it the best advice
To ask for freedom just to leave?
The king will give us gold and silver;
He'll give us ships and give us plunder;
He'll give us everything we need
To sail the ships and feed ourselves;
He'll give the duke, our noble leader,
His daughter, Inogen, as wife.
And then we'll go to seek new homes
In lands that lie beyond the sea.
For if we stay in Greece with him—
If bad we've had, then worse we'll have:
We'll never share this place with Greeks,
For never will these men forget
Their fathers, uncles, or their kin,
Their cousins, nephews, or their brothers,
Or any of their bosom friends
That we have killed with our own hands.
Know that they will seek revenge
Whenever they have time and space.
A great big fool is he, they say,
Who looks for good from him he's wronged.
Never will I put trust in them;

What comes around does go around.
Now we have done them dirt enough,
And I don't think that there won't be
Trouble from those with trouble from us,
Those losing either friend or kin.
Sons and cousins still alive
Are orphans now because of us,
And these again will seek revenge,
For they will not forget us ever.
We will decrease and they'll increase,
We'll joke around and they will grumble.
And if they once can lift themselves
And come above us, you will see—
Both you and those who'll be alive—
That all the Trojans then will die,
And we will get our just desert.
I say that things will be so bad
That I would send you on your way—
If Brutus, our leader, will agree."
Great clamor rose upon these words:
"Well said! Well said!" they all declared.
They had the king then ushered out
Until he stood before them there.
They all insisted that he die
And that his brother not escape
If they were not allowed to leave
With all the things that they would name.
And then they listed all the things:
The ship, the grain, and other stores;
They asked him for his daughter too
So she could be their leader's wife.
The king perceived the force was theirs
And had great fear of losing life;
So he agreed before them all
To grant their freedom and their leave,
Saying "In prison you have held me
And have demanded my young girl.
You'll have her—nothing I can do—
Now to my mortal enemy,
A cruel and an evil man,
I'd give her, willingly or not.

But I take certain comfort, though,
That a well-bred brave man will have her.
The ships, the plunder, all the food
And stores that you have asked of me,
I'll give you fully as you please.
And if it strikes your fancy, though,
To stay right here in this our land,
You'll have your rights and liberty;
You'll also have in your possession
A third of all the land I own."
But they had no desire to stay
And would not alter their demands.
The king then sent a message out
To harbors and to ports in Greece;
He had assembled all the ships
That could be sailed upon the sea.
Only the best were picked and chosen,
Only the strongest and the biggest.
And these were rigged with sailing gear
And loaded up with all the stores:
The nicest things in all the land
And dearest too were put aboard.
The king escorted Inogen,
His girl, and gave her to the duke.
And more than this, he gave much more
Than Brutus had as ransom asked.
There was no Trojan lord or vassal
To whom the king did not give gifts.
According to his rank and class,
Each received his proper gifts.
And when they had the proper wind,
They did not sit in long delay;
They went to the port and entered the ships,
And stepped their masts and raised their sails.
There were three hundred twenty-four
Vessels that left this port in Greece.
A day, a night, and then a day
They sailed without a stop in port.
The second day they came by sail
To Leogice when it was dusk.
They landed, climbing on the isle

To find no man, no woman there.
The island was a wilderness
That no one used for anything.
Some pirates had destroyed it once,
Chased off the people and took their stuff.
So all the land then lay in waste,
But there was much wild game to take.
The Trojans took enough of that
And put enough in all their ships.
For a long time, in plenitude,
The deer meat lasted in their holds.
They found the ruins of a city
And from antiquity a temple.
It held the statue of a goddess,
Diane, by name, a prophetess.
She was a devil, who deceived
The people with her charms and spells.
She took the image of a woman
In order to deceive the people.
She had herself addressed Diane
And claimed to be a forest goddess.
When once the land was full of people,
The statue served a living cult,
And it was held in high esteem.
The ancient people came there once
To ask about and hear about
What things were coming in the future.
Diane would give them her replies
Through signs and through hallucinations.

636 For discussions of Brutus' rites in honor of Diana as sorceress/devil, see Houck, *Sources*, 200–1, 237–38, and A. W. Glowka, "Laȝamon's Heathens and the Medieval Grapevine," in *Orality and Literacy in Early Middle English*, ed. Herbert Pilch (Tübingen: Gunter Narr, 1996), 113–45, who examines the general medieval understanding of the pagan gods as demons (134–40). In these rituals, Brutus kills a deer, which is generally symbolic of the Christian longing for Christ (Psalm 42:1). Diana came to represent the salient example of the Roman gods for medieval people (as in Acts 19:23–41) and was alleged to be the demon to whom witches owed their allegiance. Her most famous temple was at Ephesus (visited by Paul), the place where legend says that Mary the mother of Jesus died. Diana thus became a sort of anti-Mary in medieval conceptions of paganism. Diana had the ability to tell the future because demons were said to have considerable powers, powers usually used to attract devotees and to bring about evil.

Brutus took a dozen elders,
From the most judicious, prudent group,
And a holy man by pagan law
Named Gerion—these men he took.
He came to the statue in its niche
And had the others stay outside.
In his right hand he held a bowl
Filled with some wine and some fresh milk,
Milk that was taken from a white deer,
Just as the goddess Diane required.
Several times he bowed himself
And to the goddess he made his prayer
So she would tell him by response
And demonstrate to him with signs
Which region he could seek and find,
One good and peaceful to inhabit.
Nine times he made his prayer request
With lowered voice and happy face;
And nine times too he kissed the altar,
Walking around it nine times too,
Carrying in his hand the bowl.
And then he poured it on the fire
That he had ordered to be lit
Before the statue near the altar.
He took the hide then of the deer
From which he made his sacrifice
And spread it out along the ground,
And over it he lay to sleep.
It seemed to him, there where he slept,
The goddess spoke these words to him:
"Faraway in the sea, past France,
Way to the west, you shall encounter
An island good and fit for life,
A very delightful place to rest.
The soil is good for growing crops,
But giants occupy the land.
The land you'll have is Albion,
And you will make it a new Troy.
From you will come a royal line
That will be famous in the world."
After the vision disappeared

And Brutus marked it well in mind,
He gave the goddess fitting thanks
And to her made his vow and promise
That if he ever reached the land
That in the dream she promised him,
He'd make for her a statue and temple
And ever after honor her;
And then he told about his vision—
In just the words that he'd been told—
To all the men awaiting him
There in the temple where they'd been.
Then one and all returned to ship;
And sailing and rowing with all their might,
Enjoying both good wind and current,
In thirty days or more or less,
They came to ports in Africa.
But there they faced opposing wind
And passed instead the Saline Lake
And altars of the Philistines;
They then passed by Rucikadam
And by the mountains of Azaie;
There they encountered outlaw pirates
Who did indeed disturb them much,
For they attacked and harried them;
But at the end the Trojans won
And took away the pirates' booty,
Which made the Trojans very rich.
They traveled past the river Malvan
And came to Mauritania.
To seek for food and water both,
They left their ships and came ashore.
And all that land they laid to waste,
Robbing it all from sea to sea.
They took enough of loot and pillage
And took their way again by ship.
They sailed right past at running speed
The pillars made by Hercules,

728 The Pillars of Hercules are now known as the Straits of Gibraltar. Since Geoffrey does not explain the Pillars of Hercules, Weiss wonders if there may be some difference in the education of the audiences of the two authors (*Roman de Brut*, 21, n. 1).

The columns he constructed once
That were the signs by which he showed
That he had conquered up to there
Where he had put the pillars up.
There they came across the Sirens,
Creatures that could harm their ships.
Sirens are monsters of the sea,
Who look like women at the top
But just like fish below the navel,
And they harm seamen many times;
They haunt the oceans in the west.
They have sweet voices singing sweetly;
And with sweet songs they lure the foolish,
Attempting to deceive them thus.
The foolish men who hear their song
Enjoy the sweetness of the song
And mindlessly forget their way;
And if they do not turn in time,
They wreck themselves upon the sea,
And many times these seamen die—
Or in their clutches lose their way.
Many times they seize the ships
And hold them and delay them so
They run on rocks or other peril.
The sirens thus are to be feared
For they are full of many tricks.
And no one can escape these harms
Unless he knows to guard himself.
The sirens are a form of fiend,
With whom it is delightful work
To stay because they seem so sweet,
So sweet that one can hardly leave.
And he who wanders from his task
Will lose his way and lose his life—
And so he fares badly indeed,
The man who hears them far too much.
The Trojans, though, perceived this threat
And recognized the song they heard;
For they had heard about the song
And did not wish at all to listen.
They kept their vessels tightly grouped,

Close in tow to keep them safe.
And with great effort they escaped,
And they approached the Spanish coast.
  There they found along the shore
Some Trojans of their very line,
Four great tribes of Trojan people,
That Antenor, one of the lords,
Had led from Troy in flight
When Greeks had brought the city down.
Corineus was master there;
He was their overlord and sire.
Corineus was very large,
Hardy and strong just like a giant.
Now he had heard and understood
That there were certain Trojan folks
Who would be searching for some land
That they could have from that time on.
He was so joyful of their coming
That he then joined their company
And a great number of his folk
Were also thrown among the troop.
Brutus loved and cherished him
And had in him a worthy friend.
  Moving from the ports of Spain,
They took their way toward Brittany,
Yet Brittany was not its name;
It was then called Armorica.
Off to the right they left Poitou;
And so they sailed and so they rowed
That to the harbor straight they came
To where the sea received the Loire.
There where the Loire entered the sea,
The navy came all in a group.
They waited there for seven days.
To see the land and its condition.
Goffars, who ruled the Poitevins,
Sent messengers to where they lay
To learn the kind of folk they were,
To see if they sought peace or war.
Humbert, who well knew how to talk,
Was charged to bear this message there.

Corineus had issued forth,
And from the ships to the woods he'd gone
With some two hundred men to hunt
And look around the countryside.
They ran into the messengers
Who then demanded with insistence
By whose leave and by whose grant
This man was hunting in their woods:
"The king," they said, "has made a ban
Prohibiting the bow and chase
And stalking of the venison
Within these woods, the king excepted.
So how dare you to take these deer
Against the orders of the king?"
Corineus responded thus:
"If your old king's forbidden it,
Of his forbidding I knew nothing,
And I will not obey at all."
Humbert drew the bow and aimed
To strike the man, who flinched and ducked.
He was enraged and sallied forth
And seized the bow that Humbert held
And beat him so about the head
That Humbert's brains came spilling out.
His fellows then were put to flight,
And they left Humbert lying there.
They gave the news to King Goffars
How Humbert came to meet his death.
The king desired to seek revenge
And chase the poachers from his land;
This servant matter grieved him much.
A man of might, he sent great force.
Brutus learned this through his spies
And had his ships filled to the brim
With pillaged goods and with supplies.
He put in all the working men
And told them not to leave the ships
No matter what they might just hear
Until he came to them again
Or ordered them to come to him.
The other people he arranged

To meet the challenge of the king.
The king advanced until they met,
And mighty strokes were dealt by both.
The Poitevins attacked them well;
The Trojans paid them back in kind.
They battled back and forth at length,
But neither side was beaten down.
Corineus felt burning shame
(For he was good in times of need)
That Poitevins could be so strong—
That they were not yet whipped or dead.
Toward the right his folk had moved,
And so they had advanced on them;
The fight had broken through the center;
Many died on either hand.
He lost his sword in this endeavor
But found himself a battle ax
That came into his grasp by chance.
Then was the battle harder still,
For he who took the ax's brunt
Was split in two from head to foot.
The Trojans and the others who
Looked on were utterly amazed
About the strength this man displayed
And the great blows that he could give.
He quickly made the host depart,
For there were none who tarried there.
Corineus alone gave chase,
And at their backs he yelled at them:
"You sorry bastards! Why do you run?
You ought to stand and fight, you ought!
Just why are you running away?
Do you want me to beat your backs?
Come on and show me one of you
Who can defend your country here.
You flee too much, you low-class scrounges;
You run away from me alone.
More than a thousand still you are,
And yet you flee from one sole knight.
You do not know just where to flee
To keep from me who'll make you die.

But you can take some mighty comfort
In meeting death through my right hand,
With which I've given many blows
And many thousand men I've killed
And many giants I have slain
And sent by scores down into hell.
And four and four, and three and three,
Come on now—Do your level best!"
Suharz, who was a royal, heard
This bombast and this savage yell.
With some three hundred knights in arms,
He turned toward Corineus.
From everywhere they ran at him—
And they believed they had him beat,
But Corineus prepared himself,
Came to Suharz and gave him such
A blow that he was split in two
From the top of his head to the soles of his feet.
The other men he slaughtered like
A lion killing sheep and lambs,
For they had no defense from him,
No more than sheep against a lion.
Brutus, meanwhile, with all his Trojans
Arrived to help among the troops.
Then grew the noise and piles of dead,
For many bodies lost their souls.
Briefly I'll tell the end of this:
The Poitevins were vanquished there.
Goffars, who grieved for all of this,
Then went to France to look for help
From the twelve peers then living there
Who split the land in twelve divisions.
Each of the twelve was held a chief
And had himself addressed as king.
All twelve made pledges to Goffars
To get revenge on all his foes,
And he expressed his heart-felt thanks.
Then afterwards they gathered troops.

920–24 Weiss sees the influence of the *chansons de geste* in this reference to the *doze pers* (*Roman de Brut*, 25, n. 1).

Brutus was joyful in success,
Glad of the plunder and the glory.
All the lands he laid to waste,
Burning the towns he stripped of loot.
They plundered much; they wasted much;
They stopped upon a little rise
And made a castle on the top,
Where there had never been a lodge
Or fort or town or even house.
But something we have read has said
The building that these people made
Was the first structure of our Tours,
The city Tours, which still endures,
Which got its name from an event
That you'll be told about quite soon
As I compose this noble poem.
The Trojans drew themselves inside
The castle when they had it made.
For two whole days they sat in there
After the time they shut the door.
Goffars appeared with all the French,
With all the counts and all the kings.
He saw the castle on the hill;
He sadly viewed the wondrous sight.
"I can," he said, "go mad from pain;
And pain should make me lose all sense.
I see the felons who pursued me
And who have torched my towns and land—
On top of this, to spite me more—
Have built a castle in my reign.
French barons, let us arm ourselves
And swiftly set upon them now."
They armed themselves and formed their ranks.
They placed themselves in twelve divisions
And to the castle came directly.
And those inside then issued forth.
The French set on them well indeed,
And these received them well in turn.
You could have seen a well fought fight.
Each man there strove to strike with vigor.
In the first clash, in the first hour,

The Trojans had the upper hand.
They threw down dead more than two thousand
Frenchmen—and even more were wounded.
They made them run away in mass,
But they regained their former strength,
For all the time their force increased—
For all the time their people came.
They forced them back into the castle.
And then the best occurred for France:
They made attacks upon the castle
Until the night forced them to leave.
But in the castle there was trouble;
At midnight they sat down and planned:
Corineus would leave the walls
And lead his people out with him
And set an ambush in the woods.
He would be stationed near enough
So that when Brutus started fighting
At sunrise, he would leave the woods;
He'd come upon the Frenchmen's backs
And have them caught on every side.
In just this way he could harass
Goffars the king and his dominion.
They took this plan as good advice.
Corineus and all his men
Went out just as the rooster crowed;
Before the dawn they lay in the woods.
Brutus had the castle guarded;
He had his best stay up all night.
And in the morning he went out
And made attack upon the French.
He fiercely fought the battle then,
But at the time the fray began,
Before Corineus arrived,
Brutus' nephew Turnus was killed.
Turnus, indeed, had great endurance,
And he was marvelous in strength.
In either strength or martial courage,
He had no peer among the barons,
And no one fought as fierce as he,
Except Corineus alone.

He was quite hardy and quite strong.
He killed six hundred of the French
With hand alone and with his sword,
Which was completely wet with blood.
But he had wandered off alone,
And Frenchmen bore down hard on him:
They had enclosed and wounded him,
And in their midst they beat him dead.
Brutus recovered Turnus' body
And buried it inside the castle.
For Turnus, who was murdered there
And placed in earth inside the castle,
The town was later named as *Tours*,
And all the country there *Touraine*.
Brutus then fought strongly on
And wanted vengeance for his nephew.
Corineus was at his aid,
And he did deeds of splendid valor.
He hit the French from a new side,
The side they'd given no regard.
Then you'd have seen a grievous battle,
Some bodies pierced, some heads cut off.
You wouldn't know just how to write
About the suffering or deaths,
The damage or the awful pain
That Frenchmen suffered on that day.
They could not suffer this for long,
For soon it had them turned in flight.
The Trojans had them in pursuit
And slaughtered them with battle spears.
Brutus had the trumpets blown
And made his fighting men return.
In council, they decided then
To go and leave the land of France.
They took their booty and their loot
And went directly to their ships.
They filled their ships with all their pilfer,
And from the land they took their leave.
Under the sun, under the stars,
Under oar and under sail,
In Totnes on the shores of Dartmouth

The whole fleet finally arrived.
This was the island that the goddess
Had promised them in Brutus' dream.
They issued from the ships to land;
They felt great happiness and joy.
For this the land that they had found,
The land they'd sought with great desire,
They put away their cares and toil
And gave the goddess all their thanks.
Now on this island giants lived,
But there weren't any other people.
The giants there were great in size
And grew much bigger than other folks.
I do not know their list of names
And I can name just only one.
The one I know, I can thus name
As Gogmagog, who was their sire.
Because he was so strong and large,
The others made him rank the highest.
He and the others fled to the hills
And left behind the flatter land
For Trojans, who despised the giants
And shot at them with bows and arrows.
One day the Trojans had a feast,
According to their usual customs:
They sang their songs and played their games,
All in the joy for this new place
Where they had been assigned by fate,
A place that had been destined for them,
Both for them and for their heirs
To hold as heritage forever.
The giants came then into view,
Issuing from the mountain caves.
Big Gogmagog was leading them;
He was their lord—that's why he led.
They ran upon the feasting Trojans
And killed a lot in little time.
With stones, with clubs, with simple spears,
They murdered more than I can say.
But when they wished to take their leave
And hurry back into the hills,

The Trojans hastened in pursuit
And gave them such a lot of strokes
With darts and lances and with swords
And with their sharp and pointed arrows,
They made them lose their very souls.
Brutus had the biggest guarded,
This Gogmagog, to learn by test
Which one was stronger in a fight,
Corineus or this big giant,
For each was marvelously large.
Corineus ran up there fast
When he discovered he should fight.
Close to the sea on a level field
Next to a cliff in that location,
Brutus called all to the fight.
They saw to his wishes willingly.
Corineus rolled up his sleeves,
Preparing himself to have success,
And belted his cloak around himself,
Stretching the cloth around his flanks.
Gogmagog prepared himself
And dressed himself for doing combat.
They joined together arm in arm
And put their arms both high and low.
You could have seen them wrestle then,
Chest against chest, side against side.
They grappled together from behind,
And hands struck out with cutting jabs.
Then you'd have seen turn against turn,
Great strength put up against great strength,
And foot in front and foot in back,
And many kinds of special tricks:
Turns like this and turns like that—
Each fighter strong and full of hate.
They butted chests together hard;
They used their legs in scissors holds.
Occasionally, they came together

1117–28 D'Alessandro says that this battle description is astonishing and has an evocative force ("*Historia* et *Roman*," 45).

So that they were heaped in a pile.
Then you'd have seen some huffing breath,
Some scrunched up noses, sweating foreheads,
Blackened faces and rolling eyes,
Eyebrows moving up and down,
Grimacing teeth and changing color,
The breaking of heads and wounding of heads,
Butting and pulling and struggling hard,
Lifting and lowering, holding back,
Adjusting up and down and around,
Jumping around and turning fast.
Many a turn of the hip there was,
And scooping under and dragging close—
For each one wished to lift the other,
And each one wished to avoid that fate.
Gogmagog increased in strength;
He stretched his arms and linked his hands
And pulled Corineus so close
That three of his ribs were broken then.
Much did he wound him who then failed
To hammer back from there below.
Corineus, who was thus hurt,
Got just as mad as he could get.
The giant squeezed with such intent
He crushed the ribs he broke before.
The man recovered soon enough
And heaved the giant on his chest
And carried him up to a cliff,
The giant swooning in his arms.
The man released his hands and arms.
The giant weighed a lot; he fell
Down the cliff upon the rocks.
No bone was left that could be broken.
The sea was red along the cliff
With blood that streamed out from the corpse.
The place was later named (and still
Is) for the giant who there fell.
So when the land was cleansed of all
The giants and their monstrous kin,
The Trojans felt secure and safe
And built their homes and plowed their fields,

Constructed towns and villages,
And sowed their wheat and reaped their wheat.
The land had been named Albion,
But Brutus changed this former name
And coined from *Brutus* a new name
And had the land called *Britain* then.
The Trojans, who fought and sailed with him,
He named as *Britons* from his name.
Corineus had seized a part
Of Britain for his usufruct;
This part of Britain got the name
Corinee from *Corineus.*
I do not know by what event
That Cornwall then became the name.
But from the name it had at first,
It still retains a part in front.
The language that was spoken then
And had been named as *Trojan*
Was named among themselves as *British.*
But later the English changed it all.
The language and the name endured
Until the time that Gurmund came.
This Gurmund chased the Britons out
And turned it over to the Saxons,
Who were from *Angles* called the *English,*
And *England* was the name from them.
And all the Britons disappeared
And never after got redress.
Corineus was granted Cornwall,
And Brutus owned the rest of Britain.
Each leader took his friends with him
And all the men from their own lands.
The population grew in size
And spread so quickly in the land
That hardly any time elapsed
Before the land was full of people.
Brutus saw the mountain ranges;
He saw the valleys and the plains;
He saw the moors and forests too;
He saw the waters and the shores;
He saw the fields and all the meadows;

He saw the ports and fisheries;
He saw his people multiply;
He saw the land yield mighty harvests;
He thought that he would build a town
And thereby re-establish Troy.
After he'd sought a suitable site
That was agreeable and nice,
He made a city on the Thames;
It was well made and nicely placed.
To keep his ancestors in mind,
He named the city the *New Troy*.
Later the name became corrupted,
And people called it *Trinovant*;
But he who studies it will see
That *Trinovant* is just *New Troy*,
Which lost by process of corruption
That which was made by composition.
In honor of Lud, who loved the city
And lived in it for many years,
It was then named as *Kaerlud*.
Then *Lud* in turn became corrupted,
And *Lud* was changed to *Ludoïn*.
For *Ludoïn* there at the end,
One says in English *London* town,
But we in French pronounce it *Lundres*.
Because of all the great destruction
That foreigners have often caused,
Who've frequently possessed the land,
A land so often seized and lost,
The towns and all the other places
Now have other names than those
That ancient people used to use,
Who first established all the names.

1223–38 Blacker observes that "place names hold great fascination for Wace; it is in his frequent comments on etymology, rather than in theoretical prologues or epilogues, that we find the greatest evidence of his ideas on the nature of historical change and the usefulness of written records. In the *Brut*, he introduces the history of the founding of London with a lengthy passage of toponymic explanations to show that peoples leave their mark on a land through language" (*Faces of Time*, 32–33).

(This time I'm telling you about
Was Eli's time as priest of Judea, 1248
When Philistines into their land
Took both the ark and tablets of law.)

1247–50 The medieval practice of connecting events with biblical chronology is derived from Eusebius.

II. Lesser Men, Lesser Kings

When Brutus had his city built
And drawn a mass of people forth,
He made them citizens and burghers
And gave them civil laws and precepts
So that they would maintain the peace
And not engage in any crime.
For four and twenty years he ruled
And had three sons with Inogen.
The names of his three sons were these:
Locrin and Camber and Albanactus.
These three, who after him survived,
Ensepulchered him in New Troy,
The city that he came to found.
They then divided up the land
In love and in companionship,
And so each one received his part.
Locrin, who was the oldest son,
The strongest and the wisest too,
Received as his inheritance
The land called *Logres* from his name;
And Camber took the area
The Severn splits from north to south,
And when he took it as his own,
He named it *Cambria* from *Camber.*
He made great palaces and halls.
But now it's called *Cambria Wales,*
Cambria first but *Wales* much later
In honor of the Queen Galaes—
But Wales, however, may have gotten
The name to honor Duke Gualon.
For Wales was very powerful
And famous for this Duke Gualon.

The youngest, Albanac, was third,
And he became the owner of
A region that was full of trees,
Which from his name was *Albany*:
Albany from *Albanac*—
The place that we call *Scotland* now.
When these three brothers split the land
As good brothers and good friends,
Without iniquity or vice
They kept fraternity intact.
Humber, who was the King of Huns,
A man of terror from the sea,
Who came to devastate the towns
And rob and pillage on the coast,
In Scotland came into a port
And fought against Duke Albanac
For that land, which he pillaged and robbed.
This cruel man had many troops;
He beat and conquered Albanac,
Slaughtering him and many others.
The few who managed to escape
Fled south to Britain and to Locrin.
Locrin and Camber joined their forces
And marched to get their brother's vengeance.
Humber from the Scottish Water
Journeyed far to counter them,
But he was smashed and put to flight
And in a river he was driven
That takes its name from Humber's name.
For *Humber River* comes from *Humber*;
The river got this name from Humber,
Since Humber died within its depths.
Now he had been in Alemania,
Where he had robbed and wasted things.
There he had stolen three young women
And thrown them in his sailing ship.
One was a daughter of a king;
Her name was Estrild, and she was gorgeous:

1307 The Firth of Forth (Arnold, *Roman de Brut*, 2.795).

No man could find beneath the sky
A woman equal in her beauty.
When Humber met his wet demise,
Locrin and his brother Camber
Came up upon the fleet of ships
To claim the treasure in their holds.
And there inside they found three women
That Humber had by force abducted.
Locrin fell in love with Estrild
And ordered men to guard her close.
He said that he would marry her
And would not have another woman,
For her great beauty pleased him well;
She was delivered to the guards.
Corineus was still alive,
And he was father to a woman
That Locrin was supposed to have;
But Locrin left her for Estrild.
For love of Estrild he let her go
And broke his promise and his word.
Corineus became enraged
And sought for Locrin till he found him.
He came before him angrily
And spoke all swollen up with ire,
A monstrous ax upon his shoulder:
"Locrin," he said, "you filthy traitor,
No one can guarantee that you,
A fool, are not about to die.
Have you refused my little girl
To whom you were engaged to marry?
How can it be that you won't take her?
Are these the thanks that you return
For all my service to your father
And for the evils that I've suffered
In all the battles and the fights
Against the folk of other lands?
To set your father up as king,
I suffered much in terms of sweat
And many tribulations too,
And now you give me this reward,
That you for some unknown strange woman,

Dump my daughter Guendolienë.
I suffered perils for your father,
And now for someone called Estrild,
You cannot look on me alive
And jilt my girl whom you should take.
Now I cannot reject revenge
As long as I have any strength
In arms that I have ever raised
And that I used to kill the giants.
You'll die! I'll tear you limb from limb!"
As soon as Locrin understood
How much the other wished his death,
The other moved to do the deed;
But friends of both stepped in between
And kept the two of them apart.
They put Corineus at ease
And gave Locrin the good advice
That he should keep his covenant
And take the woman ere worse came.
Then Locrin under such conditions
Took Guendolienë as his wife,
But he did not forget at all
Estrild, who was his concubine.
Through one of his good serving men,
He had a cellar dug in London
Below the surface of the ground,
And there he had Estrild in hiding.
For seven years he kept her there,
Hidden beneath the earth like this.
Whenever he desired to see her
And spend a little time with her,
He had his wife believe that he
Was making sacrifice to gods
That he could not perform unless
He did it all occultly there.

1386 Locrin's underground assignations with Estrild become a more obvious joking reference to the orgies of heretics in Lawman (see Glowka, "Laȝamon's Heathens," 133–34). J. Zatta, "Translating the *Historia*," 151, argues that lust draws Locrinus to Estrildis in Geoffrey but in Wace "love, not lust," is responsible for the same. In either case, Locrin becomes less of a man (see Glowka, "Masculinity," 420).

He had to do with her so much
That Estrild had a baby girl,
Abren her name, who was much fairer
Than Estrild, who was her mother,
Who was a striking beauty too.
Guendolienë had a child,
A boy, within that very year,
Who was called Madan by his parents.
As soon as Madan learned to walk
And learned to talk and understand,
They sent him to Corineus
To raise him and to teach him things.
Finally the time at last arrived
When old Corineus passed away,
And Locrin, who no longer feared him,
Sent Guendolienë to her homeland
And honored then Estrild so much
That she was raised up as his queen.
Guendolienë grew enraged
At Locrin, who had sent her home;
In Cornwall she began complaining,
There where her kinfolk had their home.
She then assembled many kin
And asked the help of other folk
And then from Cornwall led this host.
She came to fight against her spouse,
This woman sure and confident.
Upon the river now called Stour,
The armies met in Dorsetshire.
But Locrin with a flying arrow
Received a mortal wound and fell,
And all his people ran away.

1397–1401 "In *HRB* Hestrild's daughter is *Habren* and the Severn (Sabrina) is called after her (chap. 25). Wace changes it to *Avren*, from which the river Avon takes its name" (Weiss, *Roman de Brut*, 37, n. 1).

1424 According to Robert Caldwell ("Geoffrey of Monmouth, Wace, and the Stour," *Modern Language Notes* 69 [1959]: 237–39), the battle between Guendoliene and Locrin did not have to take place along the Stour in Worcester. It is more likely that the battle took place along the Stour in Dorsetshire: Guendoliene was moving out of Cornwall; Locrin was moving out of London. After the battle, Guendoliene takes the throne, and *then* Estrild and Abren are cast into the Severn.

Guendolienë was the victor
And took the land and seized it all.
She had men toss into a river
Estrild and Abren so they'd drown;
But also she commanded all
That for the honor of her spouse,
Who had this Abren sired and fathered,
She'd place this name upon the river:
Because this was the water where
The girl was thrown, it got her name:
Avren, which got its name from *Abren*,
At Christchurch falls into the sea.
Guendolienë was a ruler
Very strong and marvelous.
She'd been with Locrin for ten years,
And afterwards she ruled fifteen;
But then she wished her son to rule,
And so she had him take the land.
When she had abdicated all,
To Cornwall she returned again.
There she retained that piece of land
Which was her right by birth and blood.
(Then Samuel was the Hebrew prophet,
And Homer was the best of poets.)
　Madan married and had two sons,
The one called Malins, the other Membriz.
For forty years he ruled, then died;
He left his reign to his two sons.
But these two brothers disagreed
And for the kingdom came to blows.
Each one desired to have it all,
And they could not agree on such.
But Membriz, who was treacherous,
Deceived his brother Malins, though.
He took a truce and granted truce
And called him to a parliament;
There where he was at the talks,
At which there was not one ill word,
The older killed the younger one;
Thus Membriz seized the throne and crown.
(Then Saul was King of Israel;

Eristeus, the King of Greece.)
Now Membriz hated all his kin
And all the men of noble birth.
Indeed, there was no man of class
Who had a piece of any land
Who was not killed by poison drink
Or force of arms or treachery.
He tossed aside his lawful wife
And took to doing heinous things
For which the Sodomites were killed
When they were wasted in their city,
Falling alive into the abyss.
For twenty years, he was the king,
But in the end he went out hunting
In the woods and met his end.
He parted from the other hunters—
For buck or doe I cannot say—
And wandered in a valley where
He came upon a roving pack
Of wolves, frenzied and wild with hunger—
They chewed him up and swallowed him.
And so was Membriz thus dismembered,
Torn apart and eaten up.
    Ebrauc, the son he had upon his wife,
After his father, took the throne.
This son was marvelously strong
And very large and full of vim.
He honored the rich among his kin
And raised the poor among them up.
There was no man who'd bring him war
Or even dare to mess with him.
He was the first to cross the sea
And raid somewhere outside of England.
He put a fleet of ships together
And took a number of his men
And went to war against the French,
Against the Flemish and the Germans.
He raided all the coastal towns
And took away a load of loot.
For many years there was great honor
And happiness in England's realm.

(During this time that Ebrauc reigned,
David composed the holy psalms
And built the town of Bethlehem
And tower of Jerusalem;
And Silvius Latinus ruled;
And Nathan made his prophecies.)
Ebrauc, who had sufficient wealth,
Near Scotland built a pair of towns:
The name of one was *Kaer Ebrauc*;
Aclud was the other one.
The one that had the name of *Ebrauc*
Was later named as *Eborac*.
The French corrupted this yet more,
And *Everwic* they made the name.
The other town he placed more north
And built it on the mount of Agned,
Which had the nickname Maidens' Castle,
But I don't know the reason why
The castle had the name of *Maidens'*
Rather than *Ladies'* or even *Girls'*.
I wasn't told, so I don't tell;
For I have never heard all things;
And I have never seen all things;
And I don't comprehend all things—
A man would have to know a lot
To offer reasons for *all* things.
Ebrauc lived a good long time
And ruled the kingdom very wisely.
For sixty years he lived all told,
And twenty sons on twenty dames
He sired—and thirty daughters too.
Hear the names of all the sons:
Brutus Greenshield, Margadud,
Sisillius, Regin and Bladud,
Moruid, Lagon and Bodloän,
Kimcar, Spaden, Gaül, Dardan,

1519–24 Kaer Ebrauc, Ebrauc, Eborac, and Everwic refer to York.

1532–36 These lines provide an example of Wace's interest in the truth and his frequent admission of ignorance of details not found in his sources.

Eldad, Cangu, Kerim, Luor,
Rud, Assarac, Buël, Hector.
You've heard the names of all the sons;
You have to hear the daughters' too:
The first one born was Gloïgin—
Otidas, Ourar, Innogin,
Guardid, Radan, Guenlian,
Angarad, Guenlodë, Medlan,
Mailurë, Ecub, Tangustel,
Stadud, Kambreda, Methaël,
Gad, Echeïm, Nest, and Gorgon,
Gladus, Ebren, Blangan, Egron,
Edra, Aballac, and Angues,
Anor, Stadiald, Galaes.
Galaes was beautiful and noble,
More so than all the other girls;
Methaël was the most stupid;
Guendlodë was the happiest;
Ourar was the best at work;
Innogin the best at talk;
And Anor was the courtliest,
Knowing most about display.
Gloïgin, who was the oldest,
Was also the greatest and the wisest.
All these ladies formed a troop
And were led off to Lumbardy
To kinsman Silvius the King,
Who'd marry them in pomp and splendor
To lads of Trojan lineage;
For it had been a long, long time
Since all the Lombard dames—
I do not know the cause—
Had chosen not to enter marriage
With anyone of Trojan blood.
This is the reason why these women
Were sent and given to these Trojans.
The brothers who remained behind
Assembled arms and sailing ships
And went to Alemania
With all the best of Britain's youth.
Assarac, the smartest one,

Became the leader of the brothers.
They captured castles, towns, and cities
And conquered all the German land.
  Ebrauc kept the oldest home,
Brutus Greenshield was his name;
After his father he was the king,
Ruling thus a dozen years.
Leïl, his son, upon his death,
Was king for five and twenty years.
A town, according to the story,
Was made in memory of him,
Kaerleïl by name, up north.
Leïl was good, but near the end
He got a little age-impaired
And could not firmly rule the land.
So men began to enter wars,
Without regard to his opinion;
And not for him or for his strictures
Did they do any right or wrong.
They made a mess of everything.
One of his sons, Ruhundibras,
Was later a great king of justice,
Who brought the land a time of peace.
He made the barons get along
And promise peace and guard the peace.
He built Winchester, Canterbury,
And also Chesterbury's castle,
Which was upon Mount Paladur.
On this specific castle's walls,
They say an eagle came to speak—
I do not know what things it said.
For almost forty years he reigned
After his father Leïl's death.
(So now, as I have found by reading,
At this time, Solomon was king,
Who built the temple of the Lord
Exactly as God had ordered him;
The prophets then of Israel
Were Amos, Joel, and Haggai.)
  When Ruhundibras was dead,
Britain was held by his son Bladud.

Now Bladud had a host of powers
And knew a lot of necromancy.
He founded Bath and made the baths,
Which never had been there before.
Bladud was the source of *Bath*;
The second letter *l* was dropped.
Or maybe *Bath* came from the *baths*,
The marvelous facilities.
The baths are warm and health-promoting
And full of profit for the people.
Nearby he built Minerva's temple
And demonstrated his devotion
By making a fire that always burned
And never even flickered any.
Bladud constructed many marvels,
Delighting in such things as that.
Bladud it was who tried to fly
To stimulate more public notice.
He bragged that he would rise in flight
And that he'd fly to London town.
He made himself a set of wings
And vowed to fly and flew indeed!
But in the end he came to bad,
For on the temple of Apollo,
He took a fall and crashed and smashed—
So stupidly did this man act!

King Bladud ruled for twenty years
After Ruhundibras' demise.
After Bladud's death, his son,
Leir, came to hold the royal honor.
King Leir, in his prosperity,
Founded a city in his name,
Kaerleir its name on River Soar—
We call it *Leicester* in these times—
But all the names mean "City of Leir."
In days of old, the city was great,
But through the fault of warring men

1627–54 Wace adds a note on the naming of Bath and "a comment on Bladud's folly" (Weiss, *Roman de Brut*, 43, n. 5).

It suffered later great destruction.
Now Leir held onto actual power
For sixty years in steady succession.
He had three girls, but no male heirs;
No longer could he sire a child.
The oldest girl was Gonorillë,
Ragau next, Cordeillë last.
The prettiest was the latest born;
Her father loved her best of all.
When Leir's old mind began to fail,
As happens when a man grows old,
He took a mind to start proposing
Marriage for his three grown daughters.
He said that he would wed them off
And split his realm among the three,
But first he wished to know by test
Which one of them held him most dear.
For he would give the biggest share
To her who loved him most of all.
He called his daughters one by one,
The first one born the first to test:
"Daughter," he said, "I wish to know
How much you love me, tell me true."
Gonorillë swore to him
By all divine that lives in heaven
(The biggest part was full of lies)
That she did love him more than life.
"Daughter," he said, "for this great love
You'll find yourself quite well rewarded,
For you have prized my dotage better
Than either life or your sweet youth:
For your reward you thus will have
The most aristocratic lord
That you can find in all my realm
As husband, if I can arrange it,
And of my lands I'll give to you
A third of all to hold fee simple."

1691 Wace adds this comment on the deviousness of Gonorille (Weiss, *Roman de Brut*, 45, n. 1).

He questioned then his Ragau next.
"Daughter, say how much you love me."
And Ragau'd heard her sister's answer,
Just how the woman had responded,
Over whom her father knew such joy,
Because she said she strongly loved him.
She wanted that reward herself,
So she applied the same sweet pressure:
"I love you over every creature,
And I can't say it quite enough."
He said, "This one's love is so great
That I could never ask for greater.
And I will give to you a lord
With a third part of all my land."
He spoke in turn then to Cordeillë,
Who in fact was his youngest daughter.
Because he loved this daughter more
Than Ragau or the oldest one,
He hoped that she would make it known
That she did love him best of all.
Cordeillë, though, had listened close
And well had noted in her heart
How her two sisters had professed—
How to her father they had lied.
She wished to test her father's thinking,
By testing thus to demonstrate
Just how his daughters flattered him
And served him up with bare-faced lies.
When Leir had put her to the test
Just like the others, she then said:
"Just where is there a girl who's said
Preposterously to her dear father
That she loves him more than she ought?
I know of no love greater than
The love between a child and father
Or that between a child and mother.
My father you are; I love you then
As much as I should love a father.
And thus I'll let you know for sure:
My love is equal to your worth."
At that she quit; she wished no more.

He father then was full of ire;
His mood was more than slightly ill;
He found great fault with what she said.
He flat believed that she was scorning
Him, deigning not or wishing not
Or through perversity neglecting
To make it known that she did love
Him just as he thought her sisters did,
Who had professed such wondrous love.
"In hatred," he said, "you hold me thus,
You who will not and who deign not
To answer me just like your sisters.
I will then give these two great lords
And all my realm as wedding gifts,
And they will have it all as heirs;
Each one will have a half of it.
But you won't get a squared-off inch
And you shan't get a lord from me
Or one small scrap of all my land.
I cherished you—I loved you more
Than any other once, believing
That you, more than the others, loved me;
It was right for you to comply.
But you confessed before my face
You loved me less than both these do.
As much as I once cherished you,
So much I must now hold you vile.
Never shall you have joy from me;
Never shall I have joy from you."
The daughter knew not what to say.
She thought she'd melt from shame or anger.
She didn't wish to fight her father,
But he'd no wish to listen either.
Without delay he used his power:
The first two born would marry thus,
And each would marry well, indeed,
The younger to the Duke of Cornwall,
The firstborn to the King of Scotland.
And so the thing was planned completely
That after him the two would reign,
With both to share as equal partners.

Cordeillë, youngest of the three,
Had naught to do but sit and wait;
I don't know what she could have done:
The king had pledged her nothing good
And he—bitter enough—would grant
To her no husband of his land.
The nice young woman felt ashamed
And suffered anguish in her heart,
More for the misdirected hate
Than for the pride she lost thereby.
She suffered from her father's anger,
But she was very fair and noble,
And much was made of all her graces.
Aganippus, a king of France,
Then heard Cordeillë praised, a woman
Who was quite ready to get married.
He sent off letters and proposals
To Leir the King by which he sought
The right to have Cordeille's hand—
If Leir would send her, he would take her.
Though not obliged in her regard,
Leir did remember often how
His daughter did once love him well;
So to the King of France he said
That he'd arranged all his affairs
And to his two daughters he'd given
One half to her who was first born,
The other half to her next born.
But if the woman was still pleasing,
She then was his—that's all he'd get.
The one who asked her hand then thought
That she was purchased very dearly.
And thus he held her more in value,
For praise had made her seem a marvel.
To Leir, about the dowry, he
Sent word that he would ask for nothing;
He merely asked for grant of her
Alone, Cordeillë, if he'd send her.
Her father granted the request
And sent his girl across the sea
With nothing but her clothes; she had

Not one thing more in her trousseau.
But she was later France's Queen,
A lady of great power and might.
The ones who won, the other sisters,
To whom the lands had been thus promised,
No longer wished at all to suffer
Leir to have a thing from the lands.
The sons-in-law then took from him
Everything—his joy was lost.
They warred against him, beating him
And stripping him of all his reign.
He lost by force to Cornwall's duke
And to the King of Scots, Manglanus.
He granted all he had to these,
But they provided for him somewhat,
For he would live with one of them
Who would support an entourage
Consisting of the former king,
His squires and forty knights with whom
The former king could go about
In honor where he wished to go.
The sons-in-law thus seized the realm
And split it up between themselves.
And Leir accepted what they offered,
And thus was stripped of all his reign.
Manglanus took Leir to his home;
At first, he had Leir's needs served well;
But soon his entourage was cut;
Its daily rations were diminished.
The first thing lacking was largesse,
But then the rations disappeared.
Now Gonorillë was quite greedy,
Tormented greatly by her father
Who kept a multitude of men
And never did a single thing.
She worried much about the cost.
And to her lord she often said:
"Just what's the point of all these men?

1862ff Example of a speech added to Wace's source (D'Alessandro, "*Historia* et *Roman*," 43).

Upon my word, sir, we are fools
For having folks like these as guests;
My father knows not what he does.
He finds himself in crazy quarrels;
Now that he's old—dementia's coming.
May he be shamed who'd trust him more
Or he who'd feed these folks for him.
His servants have attacked our own;
And one group now avoids the other.
Just who could suffer such a crowd?
Its lord is mad; its members wild.
Since spending more is wasting more,
One will not get returns that way.
Only a fool would have such people;
Too much we've suffered in their charge.
My father's had a group of forty;
From here on out, it will be thirty
That live with us, or out he goes
With all his men, for all we care."
This man had thought that she was viceless,
Without a trace of any greed.
This lady had so nagged her husband
And had so pressured him to act
That forty men were cut to thirty;
The rations also cut by ten.
The father hated all these changes;
It seemed degrading to him that
He was obliged to cut his train.
He left to join the other in-law,
Hennim, the one who married Ragau,
The one who held the land of Cornwall.
Yet Leir had not been there a year
When those two chose to treat him badly.
As things were bad before, they now
Were worse: thirty were cut to ten—
And ten were cut in turn to five.
"Damn me," he said, "for coming here!
There I was low—here I am lower!"

1900–01 According to D'Alessandro, these lines are an example of an addition of Wace's that is nearly theatrical ("*Historia* et *Roman*," 42).

So to the first he turned again;
He thought that she would better things
And as at first she'd honor him.
But she did swear by heaven that
He would not stay at all with her
Unless he cut his knights to one.
She would permit this to her father.
Then Leir began to mourn his lot
And in his heart to call to mind
All of the wealth that he once had—
The wealth that he had now all lost.
"Alas, for living way too long,"
He said, "for now I see bad times.
I once had much and now so little.
Where did it go, all that I had?
Fortune, you change the same for all;
You can't be stable for a moment;
No one should put his trust in you;
You make your wheel turn much too soon.
Too soon your color also turns;
Too soon you fall—too soon you rise.
Whomever you decide to favor
You quickly raise into great power,
But just as soon as your face turns,
You change the gifts you gave to nothing.
As soon as you have raised a wretch,
You throw him down below, destroyed.
At will, you please both king and count,
For you leave naught for anyone.
There was a time when I was rich—
When I had servants and relations;
But since—alas!—I'm now impoverished,
I've lost my friends, my kin, and servants.
I have no one belonging to me
Who might show me the slightest love.
My youngest daughter told me true,

1917ff. Leir's address to Fortune as a personification or goddess joins Wace to a tradition that can be traced to Book I, Meter I of *Consolatio Philosophiae* by Anicius Manlius Severinus Boethius (*c.* A.D. 480–524), a mainstay of medieval philosophical education (Boethius, *The Consolation of Philosophy* [London: Penguin Books, 1969]).

And I reproached my girl Cordeillë,
Who said the measure of my things
Would make me valued, make me loved.
I understood no word she said
But blamed her and I called her foolish.
My honor came from what I had,
And so did my esteem and love.
And so I've learned who flattered me
And learned who served me willingly.
For my possessions, I was flattered,
And now they turn on me, it seems.
Cordeillë spoke the truth to me,
But I did not perceive it, though.
I didn't see or comprehend,
But blamed her, and I hated her
And chased her from the land I owned
And gave her nothing good at all.
And now my daughters treat me badly,
The ones who said they were my lovers,
Who loved me more than anything—
As long as I had wealth to give.
And now I must seek out the one
I chased into another land.
But how can I now turn to the one
I exiled from my lands and realm?
But I will go without believing
That I will find a bit of welcome;
But she will do me no worse harm
Than what the older daughters did.
She said the measure of her love
Was what a daughter owed a father.
What more should I then ask of her?
Shouldn't she then thus love me more,
She who promised different love?
She did this only to deceive me."
At length Leir struggled with this problem,
Slowly working out a plan.
He boarded ship and went to France,
Arriving in a port in Chauz.
Inquiring where he'd find the queen,
He soon found out just where she was.

Outside the town, he stopped to wait,
For neither man nor woman knew him.
He sent his message with a squire,
Who to the queen announced, indeed,
Her father had now come to her
And sought her in his direst need,
He told her all in proper order
Just how his daughters threw him out.
Cordeillë, acting like a daughter,
Took gifts from all the wealth she owned
And gave them to the waiting squire,
Whom she had in her confidence,
So he could take them to her father
To comfort him there where he was.
And with these gifts, Leir was to hide
In a good town or a good city,
Where he could straighten himself up,
By eating, dressing, washing, and bathing.
He was to dress in royal clothes
And have great honor doing so.
He was to keep an entourage
Of forty knights with him in train.
Then Leir could tell the King of France
That he had come to see his daughter.
When Leir had gotten all these gifts
And heard his daughter's plan of action,
The squire would carry to his lord
New gifts that would be good and nice.
Leir'd turn then to another city,
Where he could get some decent lodging.
When Leir was good and settled down
And bathed and dressed and all fixed up,
And holding court with pleasant people,
Wearing nice clothes and well turned out,
He asked the king if he could visit;
He wanted now to see his daughter.
The king himself, in great nobility,
And the queen too, in wondrous joy,
Came to him then from far away,
And willingly they honored him.
The king received him beautifully,

Though he'd not seen the man before.
He ordered all his loyal subjects
And ordered all his loyal knights
To serve his lady's father well,
Doing whatever he commanded.
They had to do the things he wanted,
And all was done as he directed
Because he rendered up his reign
And re-established Leir in honor.
He did all this for courtesy:
He called together all the French;
With their advice and with their aid,
He launched a fleet of sailing ships.
He sent them with his father-in-law
To Britain, also giving him
Cordeillë, who was with him there
And who would have the reign as heir
If they could liberate the land
And smash the sons-in-law's defenses.
The fleet soon went across the sea,
And soon they brought the land its freedom.
They took it from the evil sons
And seized it all for old King Leir.
For three more years, Leir lived his life
And held all of his reign in peace,
And to his friends, he had restored
Whatever they had lost before.
In the third year, he died, however.
In Leicester, where his body lay,
Cordeillë made a tomb for him
In Janus' temple, in the crypt.
For five years, then, she held the crown,
But she was widowed at that time.
In the fifth year, a war was launched;
Her land was put under attack
By the two sons of her old sisters,
Whom Leir had married off so badly.

2029–39 According to Pickens, Aganippus, who elsewhere may demonstrate a romantic type of *courtoisie*, exemplifies the values of *vassalage* found in a work like the *Chanson de Roland* ("*Vassalage*," 171–72).

They terrorized their aunt's domain,
And many times they waged their battles,
Sometimes losing, sometimes winning,
This Margan and this Cunedages. 2060
At last they captured Aunt Cordeillë
And put her in a prison cell.
They would accept no ransom money
But held her in her prison till 2064
She killed herself inside the jail
In sadness, a foolish act indeed.
When they had conquered all the land,
Each one of them then took a part: 2068
Cunedages from the Humber west;
Margan all that tended north.
Things stayed this way for a dozen years—
But covetousness never rests. 2072
Margan had a group of friends
Both envious and full of evil,
Who never, ever loved the peace.
They said, "It is an evil man 2076
Who makes you share a half of that
Which can be yours alone through war.
You ought to have the whole of Britain
Or not possess a single foot. 2080
It's vile, since you're the older son,
For the young son to have more land.
Cross the Humber, seize it all,
And take the land and all to boot!" 2084
Margan listened to their urgings,
But badly they misled the man.
He crossed the Humber with his force,
He burned and wasted, robbed and looted. 2088
Cunedages' men were great
And came against him when they could.
But Margan didn't dare to stop
And have a battle face to face. 2092
From land to land he went in flight,
With Cunedages in pursuit.
Margan fled away to Wales;
The other followed into Wales. 2096
Margan was taken there and killed

And then in Wales was laid to rest.
The country where this man was killed
And where he lies beneath the ground
From *Margan* takes the name of *Margan*,
And for no other reason then.
Then Cunedages held alone
A land that once was held by two.
For thirty years he lived as king
And ruled the country in great peace.
(At the same time, Romulus built
The city of Rome with Remus' help.
Brothers they were, but for sick envy
The one threw down the other dead.
Hezekiah lived at that time,
And of Judea he was king,
To whom God granted fifteen years
Of life for crying bitterly.
This also was Isaiah's time,
Who made a prophecy about
A virgin woman who'd conceive
And who would then produce a son
Who'd have the name Emmanuel,
Who'd ransom captive Israel.)

After the death of Cunedages,
A son then reigned who was quite wise.
His name was Rival; he was quite valiant,
And he was loved by all the people.
During his time, blood fell as rain
For three whole days—I know no doubters—
And such a swarm of flies arose
That many people died of plague.
Concerning the vermilion rain
And all the flies, there was great wonder.
The people had great fear of both,
And everyone could feel the threat.
When Rival the king came to his end,
The throne descended to his son,

2111–20 Hezekiah and the details of Isaiah's prophecy were added by Wace (Arnold, *Roman de Brut*, 2.798; Weiss, *Roman de Brut*, 55, n. 2). These details are another example of the influence of Eusebian chronology.

Who had the name Gurgustius.
Then followed King Sisillius;
Gurgustius' nephew Lago then;
Then Kimare, son of Sisillius.
Gorbodiagnës followed then.
He had two bad unruly sons:
The oldest one was Ferreus;
The second one was Porreus.
They always fought like cats and dogs
And never once could keep the peace.
They had a father still alive
When they began to fight their war
For overlordship and the throne,
For envy and for jealousy.
The oldest one said he'd have all;
The other said he could not have it.
Porreus had a felon's heart
And wished to kill his older brother
Through treachery or some cute trick.
Ferreus knew what Porreus planned;
He fled to France across the sea
And served its King Suart so well
That he returned with an armada
And with an army of great knights.
He waged a war against his brother,
But badly things fell out for him,
For he was killed right at the first,
And after him his army too.
Judon, their mother, was still living
And felt like dying wretchedly
Over the evil cruelty
That led one son to kill the other.
Now she had loved the dead one more
And held the live one in despite.
One night when he was in his bed
And slept secure in confidence,
There came the mother with her maids;
Cutting his mail above the shoulders,
They slit the throat of the sleeping thug—
Was ever a mother so enraged?!
God! Who has ever seen more sin!

They chopped him up in little pieces.
There was much talk for a long time
Of Judon and her gruesome vengeance,
Who murdered one son for the other,
Losing two because of one.

With Ferreus dead and Porreus too,
There was no son or daughter left
Or heir of their close relatives
Who could inherit all their riches.
The men of means then fought and struggled;
The strong tortured the weak and feeble;
Each man according to his strength
Destroyed the poor who lived nearby.
There was no man of righteousness
Who might preserve the laws and rights.
Many a man was treacherous,
And even kinfolk killed each other
Both for their goods and for their land:
On every hand was mortal combat.
There were five lords of consequence
Who had great power and great wealth,
And to these men the others bowed
And handed over all their land.
Each one of these was overlord,
And each one claimed to be the king;
Each one of these attacked his peers,
And each one wished to grieve the other.
In Scotland ruled Stater the King,
And Pinner was the King of Logres;
Rudac was the King of Wales,
And Clotem was the King of Cornwall.
This Clotem should have had the throne,
For no one knew who'd better claim;
But those who had the greater power
Had no interest in this solution.
But Clotem had a noble son,

2207–10 "Wace adds Cloten's strong claim to kingship" (Weiss, *Roman de Brut*, 57, n. 1).

2211–18 Pickens argues that Dumwallo Mulmuz is *courteis* according to the values of *vassalage* found in a work like the *Chanson de Roland* ("*Vassalage*," 170).

Who was a very doughty man;
Handsome and skilled and very tall,
Dumwallo Molmuz was his name—
Yes, strong and handsome and polite.
He superseded every king
That ever held the crown in Britain
As far as looks or bravery goes.
From the time he could first bear arms,
He never wished to sit around:
He conquered thus the land of Logres,
Killing old Pinner, who was king.
He wished to take then Wales and Scotland,
But these two kings put up defense.
Against this man they made alliance
Both by swearing and by oath.
Within his land, they led their forces,
Destroying much and wasting much.
Rudac was there with all the Welsh,
And Stater there with all the Scots.
They went about seizing the castles,
Wasting the manors and the farms.
Dumwallo moved to counter them
With thirty thousand men in arms.
Great confusion with blowing of horns
Was what they had when they first met;
And many blows were then exchanged,
As many men were killed or wounded,
As many shields were pierced or broken,
Helmets crushed or hauberks split.
The battle had gone on at length,
And long had been the nagging doubt
About who'd win and who was stronger,
For each side fought with all it had.
Dumwallo was ingenious
And very covetous of victory;
He took aside six hundred men,
The hardiest and most proficient;
With all the arms of their opponents,
Who lay in death upon the field,
He armed his men in secrecy
And armed himself in the same way.

And then he said, "With me you'll come,
And that which I will do you'll do."
He watched and waited then awhile,
And through his spies he came to learn
Where Rudac and Stater could be found
And in what place they waged their war.
And then he ran right up to them
Just as if he'd come there with them.
He threw his men at the two kings
Crying the while "Strike on! Strike on!"
With ease the men fell on the kings,
And so the two were killed by many.
Then quietly and secretly
They all returned to their own lines,
Donning the armor they'd cast aside
And doffing the armor that they'd worn
So that they wouldn't shock them there
And then be killed disguised as others.
When they were once again in arms
And reunited with their people,
They reassembled for the fight,
But they met no resistance then.
Because this pair of kings had died,
Their followers had left the field.
Dumwallo ran behind them, though,
And they were quickly vanquished then.
When he had conquered thus the land,
Through all the reign he set up peace.
There was no peace before or since,
Nor will there ever be, I think.
A crown of gold was made for him;
I've never heard of any king
Who ever ruled as British king
With a gold crown upon his head.
Dumwallo made a slate of laws
That he enforced with a firm hand,
Whereby the temples and the towns
Were held with such respect and awe
That one—no matter what his crime—
Who reached a temple or a town
When he had been accused by men

Could leave with all the charges dropped.
Released from claim, he could go home;
Released from claim, his goods were safe.
Dumwallo set up such a peace
That no one would attempt to harm
People who stood in plowed-up land
Or people who traveled to the towns
Or to a temple or a market.
And anyone who reached such places
Had mercy granted on his life,
Just like a pardon for his crime.
Dumwallo made the laws and statutes
The English people still uphold.
For forty years he ruled, then died;
His people buried him in London
Close to Holy Concord's temple,
As history itself records,
A temple that he had erected
To guarantee both peace and concord.

III. Belin and Brennës

Dumwallo's wife bore him two sons,
Nobles who were of noble lines:
Belin, the older; Brennës, the younger.
Between themselves they split the realm.
Brennës, who was the younger one,
Happened to get Northumberland
And Caithness and some other places,
Whatever lay north of the Humber.
Belin wouldn't part with more
And granted what he granted only
If Brennës served him as a vassal
And recognized him as his lord.
Belin retained as his own land,
Logres and Wales and Cornwall too.
And so there were some five good years
When one did not defy the other.
But bad-mouthers surrounded Brennës,
And liars and prevaricators
Who nagged and ranted for so long
That brother fought against his brother.
One man was very treacherous
But was quite able as a speaker.
He knew quite well just how to reason

2313ff. J. Zatta, "Translating the *Historia*," 154, notes that "in the vernacular *Bruts*, Belinus's actions toward his brother are complicated and made more dubious" than they are in Geoffrey. "In Wace, Belinus attempts to extract his brother's allegiance by force. . . . Brennius's decision to rebel is prompted by a wicked counselor whose bad advice raises the problem of right and law as opposed to strength. . . . [and] Brennius's threat to make war on his brother comes only after Belinus has refused to restore his lands." The subsequent attack comes only after Brennes's request for the return of his wife, castles, and land is rejected by his brother.

And how to run a good debate;
He also could accuse with skill
And overturn a set opinion;
And if he thought he'd win the prize,
It didn't matter who might lose.
"We wonder very much," he said—
"Although I do not wish to tell you—
That you, of such a heritage,
From such a large and bounteous land
As in his life your father ruled,
Have taken such a little part;
And for this little bit you have—
Without apparent means of serving—
You are supposed to serve your brother
From whom it seems you have your land.
Are you some whore's or mistress' son?
Are you so vile or cowardly
That you should not be rendered homage?
Do you not have a noble family?
The one who bore you bore him too,
And both of you have the same father.
And since you're brothers in the flesh,
Born of one mother and one father,
Just why is Belin lord over you
And over your inheritance?
Break the alliance, break the trust
That lies between both you and Belin,
Who's dragged you down into dishonor.
No longer will you hold him lord.
Call for your men; call for their thoughts.
In faith, I wonder much about
A lord who has your feudal rank
To whom such villainy is done.
Belin divided and he chose.
And by what scheme did he divide?
It was his right to do the splitting,
But he who can do more gets more.
I do not know of other right,
But to the elder goes the better.
You're stronger, though, and braver too.
And many men have said as much

Ever since you conquered Ceoflo,
From whom you took the land of Scots
And who was King of Moriane
And wished to waste the land of Scots.
Can this be you allowing such,
And have you hidden all your courage
For this that now we speak about?
Let's see if we can sway you now
To take it all and have it all.
What do you fear? Why do you balk?
We will not fail you while we live,
And if you cannot summon faith
In us as knights with strength enough,
Go to Norway to look for help.
Elfing the king will give you aid
And throw his daughter in to boot.
Take the woman if he gives her,
And he will have you take some Norsemen.
So many Norse, so many Scots,
So many others and us too—
You can—so please you—use this host
To lay a lot of realms to waste.
If brother dear won't be your man,
He will not have a reign at all.
But go away and come back soon
And keep your plans in secrecy
So Belin gets no wind of them
And then deceives you with some trick."
When he had given this advice
And all the others had consented,
Brennës believed them willingly—
Despite good thoughts, he wasn't good.
He went across the sea to Norway
And asked for Elfing's daughter's hand;
And Elfing gave the man her hand
With loads of other fine possessions
And promised that he'd give the aid
Required to render Britain Brennës'.
There were enough informing Belin
Where Brennës went and what he sought.
Belin believed and quite suspected,

When such a move was made in secret,
That soon there'd be a lot of trouble.
Against a trick he'd use a trick;
If Brennës wished to use a ruse,
He knew just how to pay him back.
Belin seized Northumberland,
Took the castles, and made them his.
There was no scrap of anything
That Brennës could then use for war.
Belin put guards in all the castles
To have them watched all of the time
So that his brother'd never have them.
He had them filled with arms and grain.
With his own forces he himself
Occupied the ports and coasts
So that his brother could not land
Without attack or interdiction.
Brennës, however, heard the news
That brother Belin had seized his land.
He took his wife, arranged affairs
And started back with a great host.
The lady was both fair and noble,
But very sad about these things.
For she, for a long time, indeed,
Had been in love with Denmark's king,
Guthlac, who'd loved her in return;
She was supposed to go to him,
But Brennës had disturbed their plans.
She sent a letter to King Guthlac
And told him plainly what had happened,
That Brennës had what Guthlac lost,
And, even if he followed fast,
She'd never dance in his embrace.
Guthlac, the Danish king, thus learned
That Brennës had usurped his woman.
With all the ships that he could get,
He searched the seas for Brennës' fleet;
He planned to take his woman back
If he could come to where she was.
He said that he would have her now
If he'd not lost her to the other.

The two armadas came together;
The warring ships engaged each other,
Blow against blow, force against force,
Strike against strike, lance against lance.
Some lances broke; some lances pierced;
Many were killed; many were drowned.
Forces were here; forces were there;
But Brennës' navy took a beating
And turned its tail to run away.
And Guthlac, as his fortune turned,
Happened upon one of their ships—
The woman's ship—he took her back.
He had no interest in the others;
He kept hers back, and it remained.
And Brennës left, fleeing away,
Missing his woman very much.
When Guthlac had regained his prize,
He wished to be on *terra firma*,
And he was making his return,
But now just listen to the tempest!
A giant storm arose at sea;
The weather changed; the wind did too;
It rained and thundered; lightning flashed;
The skies blackened; the air was stirred;
The sea was churning; waves were rising;
Expectations rose and fell.
The ships were thrown in certain peril:
Planks and pegs began to break;
Seams were split, and planks were cracked;
Sails were shred, and masts were broken.
A human could not lift his head
Because the tempest was so great.
The ships were scattered very soon
And blown to many different lands.
For five whole days they suffered this
In the sea's force, in the great wind.

2479 ff. Although most readers would find no fault with Wace's storms, Joël Grisward concludes that the storms are formulaic with essentially meaningless, interchangeable parts ("A propos du thème descriptif de la tempête chez Wace et chez Thomas d'Angleterre," in *Mélanges Jean Frappier*, 1: 375-89).

Guthlac, with only three ships left,
Ran before the wind until
He came to England on day five.
Happy he was to come to land
Next to the woman whom he loved.
But he'd no knowledge or no notion
About which land he'd happened on
Since he was far away from home.
The men who guarded coasts and beaches
And kept the watch on ports and harbors
Arrested Guthlac, his companions,
His woman, and his prisoners
And led them all before the king.
Belin gave them to the care
Of those who guarded all the coasts
Against his brother Brennës' coming.
The men arrested with the woman
Confirmed the truth before the king
About his brother Brennës' deeds:
How he had been with Norway's king
And how King Guthlac crossed his path
And forced his navy to retreat.
Brennës, though, did not delay;
He got another fleet together
And landed on the shores of Scotland
With a great fleet and a great army.
To brother Belin he sent word
And pleaded with him through his envoys
Not to retain his lawful wife,
But to deliver her to him,
Along with all his captured castles,
And to take leave and go back home.
If he did not give them back soon,
He'd waste his land with torch and flame.
Belin did not fear these threats
Or anything that Brennës did,
So Belin plainly turned them down.
When Brennës came to understand
That he would not succeed with niceness
And that requests would get him nothing,
He had his men take up their arms;

He set his forces in formation.
Near the Woods of Calatere,
The forces of the brothers met.
One despised the other greatly;
One felt envy of the other.
One had his knights ride at the other;
One threatened the other with attack.
When these two brothers finally met,
They fought a very heated battle.
Spears were launched in countless numbers;
Massive stones were also thrown;
Lances wounded many men;
And swords made many slashing wounds.
They threw, they launched, they struck and pierced;
They fell, they kicked—they breathed their last.
The Britons were the better men;
The Norsemen were just mercenaries.
The latter could not long endure,
And to their ships they made retreat.
But Belin went in hot pursuit,
Crushing many as he went.
By scores, by hundreds, and by thousands,
They died in fields and on the paths.
Brennës, who started all the trouble,
Escaped at great cost to himself.
He found a ship nearby in port
And with six dozen boarded it;
No more than these could he lead there;
And then he crossed the sea to France.
All of his friends were left behind,
Dead or wounded or detained.
When all the dead were laid in earth,
They numbered five thousand or so,
And there was none who got away
Unless he ended drowned to death.
When this affair had reached its end
And Belin's brother was in flight,
Belin summoned his advisers

2537-38 "In Scotland, later situated by Wace near Alclud (Dumbarton)" (Weiss, *Roman de Brut*, 65, n. 1).

At Everwic, inside the town,
And sought advice on what to do
Concerning Guthlac, whom he held.
Upon command, Guthlac the King
Was brought from prison, where he was;
This king would hold his throne from Belin
And thus become his feudal vassal;
From Denmark by command and levy
He'd render tribute every year.
He guaranteed what he would do
With hostages and promises
If Belin would then set him free
And let him take his woman home.
Belin had great desire to make
Denmark a tributary nation.
With the advice of lords and barons,
He let go Guthlac and his woman.
But first he took the feudal pledges
With Guthlac's hostages and seal
To make the covenant secure,
And so he let him go like this.
Guthlac took his leave from there
And made his way back to his land.
He took along his woman too,
Whom he had purchased with great pain.
  Belin had an active reign,
And wisdom was his guide in life.
He lived in peace and thus loved peace,
Established peace and guarded peace.
He traveled all about his Britain
And journeyed through the countryside.
He saw the moors and saw the woods;
He saw the waters and the roads
Upon which one could barely go
To pass from one town to the other.
Throughout the valleys, moors, and mountains,
Belin constructed roads and bridges;
The bridges were good; the roads were great,
Made of stone and sand and lime.
The first-made was a thoroughfare
That still can be admired and seen,

Stretching the length of the great land.
The peasants call the highway Foss,
Which starts in Totnes in the south
And ends up in the north in Caithness;
Yes, down in Cornwall it begins
And ends up in the midst of Scotland.
From Port Southampton by the sea,
He paved a thoroughfare that led
Completely to St. David's, Wales,
Where at another sea it ended.
From town to town the road has run
As long as the land itself has lasted.
Belin made these two great roads,
Which cut across the countryside.
And when the king had made the roads,
He ordered that the peace be kept—
Complete tranquility and peace—
And that if someone in his realm
Then violated all this peace,
He had to forfeit his estate.
Brennës, who had gone to France,
Suffered great shame about his land—
And great chagrin about his wife,
Whom he had lost with great dishonor.
Six dozen of his loyal friends
Served the king and all his barons.
Courteous and able knights,
They made themselves the friends of all.
They never lacked for proper clothes
Or ample funds or generous gifts;
For they were prized for all their prowess
And were much loved for their largesse,
For freely they would share their goods,
Giving away and spending much.
When they became the friends of all
And had been praised through all the land,
They asked for aid and asked for help
To fight a war to get the land
That Belin had usurped by force.

2616 The name is Wace's addition (Weiss, *Roman de Brut*, 67, n. 1).

At last, however, Brennës went
To Burgundy, to Duke Seguin,
Who honored Brennës very much
And gave him much of his fine stuff.
Brennës conversed with courtesy;
Indeed, he was refined and polished.
He knew about the woods and streams
And entertained in many ways.
His body was fine; his face was handsome;
He looked just like a noble man.
The duke himself was powerful,
But he'd no children or an heir
Except one daughter that he had,
And she was then of such an age
And so grown up and well turned out
That she could well be married off.
Brennës served the duke quite well
And spoke to please him well enough.
His handsome face impressed the duke,
Who liked to have this man around.
The duke endowed him with his daughter
And all the land that she'd inherit
If he himself would have no son
Upon his wife before he died.
The nobles liked Brennës a lot
And held him in esteem and love;
And he knew how to get this love
By speaking well and giving wisely.
It wasn't even a single year
After Brennës married the daughter
Before his father-in-law was dead;
Then Brennës took the title *duke*.
The barons who before had loved him
Loved him now the more, if able,
For he was very generous
And spoke to them with friendliness.
The men of Burgundy loved him much,
Both the barons and the knights.

2686-94 According to Pickens, Brennes has *courtoisie* beyond *vassalage* ("*Vassalage*," 184).

He had enough money and land;
He had a noble, gorgeous wife.
But he had not forgotten yet
That Belin disinherited him
And confiscated all his fiefs.
When Brennës saw both time and place,
He called his folk, requested knights,
Called his neighbors, and drafted soldiers.
He came to Normandy in force
And there prepared a naval fleet.
When he was set and had good wind,
He crossed the sea completely safe.
Belin, who knew of his arrival,
With all the folk that he could get,
Then came against him in a battle.
They had great armies on both sides.
They were just at the point of fighting,
Of giving strokes and taking strokes,
When Tonwenne came between the two,
The mother both of Belin and Brennës.
Trembling she came between the hosts;
She was so old she barely moved.
She sought Brennës and asked for him
Until the lords pointed him out.
She threw her arms around his neck
And kissed and hugged him many times.
Not much time passed before she spoke,
For she had sought him quite awhile.
She ripped her clothes completely off,
Down to her belt right in the front.
She showed the man her naked breasts,
Withered with age and somewhat hairy.
Crying, she spoke to Brennës her son,
Interrupting her words a lot,
For frequently she stopped to sob
Or heave profoundly with her sighs:
"Beautiful son, listen to me.
Remember, please, remember, please,

2729-40 The bare-breasted mother's appeal for her son to abandon fighting is as old as Homer, *The Iliad*, Book XXII.

These breasts that you now look upon,
That many times you sucked upon.
Remember too that you came out
Of this womb here when you were born.
Remember also all the pain
I suffered many days for you.
Remember, son, this body too,
Which the Creator put you in,
Who made you when you were not there.
Remember, please, and hear me now:
Put down the arms that you now bear,
You who now come from a foreign land,
Leading a force of foreign folk
In order to destroy your land.
Are you so happy with your friends
That you can't see a single thing
Of the good state to which God's raised you?
Do you then give us such good thanks
That you have come to kill your brother?
Calm yourself down; appease your ire.
You'll never have a brother or sister;
Your father's gone; your mother's old.
Should you have come then to this place
To put your poor kinfolk to death?
You ought instead to bring to us
Your pretty things for show and tell
And have us look at your great wealth
And boast about your high estate.
You ought to come in peace to us
And make us gifts of your nice things.
And you now come to pillage us,
To whom you should give loving help.
Please abandon this foolishness!
If you desire to sue your brother,
I'll make you judge of all this case
And make you plainly see what's right.
Now if you say he chased you out
And exiled you from your own land,
You're wrong, for you don't speak with reason.
No one exiled you but you.
You have the blame for everything,

For you yourself caused all the trouble.
He's in the wrong, so people say,
Who goes and starts all of the trouble.
Everyone knows that you began it
Crossing to Norway on the sea
And marrying among the Norse,
For you did not take open leave
And went off there among the Norse
To exile your brother, but you failed.
If you had not defied your brother,
He'd not have taken all your land.
You wished him dead or without land;
Everyone knows you failed in this.
Belin had never exiled you
Before he did to Burgundy
To get new things—more than he took.
And now you are indeed a duke
And ought not be enraged at him
Who made you lord of Burgundy.
He's raised you up from small to great;
He's made you go from rags to riches.
The reign of which you might have part
You might as well have thrown away;
And still if it would please you any,
Northumberland could still be yours.
You left it for a better deal.
You really ought to thank your brother
Because of whom you had to flee
And go into another country
In order to receive the land
Of which the Lord God made you lord.
You have one brother; you should love him;
But he should hate you very much,
For you have done him many wrongs,
You who've led these men against him
To disinherit your own kin
And lay our homeland all to waste,
And they would treat you otherwise
If they had really done you wrong.
Dear son Brennës, what do you think?
Put down your lance, put down your shield,

If you believe your mother's counsel;
And make your peace with your own brother.
Apologize for your ill will,
And he will do the same to you."
Brennës heard his mother well;
He was so moved that he believed her.
He took his sword and helmet off,
And doffed the armor of his hauberk.
He went out front onto the field,
And Belin also did the same.
The mother brought them both together
And ordered them to kiss each other.
There was no count of any worth
Who was not subject to her orders.
They moved forth to embrace each other
And sweetly they gave kisses too.
And this was how the war was won
And how the brothers' anger died.

From there they went to London then,
And there they went into their council.
The end of all their talk was this,
And all of them agreed to this:
That they would cross the sea toward France
And conquer every part of it.
Then Belin called his British folk,
And Brennës took Burgundians;
At the appointed date and time,
They came to port and entered ships
And sailed across the sea to France.
The people there were all afraid,
And all of them felt awful fear
That in the end they'd all be dead.
Now at this time there were in France
Several kings who ruled the French;
They were agreed by common counsel
To be allied and act as one.
They fought against the pair of brothers,
But the two brothers conquered them;
They could not make defense against them,
And they surrendered, pressed by force.
And there was none so wealthy there

Who did not give his castle up.
They took the castles and the towns
And conquered France in several months:
All the people trembled before them.
The brothers spoke together then
And said that they would go to Rome
And up to there they'd leave no man
Who had a town or a good castle
Who'd not become their underling.
They summoned up their folks again
And made their royal forces one.
They led as many as they could
And passed Montjoie and Mount Cenis
And captured Turin and Ivrea
And all the towns of Lumbardy:
Cremona, Pavia, and Vercelli,
Milan, Bologna, and Piacenza.
They passed the Taro River by
And then they passed Mount Bardon by.
They took and pillaged Tuscany,
A land that lost its feudal rights.
When they went further seizing all
And came yet closer still to Rome,
The folks in Rome then made a stir,
The ones who'd heard the news reports.
In this the year of which I speak,
The Romans had installed in office
Two counts who oversaw the wars
And made arrangements for defense.
The name of one was Count Porsenna;
The other was Count Gabius.
These two conferred with senators

2865 Roland Blenner-Hassett and F. P. Magoun ("The Italian Campaign of Belin and Brenne in the Bruts of Wace and Lawman," *Philological Quarterly* 21 [1942]: 385-90) say that Wace drew knowledge of Italy from the *chansons de geste* and perhaps diaries or firsthand accounts of clerical travelers. These scholars claim that the route of Belin and Brennes makes good geographical and military sense: the two Britons entered Italy in a pincer movement of two columns, joined their columns, sent out splintered columns, and then joined all their forces for the march on Rome. Weiss notes that Wace "adds this route into Italy, which Arnold suggests is a pilgrimage one, passing along the old Via Flaminia to Bologna" (*Roman de Brut*, 73, n. 2).

And sought their counsel and advice
On how they'd manage their defense:
Should they go fight against the brothers
Or hand the city over now
And recognize their overlordship?
The senators were quite afraid
And in their senate meeting voted
Not to go to war with them;
The brothers with their troops were strong.
But if the Romans could get peace
Through promises and gifts and such,
They ought to seek the brothers' peace.
They'd give them so much gold and silver
That they would not then ask for more,
And in addition they would pledge
To give them payments every year.
And thus they'd make them turn away
Before their town was laid to waste
And all the country set on fire.
Should I then make the story long?
With this advice, the counts approached
The brothers, and they brought for them
Many great things to give as gifts;
And to secure their future friendship,
They promised them and pledged their word
To render Roman tribute yearly.
The brothers took the offered goods.
To guarantee the covenants,
They kept behind a hostage group
Of twenty-four young Roman children
With very rich and powerful kin,
And so a friendship was secured
That had a very short duration.
The brothers two withdrew their forces;
They went across through Lumbardy.
They marched up toward the Alemans
To get the tribute they demanded;
The Romans, though, disturbed their plans
And did not keep the covenant.
They thus gave up their hostage children,
Who were of noble family lines,

And rendered all their friendship null,
Which certainly was shortly lived.
For when King Belin took his leave
And Brennës turned away from Rome,
The Romans dropped their former fear
And got their bravery back again.
And so they got some knights together—
I do not know how great the number—
Armed to the teeth and well prepared;
And then they sent them at the Britons
To hassle them and set an ambush
And take them in a mountain pass.
They also took some other troops
And sent them up to Alemania
So they could join the Alemans
And put their forces both together
To stand a watch along the pass
So that the brothers would not cross.
This part of the force would set this trap
(Or so they thought, but they were wrong)
There in the pass of the great mountains,
There with the press of their great forces
So that the brothers'd be enclosed:
Behind their backs the Roman army,
Before their faces the Aleman.
Thus all the Britons would be killed;
The mountain pass was nowhere straight,
But it was crooked, long, and narrow.
He who was caught in such a pass
Would be embarrassed easily.
A little troop could there harass
Much greater force or greater power.
When Belin and Brennës learned all this,
They were advised, if possible,
That Brennës should return himself
And offer combat to the Romans
And for their lying perfidy
To seek revenge, as he was able.
Belin would cross the mountain range
And take the Alemans to task;
The one who beat his foe the first

Would run to help the other brother.
The French and the Burgundians
Were led by Brennës into battle;
And Belin had his many friends,
The Welsh, the Scots, and all the Britons.
But when the Romans understood
(The ones who were in Germany)
That Brennës had then turned around
And thus was heading back to Rome,
They then decided that they'd leave
And run to help the folks in Rome;
And by a road they knew about,
They'd march ahead of Brennës army.
Belin knew well by espionage
The route this Roman company took;
He knew the time of their return
And parts through which they'd have to pass.
He had some locals as his guides
(With promises he hired a number)
Who as directly as they could
Led him to the returning Romans.
He came on Montjoie's sloping flanks,
And day and night he marched so much
That he came to a valley pass
Through which, the guides had pointed out,
The Roman army'd have to march,
From which it could not turn away.
Belin waited and forbade
The host from making cries and noises.
The air was nice just like in summer;
The night was clear; there was no breeze;
The moon was shining clear and bright.
Belin had hidden in the valley;
The Romans held onto their route,
Very secure, feeling no fear.

2981ff "The whole episode of the Britons ambushing the Romans in the pass is far more exciting in Wace than in *HRB*, partly because Wace is good at making the topography come alive, partly because he has an eye for ironic contrast—between the fine, still night and the horrors round the corner—and partly because of the bloody savagery of the fighting" (Weiss, *Roman de Brut*, 77, n.1).

Below the moon, which shone so bright,
They went along in a hasty march
As they approached the ambush trap.
And they saw shining in the moonlight
The helmets, the saddles, and the shields.
And now you see them totally lost,
And those who had been waiting there
Without delay began to strike.
When Belin hollered out his signal,
There was no coward lacking courage.
From every side the men attacked;
The Romans fled and left the field.
But they could not escape at all;
They did not have a place to hide.
The Britons slit their bellies open
And chopped them up and cut their throats
And cut the heads off many men
And slaughtered them like animals.
All the killing did not stop
From morning when the sun arose
Till evening when it went to rest
And when the darkness made them part.
The ones escaping with their lives
Turned and fled into the valleys.
  The second day, when it was dawn,
Belin set out on the road;
He followed his brother down to Rome;
Brennës knew and bided time.
For when the brothers joined their forces,
They'd march securely in their strength.
To Rome they'd go and occupy it,
Laying a siege in several places.
Stone-throwers, catapults, and rams
And other types of siege machines—
They had these built to weaken the wall
So they could break it into pieces.
The Romans waited at the wall,
Defending themselves quite wonderfully.
With slingshots and with arbalests
That they had ready near at hand,
They threw down rocks and shot off bolts.

They showed no fear of anything.
They launched off darts and leaden balls,
Crushing many and killing many.
They forced the men attacking back
Before they breached or broke the wall.
For a long time, in all attacks
The brothers had the worst of it.
For they were beaten almost senseless
And suffered losses of their men.
But they then ordered, for revenge
And ire, that gallows be erected.
The eyes of those inside looked on;
The friends looked on; the kin looked on:
The brothers brought the hostages
And had them raised high on the gallows,
The four and twenty Roman sons,
Sons of the proudest men of Rome.
The sadness felt was very strong
For both the friends and relatives,
But they were not all vexed at this.
Stronger and fiercer they became,
And so they said and so they swore
That they would have no peace with them.
The Romans were quite powerful,
And so they placed a lot of hope
In Gabius and in Porsenna,
Who just awhile before had gone
To look around in Lumbardy
And up in Pully for some help.
The men in Rome awaited them.
Upon the day on which they knew
The counts would be arriving there
With all the help that they were bringing,
They acted very fierce and brave
And charged the people of the host.
According to plan they went outside
And started fighting with some fierceness.
And then the counts made their appearance.
Then you'd've heard both hue and cry!
The Romans were on one side fighting,
With Pullese and Lombards, on the other:

Burgundians were felled like trees.
"Whoresons and cowards," the Romans said,
"Didn't you come to get some tribute?
You'll be apart from it for ages.
For now we'll make you drink your blood
To save the water of the Tiber.
Didn't you come here from Montjoie
To challenge the people of our land?
We are not one bit happy now,
For Rome belongs to us alone.
In sin and villainy you acted
When you strung up our hostage children;
Ignorant, evil counsel you took,
But bad will come to you, please God."
The Romans thus provoked the Britons,
Demeaning them unpleasantly
And throwing giant insults at them;
They were quite bad and threatened worse.
The Romans made them all pull back
And made them cry and bray a lot;
Each man laid on his adversary,
And no one knew how to be sparing.
Belin and Brennës got quite angry
Over these Romans getting pleasure
Destroying their men and beating them,
Hitting, striking, killing, winning—
Even the strong suffered disgrace.
The Britons drew themselves aside
And had themselves a little talk
To gain their hardiness again.
They made their folk feel reassured,
Had horses harnessed and men armed;
And then they set their troops in groups
Of thousands, five hundreds, and hundreds.
The hardiest and the most helpful
Were made the constables and masters
Within each level of command,
Their job to keep the lines in order.
The hardiest of all the warriors

3120ff "These military tactics are added by Wace" (Weiss, *Roman de Brut*, 81, n. 1).

They put in front of other soldiers;
And to the left and right of these,
They put their crossbows and their archers.
The best and highest of their men
Would climb down from their mounts and horses,
And in the field they'd go on foot
Arranged and set in ordered ranks.
Some of them threw their lances forward
And threw heraldic symbols down.
They marched one foot before the other
To strike the press in unison.
Not one of them at all broke ranks
Or even flinched for any man.
They blew their horns and bugles then
And in this way prepared to strike.
Soon enough they came to do so.
Then you'd've seen the clashing armor,
The flying splinters of the spears,
The falling and the tumbling men.
I cannot give you full account,
But many died on either half.
The Romans, though, were finally vanquished;
And sad misfortune fell to them,
For Gabius was cut down there,
And Count Porsenna was a captive.
The brothers entered Rome by force
And found great riches there inside.
They did whatever came to please them:
One found the things he wished to have.
When they had taken all the city
And conquered all the countryside,
Brennës remained in Lumbardy
And held the lordship over Rome.
He later acted cruelly there
Just like a man with massive power.
And Belin, who returned from there,
Then made his way back home to England.
He reinforced his ancient towns
And fixed up all the broken walls;
He renovated ancient towns
And also built some new ones too.

In Wales he had a city founded
That he had named as *Kaerusc*
Because it sat upon the Usk,
A river running right before it;
Men later called it *Kaerlion*,
And now you'll hear about the reason:
Along time after Belin's death
And after Brennës met his end,
It happened that the Romans here
Held England as their own possession.
To keep it there in their domain,
They had to suffer pains at length
At many times and at great cost.
While they were there they always had
Two or three or four good legions
To fight against their enemies.
The Romans then were very strong.
Six thousand six hundred sixty-six
Was what it took to make a legion.
This is the explanation of it.
So when the legions spent the time
In which they did not have to fight,
They passed the winter every year
At Kaerusc there in Glamorgan,
Both for the pleasure and great plenty
That could be found within this city.
In honor of the legions, I said,
Who passed away their time in there,
Returning there through use and custom,
They called the city *Kaerlion*:
That is, "the city of the legions."
And then men changed the name a bit.
Kaerlion for *Kaerusc*,
The right name being *Kaerlegion*—
But foreign people have the name
Abridged by thus subtracting part.
From *legion* they have made *lion*;
They've also simplified *Kaer*

3182ff Details of the legion are added by Wace (Weiss, *Roman de Brut*, 81, n. 2).

And from the whole said *Karlion*.
And so they made the name much shorter.
When Belin had made Kaerusc
And drawn a mass of people there,
In London, his big urban center,
The place where he sojourned the most,
He made a marvelous kind of gate
Upon the navigable river.
The gate was on the River Thames,
Placed there with some wondrous skill.
The English call it *Belnësgate*,
But it should be *Belinësgate*
For Belin, who constructed it.
I do not know another reason.
Above the gate he made a tower,
Very large and very tall.
He re-established his father's laws
And made them very firm and strong,
And he himself was a good ruler,
A king maintaining laws and rights.
During his reign there was great plenty:
There'd never been that much before
And there have never been as many
Things to drink and things to eat.
So Belin ruled and lived his life
In great power, through constant vigil.
He was in London at the end.
God! How the people cried for him!
The corpse was burned, the ashes taken
And put into a golden cask,
Into a cask made all of gold,
Which had been found within his treasure.
Then someone put the cask up high—
Completely sealed and tightly closed—
Fully in view atop the tower.
The body had no other tomb.
For exaltation and for honor,
The corpse was placed so high above.

3214 Billingsgate (Weiss, *Roman de Brut*, 83, n. 1)

IV. Belin's Heirs

After Belin a son of his
Who was named Gurguint held the land;
Gurguint Bertruc was his whole name.
He had the very best intentions;
For he was wise and moderate;
He loved both peace and righteousness.
In having peace and guarding peace,
He was the equal of his father.
His father was rich, and so was he;
And no one ever turned him down,
Except the Danes in their rebellion,
Who did refuse to pay the tribute
That Gudlac had first given Belin
When Belin freed him and his woman.
Gurguint knew well that he had rights
Regarding what his father owned.
He called his people, boarded ships,
And had the sails and masts put up.
By force he entered Danish land;
There wasn't city, march, or castle
That he did not obtain with force,
Unless it gave up to have peace.
He waged there many a hard-fought battle.
He even killed the king himself.
And so he got his tribute back,
Just like his father'd gotten once.
From all the lords he gathered homage
And hostages and oaths of fealty.
When Gurguint took his leave from there,
He traveled through the Orkney Islands.
And there he found some thirty ships
Assembled in a company,

Filled with women and with men,
And decked out rather nattily.
Pantaloüs governed them;
He was their sire and guided them.
Gurguint asked what folk these were
And where they went and what they sought.
Pantaloüs bowed before him,
Asking him for peace and truce.
When Gurguint granted him the floor
And gave him leave to speak, he said:
"I have been forced to leave from Spain,
Both I and all this company.
We go as one to seek by sea
Some land where we can settle down.
For eighteen months we've wandered now
With hunger, thirst, and useless wind.
We've yet to find a decent place
Where we can stay and hold a fief
Or where we can remain at all,
And so we all have heavy hearts.
We've sailed and sailed for so long now
That all of us feel very low.
But if it comes into your pleasure
That you might wish to keep us here
And see perhaps a bit of land
That you perhaps might give to us,
We'll serve you with a ready will
And so become your loyal men."
Gurguint did not desire to let
Them have some land in his domain,
But gave them counsel nonetheless.
He put them on the route to Ireland—
Indeed he asked them to go there
And put this land to cultivation.
Ireland was still not populated
Or lived in by a single soul.
And so these people sailed to Ireland,

3293-300 Example of Wace turning indirect discourse into direct discourse (D'Alessandro, "*Historia* et *Roman*," 43).

And King Gurguint assigned to them
Some mariners who'd serve as guides
And who'd put Ireland in their hands.
And so they sailed and so they went
Until they came at last to Ireland.
The land was still a wilderness;
There was no house or place of lodging
Or any other sign of farming,
But it was fair and well endowed
With waters, woods, and mountain ranges,
With fields and plains that could be plowed.
There they made huts and homes of branches
And from the land made fields and farms.
The people grew and multiplied;
The man more able plowed more land.
Pantaloüs ruled these people:
He was their lord and source of justice.
Meanwhile Gurguint returned to England,
The man who sent these folks to Ireland.
He held his kingdom peacefully
Until his life came to its end.
When he had finished up his time,
He died at Kaerleon on Usche,
And when he passed beyond this life,
The reign was passed to Guincelin.
   Guincelin enjoyed his life,
And Marcie was his spouse's name.
She was a wise and learned lady,
Of high regard and worthy fame.
She focused all her wit and care
On learning how to read and write.
She learned a lot and studied much;
She even wrote a set of laws:
The laws were called the *Marcïene*,
Which is the name it has in British.
Alfred the King, as now it's claimed,
Translated and wrote out the law.
When he had turned it into English,

3335ff "Wace virtually ignores Guincelin . . . to expand on the portrait of his wife" (Weiss, *Roman de Brut*, 85, n. 2).

It had the name *Marcenelaga.*
The queen who learned so many things
Produced a child for Guincelin;
Sisillus was the baby's name.
She never had another child.
Sisillus was not very big
And was not more than barely seven
And had not reached the age of reason
When his father passed away.
The mother, when the father died,
Maintained the kingdom for the child
In peace and in tranquility.
And when the son was old enough
To know just how to rule the land,
The mother had him crowned as king.
He was still in the best of health
When he came to his final day.
Then Rummarus his son was king,
And then his brother Damus too.
This latter had a bastard son,
Who was the king through force of arms.
Morpidus was his name; he was
A very fierce, strong, hardy knight.
He was esteemed for his good deeds,
But he was also very cruel.
He lost his temper to excess;
He always wished to kill someone.
Whenever he would lose his temper,
He knew not how to spare a man
But always put him to the sword.
There was no thought of former love:
At once he always killed the man,
Whether wrong or whether right.
As long as he was not in anger,
He acted as one wished he'd act.
In all his reign, which was immense,
There was no man of his great strength.
He had a handsome face and body;
He gave great gifts and did so often.
The man's largesse went to excess;
He had no wish to gather wealth.

The Duke of Moriane invaded
During the reign of Morpidus,
Coming by sea, wasting the shores,
Capturing men to hold for ransom.
He brought an armored troop with him
Who were both scary and quite frightful.
They landed in Northumberland,
And there they started their destruction.
Concerned about this, Morpidus,
With Britons whom he called together,
Waged such a war against the duke
He overthrew and vanquished him.
One says this thing in truthfulness—
I do not know how it was proved—
That Morpidus defeated more
And with his hand killed more in battle
Than did the whole assembled force
Of people that he'd called together.
When he had taken all the field,
There was not one he caught alive
That he did not then disembowel
Or with a sword decapitate.
He made a pile of those he killed,
And when he had grown tired of killing,
He had the rest then skinned alive
And placed upon the fire and grilled
To satisfy his giant ire,
Which he could never moderate.
When he was in the prime of life,
When he was strong in will and heart,
There came up from the Irish Sea
A marvelously giant beast,
A sea monster, a horrid beast,
With horrid head and horrid body.

3420-24 The description of the sea monster has been amplified from that in Geoffrey (D'Alessandro, "*Historia* et *Roman*," 44). According to Weiss, "Wace extends the battle with the sea monster—a sort of external symbol of Morpidus's own cruelty—and makes it more satisfactory in that Morpidus wounds and kills it, though himself swallowed up" (*Roman de Brut*, 89, n. 1).

It was a creature of the sea;
A bigger one was never seen.
Both in the towns and on the shores,
It brought great pain and great destruction;
The beast devoured both men and women;
It ate the beasts out in the fields.
The people ran away in flight,
Abandoning their homes and towns.
They fled into the woods and mountains,
And still they feared that they would die.
Their cries were heard by Morpidus,
Who had a very hardy heart.
He trusted in his manly strength
And went to face the beast alone.
He went to fight as one sole body;
He never wanted any help.
It's foolish to be way too brave;
A fool trusts too much in himself.
Morpidus in bravery
Came to the monster without fear.
He shot his arrows, threw his spears,
And wounded it in many places.
When he'd naught else to thrust or shoot,
He set upon it with his sword.
But with a great stroke the sword broke—
The monster opened up its mouth,
Devoured the man and swallowed him:
Dead was the king through foolishness.
The beast, however, did not live:
The king had beaten it so much,
And slashed and wounded it so much,
That it expired right then and there.
There was no peasant not rejoicing.
For the dead king they took some comfort
In the great beast who fell down dead.
They had great sorrow for the king,
But they then felt a little better
To know the monster died as well.
Among them then the joy so grew
That Morpidus was all forgotten
And all the sadness went away.

He was the father of five sons:
Gorbonian who was first born—
Then Argal, and then Elidur,
Then Jugenës, then Peredur.
Gorbonian, who was the first,
As king was keen on laws and rights.
More sweetly never has a king
Governed a country's citizens:
He never lied if he could help it;
He never wronged a single man;
He never was immoderate;
He wanted to do right for all.
Loyal he was; in loyalty
He came at last to his life's end.
His tomb in London was prepared
With great attention to detail.
Argal, who after him was born,
Was after him raised up as king,
But he behaved disruptively
And was no copy of his brother.
He set the noble people low
And raised the low-class people up.
He dispossessed the folks with wealth;
He lied when he should tell the truth.
He put together a great fortune,
For he was covetous and greedy.
He never loved a loyal man;
He always liked an evil one.
Argal's evil way of life
And badness lasted for so long
That noble men banded together
And threw him right out of the land.
The third brother was then led forth,
Elidur, who they then crowned.
This one extended friendship freely,
For he had sympathy and sweetness.
Argal, the one who lost his kingdom,
Left to wander through many lands,
Seeking help, asking for aid
So that his reign would be restored.
But he did not know how to buy,

Request, or ask for such a thing,
And so he never found or saw
A person who would promise help
Or restoration of his loss.
In dire distress and poverty,
He sought his brother five years later
Within the wood of Calatere.
Argal encountered Elidur;
He sought his mercy and received it.
The king looked at his needy brother,
Felt touched enough to grant him mercy,
And many times he gave him hugs,
Patted his back, and gave him kisses.
To Aclud then, a town that lay
Nearby the place, he led the man.
Secretly then in his own chamber
He had him put away in hiding.
God! Who ever saw such pity,
Such love, or such fraternity!
The king pretended to be sick
And to be fearful of his death.
He had his barons all commanded
To come to him to pay a visit;
He had no hope that he would live;
They should come see him very quickly.
When they were all convened together
Upon the day that he had set
And were prepared to talk to him,
He had them pulled aside and asked
To come to peace agreeably
And not to make a noise or cry;
Each would come in his room alone,
And each would speak to him alone
Because his head was hurting badly
And noise would make him feel much worse.
These were the things that he commanded;
They could not enter otherwise.
As each one came into the chamber
And sought to parley with the king,
The king himself would grab each one
And hold him down and keep him still—

With servants that were there inside
Who carried drawn and naked swords—
Until he paid his brother homage.
There was no peer of such high birth
Who could deny the king's request
Without a hasty execution.
When Elidur had made all come
And thus become Argal's liege men
And when they had all sworn their oaths,
He led his brother to Everwic,
Where from his head he took the crown
And placed it on his brother's head.
He re-established him as king
And rendered all the reign to him.
For all the honor and the pity,
For all the goodness and the friendship
He tendered to his needy brother,
He then was always called "the pious."
Argal behaved himself so well
And left his evil ways so well
That there was never king so balanced,
So peaceful, or so full of honor.
For some ten years he ruled with strength,
But then he fell into disease:
He was to die (he had no choice),
For that's what pleased the King of Heaven.
Then Elidur was remade king
Just as he'd been in olden days.
He reassumed his dignity.
If he had been a good king once,
He then became a better one.
But his two younger brothers then
Combined their forces into one
And waged a war against the king
And met him one day in a battle;
But he had so few folk—they won.
I do not know just how they took him,
But they put him into safe keeping.
In London in a great big tower,
There Elidur spent many days.
They split the realm into two parts:

From Humber down toward the south
And all below and toward the west,
The land was owned by Jugenës;
Peredur owned the other part
But later ruled the land alone,
For Jugenës did not live more
Than seven years and then he died.
And Peredur then seized the throne,
But he did not enjoy it long,
For Death with violence took his life.
Badly he lived; badly he died.
For the third time then Elidur
Was made the king, and this was right.
From London's tower he was taken
And was made king for a third time,
And so he had redress for all
That he had suffered from his brothers.
He was a model king for justice
And for compassion and largesse
For all who would come after him
And hold the land when he was gone.
He never did a thing with blame;
He lived life well and died well too.
One of his nephews then took power,
Son of the oldest of his brothers,
The noble King Gorbonian.
Then Argal's son Margan was king.
Margan possessed a pleasant nature
And went to trouble to do well.
Much was done for the people's love,
And all the people wished him honor.
His brother, who was called Eumannus,
Obtained the kingdom after him.
He had a very cruel streak:
He lacked the wit to have a friend
And was not able to possess one.

3611ff Wace adds to the details concerning Merian, Bledudo, Blegabret, and Pir (Weiss, *Roman de Brut*, 95, ns. 1, 3, 5).

3619-36 "Wace expands on the wickedness of Eumannus" (Weiss, *Roman de Brut*, 93, n. 1).

All of the people hated him,
And so he hated all the people
And so did evil when he could.
Even the servants hated him
And served despite their own desires,
Since they had found him very cruel.
But they did not dare do a thing.
For six years he ruled as tyrant
With cruelty and foolishness,
And then they threw him from the realm
With the consent of all the land.
He was chased out and so he fled
And never came back there again.
They then elected as the king
Iwallo, son of Jugenës.
Iwallo could do heavy work
And march a lot without much sleep:
He was just like his ancient fathers
In deeds of arms and good behavior,
But he was not the king for long.
Because of this his men were sorry,
But against Death, he had no refuge.
Then after him the King of England
Was Runo, the son of Peredur;
Then Geronces, Elidur's son;
His son Catullus was then king;
After Catullus came Coïlus;
Then Porreus and then Cherim.
Cherim was given to fine drink,
Devoting himself to fine old wines.
He spent his youth completely
In drinking and in drunkenness—
He had no other claim to fame.
And God allowed him such good luck
That no one ever warred against him.
Three sons that he had with his wife
Controlled the kingdom in succession.

3652-58 "Wace adds Cherim's love of wine and undeserved good fortune" (Weiss, *Roman de Brut*, 93, n. 2).

They had the names Fulgenius,
Eldadus, and Andragius.
All three held England in succession,
With each one taking his own turn,
But little was the time they ruled,
And little was it till they ended.
Andragius' son, King Urian,
After his father ruled one year;
After Urian, Eliud
Ruled the country in great peace;
After Eliud, Cledaucus,
Then Doten, then Gurgustius,
Then Merian, who was good-looking
And who knew much of hounds and birds
And much of riverbanks and woods.
When he desired to hunt a thing,
He would not seek another pleasure,
For this diversion pleased him much.
He was attractive to the ladies
And much sought after and much loved,
But he did not have any lust
For any woman but his own.
Bledudo came to power next,
The son, who was just like the father,
But who was greater in largesse
And did not know how to say no
Or keep a thing for his own good:
He wished to give his things to all.
He had great goodness in his heart.
Succeeding this free-handed noble,
Cap was the king, Oënus next;
Then Sillius was after him,
But he lived just a little while.
Blegabret ruled after him.
He knew the ins and outs of song;
No one's known more or quite as much.
He mastered all the instruments,

3673-82 The *efficitio* of Merian is added by Wace as "an effort of personal fantasy" (D'Alessandro, "*Historia* et *Roman*," 46).

And he knew all there was of singing.
He knew plenty of lais and airs;
He played vielle and played the fiddle;
He played the harp and played the zither;
He played the lyre and psaltery too.
Because he had such gifts in music,
The people of his time would say
He was the god of all jongleurs
And also of all vocalists.
The king was such a pleasant man
That all would serve him out of joy,
And he was joyous all the time
And never cruel or filled with ire.
His brother, Archinal, then held
The reign in hand, enjoying peace.
His son Eldol was the next king,
Who did his best to be a fool,
For he was very lecherous
And very covetous of women.
Now there was not a noble woman
Who was of such high lineage—
Whether a wife or unwed maid—
Because she seemed attractive to him—
That he did not attempt to bed.
He made himself despised by many.
After Eldol came Redion;
Then Rederch had the kingdom next;
Then Famu Penissel was king;
Then Pir, who had a pretty head;
Now, with his head and with his hair,
Nature strongly honored him.
Caporus ruled then after Pir,
And then his son Eliguellus.
The latter acted very wisely
And also very temperately.
Heli, his son, who then ruled next,
Lived for forty years a model king.
This man Heli fathered three sons:
Lud was the name of the first son;
Cassibellanus was second born;
And after him was Nennius.

After Heli, Lud had the land,
Who was quite brave and skilled in war.
He was a very glorious knight
And marvelous host at feasts and such,
Where he would give with willing hands
And honor knights with plentitude.
King Lud built towns, and he built castles,
Restoring the old and building the new.
He built a wall surrounding London,
Which was the greatest of his towns.
Lud had the great enclosure made
Of the old walls that are still standing.
And for the people and the lords,
Lud constructed wondrous houses,
Provided that a man could say
That near the place he did not have
A house that was so nicely made
Or was so richly put in order.
Until his time and long before it,
Trinovant was London's name,
But for King Lud, who honored it
And spent much time sojourning there,
It got the name of *Kaerlud*.
Later, foreign men arrived,
Who did not know the language there,
But they said *Londoïn* for *Lud*.
Angles and Saxons later came,
Who even further changed the name,
Saying *London* for *Londoïn*,
And they used *London* a long time.
The Normans came and Frenchmen too,
Who did not know the English tongue
And did not know how to say *London*;
Before they knew what they should say,
They came to call the city *Lundres*,
And they kept their pronunciation.
Because of change and fluctuation
In languages of foreign people,
Who've often had the land by force
And who have often won and lost it,
The names of towns have suffered change,

By lengthening or shortening.
As I have heard and understood,
A person can find very few
Things that have completely kept
The names that they had from the first.
When good King Lud had met his end,
He was ensepulchered in London
Near to a port that had the name
Porlud in British from his name;
The English changed the way it's said:
For *Ludgate* is its name today.

V. The Coming of the Romans

Two children came from Lud the King,
But they were hardly grown up then.
Androgeus was the first born;
Tenuancius the second born.
Their uncle was Cassibellan,
A noble man, their father's brother.
He ruled the kingdom for his nephews;
He was proclaimed the king of all.
He was a good administrator,
A good knight, and a generous man.
He well knew how to run a country
And tried to make himself of service.
When the nephews were wise enough
And came to be of such an age
That they could manage property,
He gave them charge over two counties.
Androgeus, the older one,
For whom he had the greater love,
He charged with London and with Kent
To have and freely hold from him.
Tenuancius, the younger one,
He charged with Cornwall as his fief.
And so each one received his county,
And so they both were named as counts;
But they were vassals of their uncle,
And they regarded him as lord.
He was their sire and overlord
And held the rest of the land himself.
As long as they were in accord,
Their strength and power were sufficient;

They later suffered from some discord
(As witnessed and recorded by
This book's own author, Master Wace).
This discord was the evil cause
That let the Romans get some tribute
That they could never get before.
Some sixty years before the birth
Of Jesus Christ from Holy Mary,
Julius Caesar was on the move
And came to France from out of Rome
To conquer in a westward direction
The faraway regions and lands:
Julius Caesar, the valiant one,
The strong, the brave, the conqueror,
Who did so much and tried so much
He made the whole world his through conquest.
No man ever, before or since,
Of whom we know conquered so much.
Caesar was emperor of Rome;
A very wise and generous man,
He was a worthy knight in arms;
A learned man, he read and wrote.
Now when the Romans had subdued
All the land surrounding them,
Caesar received Roman permission
To go and conquer distant lands.
He called together the best youths;
He passed Montjoie and Lombardy.
First he conquered Burgundy,
Then France, Auvergne, and Gascony,

3821-25 J. Zatta, "Translating the *Historia*," 156, argues that "If Geoffrey's story of Cassivelaunus functions as does the story of Belinus and Brennius to warn that disobedience and insubordination to the king result in the subjection of a nation, the vernacular *Bruts* make the opposite point: that a king who fails to appreciate and treat fairly the vassals by whose strength he has prevailed over his enemies suffers inevitable defeat."

3833ff Wace's praise of Julius Caesar draws sympathy away from the Britons (Blacker, *Faces of Time*, 97-98), although "Wace omits Caesar's contempt for the 'degenerate' Britons in *HRB* chap. 54, mentioning, on the contrary, the achievements of Belin and Brennes" (Weiss, *Roman de Brut*, 99, n. 2). Wace regards Caesar as "an ideal ruler, although he mistakenly thinks he became emperor" (99, n. 1).

Brittany, Normandy, and Poitou.
He then campaigned in Germany.
At many sites, he built new castles
And towns and fortresses with walls.
He managed his resources well;
He came to Flanders and Boulogne.
He looked out on the sea from there
And saw an island and then asked
What land it was that he could see
And who the people there might be.
And so the natives let him know
That he could see a good-sized island
That Brutus settled first of all
And led the Trojan people there.
He named it Britain for himself,
For he was made the king and leader.
Successors who came from his line
Possessed the kingdom after him.
And Caesar gave them this response:
"I know," he said, "who Brutus was;
Both he and we are from one line.
The heads of our respective lines
Had their beginnings back in Troy.
After the great destruction there,
The barons left and went away
And got their hands on many lands.
From this island of Britain came
Belin and Brennës, who grew in strength
Until they took the city of Rome
And wrecked the power of our senate.
But we should let them know for sure
That Rome now has a different strength:
Lady Fortune has turned her wheel,
And Rome has been invigorated.
It's right for them to hear us now
And render tribute now to Rome.
We surely ought to take back that
Which long ago they took from us.
By letter I will summon them;
I know that they will want to answer.
I do not wish to cross the sea

If they will peacefully agree
To render tribute unto Rome
And then to hold their fiefs from us."
He had his letters made and sent
Across the sea to Cassibellan
And ordered him to be his man
And render tribute to the Romans.
Cassibellan, who was upset,
Had letter made to answer letter:
He did not wish to scribble greetings,
But sent instead a note of anger:
"Caesar, it seems to us a marvel;
And marveling, we find distasteful
The Roman brand of haughtiness
That goes too far and lasts too long.
Such greediness cannot allow
Freedom for any, but the Romans.
All gold and silver in the world,
The kings, the counts, the other folks,
They wish to put beneath their rule.
No one at all can suffer them;
They want to grab up everything—
What can they do with all of this?
We, who live at the world's top,
Here on an island that we own,
Will not be passed then by the Romans
Before they make demands of tribute.
Caesar, you test our strength indeed
Demanding that we pay you tribute
And wanting us as tributaries.
But you will not get anything.
We've always lived completely free,
And freely we have held our land;
And we should live in liberty
Just like the Romans do with right,
For we descend from the same root,
From the same people and same race.
Caesar, if you yourself consider
And if you have regard for reason,
You should feel quite a bit of shame
For asking us to pay you tribute

And wanting us to be your servants
Since we are relatives of yours.
We ought to be the peers of Romans
Since we descend from the same line.
A man as wise, a lord as noble
As you must be—how dare you say
That we should now become your serfs
When we have never learned to serve,
And never, please God, ever will—
Do you conclude that we could learn?
We always have been such free men
That no one of our ancestry
Has ever known or now does know
How one should live in servitude.
We do not know, unless we're told,
How servants live in servitude.
We're free and want to stay that way.
If very God Himself in heaven
Wished to put us down by force,
We'd want to fight with all our might
So that we would not lose through man
What we have owned for a long time.
You should know now—for we hide nothing—
That, while we are all still alive
And can still keep ourselves together,
We will defend our liberty.
We wish to live with freedom and honor
Just as our ancestors once lived."
As soon as Caesar had seen the letter,
He very plainly recognized
That he would have to cross the sea:
He had no other choice or option.
He had great ships and barges built;
Eighty of them that were so large
That there were never any larger
For bearing people and their cargo,
Not counting other smaller ships
That came about on every hand.
When Caesar had them all prepared
And had good weather and good wind,
He had men cry: "To ships! To ships!"

They entered and they raised the masts.
They had good wind and soon they sailed;
They came to port and thus arrived.
They had just barely come to land,
There where the sea receives the Thames,
When through the whole country was spread
The news that they had come ashore.
Cassibellan, who knew right well
These people would be coming there,
Had all his barons come together,
Who had been summoned from all parts.
He had a lot of lords and vassals:
Belins was there, his seneschal,
Who was his privy counselor
And under him the master justice.
He had his pair of nephews near
In whom he trusted over all,
On the one hand Androgeus,
And on the other Tenuancius.
Androgeus led the Londoners;
Tenuancius led the Cornishmen.
And Nennius of Canterbury—
One could not choose a better man—
The younger brother of the king,
Was right next to this pair of nephews.
Beside the counts there were some kings,
Who'd come as three to join the host.
And each one had a fighting force:
Eridious the King of Scots
And Britaël of Northern Wales
And Guertaët of Southern Wales.
Each one had come there willingly
In order to defend his rights.
They all gave counsel to the king,
And all of them gave firm approval
That he should move against the Romans
And not let them get off the beaches

3990 The addition of the mention of trust emphasizes "sharply the poignancy of later betrayal—a recurrent theme" (Weiss, *Roman de Brut*, 101, n. 2).

And set the land under a siege
And build their forts and battlements.
This counsel taken, all were armed.
When they were all prepared for war
And each one had arranged his troops
In ordered ranks without confusion,
They set out then to beat the Romans.
Caesar, who'd seen them coming on,
Cried to his men: "Arm yourselves!
You'll see them coming on us now!"
Right then the battle was engaged,
Which on that day was very frightful.
You could then see horses well spurred,
Lances brandished, knights engaged,
Shields pierced through, saddles emptied,
Soldiers felled and wounds cut open.
Knights joined jousting; archers drew;
They fought and hurt each other well.
The arrows fell just like the rain,
Pleasing these, annoying those.
You could have heard the skullbones crack;
You could have seen the wounded die.
All of the grass was red with blood,
But this was not a wondrous thing,
For living men were on the dead
And fought above the ones who died.
Caesar had in his company
The best of all his knights in arms,
Who pressed on hard, defended hard,
Gave battle hard, and labored hard.
No one who went against them there
Had any guarantee from death.
Androgeus, with men from Kent,
And Nennius, with all his people,
Drew apart from all the rest
And formed a line with their two forces.
They then joined Caesar in the battle

4021ff "Wace constantly evokes the horrors of war with details like this" (Weiss, *Roman de Brut*, 103, n. 2).

And got mixed up with Caesar's men.
Nennius recognized the man
And came on him and hit him thus.
Happy he was to touch a noble
Like the Emperor of Rome.
Caesar held his shield in front
And took the blow of Nennius.
Well mannered too, he drew his sword
With which he made a lot of plays
And hit Nennius on the helmet
So that a great big piece came off.
He cut him on the head a bit
And would have knocked him down right there,
But Nennius moved from the blow,
Lowered his head, raised up his shield,
And caught the sword right in the shield.
So deeply did it sink its blade
That Caesar could not get it out—
Never had he tugged so hard.
He pulled on sword; the other shield;
Each one gripped his own thing well.
Nennius wished to turn away,
But Caesar made him stay right there.
Believe me well that Caesar pulled him,
And one retained the other one.
But Nennius' force began to grow;
Androgeus himself ran there
With a great troop of Kentish men:
From everywhere came help and aid.
Caesar dared not hang around
Since he had no one to defend him.
He threw away his shield-bound sword,
And Nennius, who had some help,
Shook the shield and took the sword,
With which he killed a lot of Romans.
He could not strike a single man
Who could fend off the blow he gave.
Using the sword that came from Caesar—
So strong a man, so high a lord—
Valiant Nennius did a lot.
Before him came Labienus,

Who was a lord of high degree,
A man in Rome with a big title.
Nennius gave him such a blow
He cut the head right off the body.
You could not try to count the dead
Or name the best of the combatants,
But many fell there many times
And died in massive quantities—
And plenty more there would have died
If night had not split them apart.
The night came on and the day failed,
And so they had to leave the field.
The Romans, who were quite upset,
Went back into their resting places.
They were exhausted and dismayed
And beaten up at the same time.
They were advised to go away
And also leave this land behind them,
For they would not get terms of peace
And they did not have ample force.
That night they went down to the ships
And thus they went across to Flanders.

When morning came and Britons knew
The Romans had made their departure,
They made joy and were very happy,
But afterwards they were depressed,
For Nennius, the hardy lord,
Could not then find a thing to help
The wound that he had got himself
When he retained the sword of Caesar.
On day fifteen he passed away.
In London at the northern gate,
He was entombed with royal pomp,
With much beauty and courtliness,
For he was brother to the king,
Who loved him as he loved himself.
Beside the body there was placed
Within the tomb the very sword
That he got from the emperor.
The sword was laid in honor there.
This sword was very high in value,

For it was marked with golden letters.
Along the pommel these words told
How it was named *Crocea Mors.*
It got this name "The Yellow Death"
Because it never cut a body
That ever could find medicine
To turn it back away from death.
Soon enough the French were told
(Such news could not be hid from them)
The Romans were in bad array.
They had made subjects of the French,
Who held themselves unfortunate
For having made their peace with them.
They got back all their bravery,
And so they grew emboldened then,
Because they had received the news
That Romans had been put to flight.
The fleer has enough pursuers;
The threatener himself has fears;
He makes his threats because he fears
And chases when there's naught to lose.
The French threatened the Romans much,
And they disdained them quite a lot
And said they'd be unfortunate
If ever they held land from them;
They said they'd love to kill them all
If they could get their hands upon them.
They had great hatred of their lordship
And were afraid of their bad deeds.
And so their hardihood increased
As news was often spread abroad
That Britons would come on the sea
And bring the battle to the Romans.
But this French pride came to an end
When Caesar had a talk with them.
Caesar knew how to ward off trouble
And moderate the pride of men;
He knew how to appease the greedy

4129-36 Weiss notes that Wace added "the gold lettering and the sword's fame" in the manner of the writer of a *chanson de geste* (*Roman de Brut*, 105, n. 2).

And make them alter their desire;
And he knew how to act quite humble
When force was not appropriate.
He saw the French with their disdain
And with their violence aimed at him
And saw his men with all their wounds
And their exhaustion from the fighting,
And he preferred to spend his goods
Than enter into doubtful war.
To dukes and to the highest barons,
He gave great gifts of gold and silver.
He added to the things they owned
As much as they had wished to get,
And more than that he promised that—
When and if he beat the Britons—
To poor men, he'd give liberty
And set them free of servitude.
To those who had been put in exile
Or chased from their inheritance,
He promised all their heritage
And restoration of their losses.
After they had seen the goods
And gotten them into their hands,
Each one then had a change of heart.
You have great power, worldly goods!
Quickly you have caused a fight
And quickly turned a war to nothing.
The ones who hated Caesar once
And who desired to murder him
Changed their hearts for yellow gold;
And each one said that he was lord
And could ask them for anything
And even lead them into Britain.
When Caesar had appeased them all
And he had all of them assuaged,
With clever ingenuity,
He made a tower by the sea,

4201 ff. "The tower of Ordre actually existed, created by Caligula and restored by Charlemagne; it was demolished in 1644" (Weiss, *Roman de Brut*, 107, n. 2; see also Arnold, *Roman de Brut*, 2.800, and Houck, *Sources*, 216).

Within Boulogne, which was called Odre.
I do not know what it looked like.
It was unusually designed:
Around the bottom it was wide,
But it got always narrower
The higher up one went in it.
It only took a single stone
To cover up the highest part.
It had a lot of floors and levels,
And each one had a lot of windows.
There Caesar had his treasure guarded
And all his precious goods delivered.
Caesar himself would go inside
Whenever he feared treachery.
For two years he remained in France.
He made his tower Odre ready;
For he had built it by the cities
And by the lands in his control,
Which were accustomed to his taxes
And which would send them all to Odre.
  In these two years, he got prepared
And got six hundred ships together.
And so he said he'd try again
To see if he could beat the Britons.
He would not prize what he had done
If he now let them lie in peace.
  When he'd obtained his fleet of ships
And was prepared to make his voyage,
He loaded his six hundred ships
With all the things that they would need.
They rowed so much and sailed so much
That they went up the River Thames.
Now they had thought and they had planned—
But they were lacking in their thinking—
That they would go upon the water
Until they came ashore in London,
And then they'd make their first appearance
And wage their war against the Britons.
The Britons were prepared for them;
I do not know just how they heard.
They put iron stakes into the Thames

That were placed well and hidden well
So that no ship that entered there
Was not imperiled in dishonor.
So when the ships came up the Thames
And made their way above this place,
They did not sail too far that way
When they were struck by the great stakes.
Then you'd have seen the floundering ships
Receiving water and sinking down,
One ship crashing on another,
Falling masts and twisting beams,
Splitting hulls and cracking boards.
They could not land at port or bank;
They'd badly sailed and badly rowed.
Caesar then looked on all this damage:
He saw the danger and the stakes
And wished for different everywhere.
He made his ships then turn about,
And reached the land and sallied forth.
Then they established their encampments
And set up their pavilions.
Then see Cassibellan on fire,
Who did not go with hesitation;
The nephews and the kinfolk did the same,
And all the barons did so too.
When the king let out his battle cry,
There was no coward who then shirked.
They went to strike them in the camps;
Then you'd have heard the weapons clashing.
The Romans stayed around their tents
And wondrously put up resistance.
They had their bravery as a wall,
And so they gave a good strong fight.
They did not try too hard at first
But then regained their hardiness.
They put them into a retreat
And made a number of them die.
The Britons later held their line,
For all the time their people came.
Their numbers were some three times greater
In knights (not counting other soldiers)

Than those that Caesar had led there,
And so they gave them a good pounding.
They had a massive force in back
And therefore killed a lot of Romans.
Caesar, the brave and valiant one,
Who never lost his head to fear,
Saw that the Britons had great force
But that his men could hold them back,
For they were fighting in a rage
And did not fear the clash of arms.
He stationed all this men in front,
And he was in a line in back.
He gave the Britons fierce resistance,
And nothing bad befell his men.
He made the ships approach the land
And made his men all go inside,
And at the end he entered too.
He had good weather, wind, and breeze;
He came ashore at Odre, his tower.
There he spent a good long time
To let his wounded soldiers heal
And let his other soldiers rest.
During the time that he spent there,
He called the barons of the land.

Cassibellan was very joyful
For his deliverance from the Romans.
He had defended his land twice
And vanquished Caesar two times too.
For happiness and for the glory
Over his double victory,
He made a promise to the gods
To hold a feast of great proportions
And render vows and sacrifice,
And named a day for such a service.
The men of his houses and estates
Were summoned and were all commanded
To come to London for this feast
And to observe the feast with him;

4297-4300 Tactic added by Wace (Weiss, *Roman de Brut*, 109, n. 4).

For none of them could be excused
Who had been in his obligation.
All of them came there filled with joy,
Dressed up in festive clothes and robes,
With all their wives and all their children
And all their other relatives.
The feast was celebrated nicely;
The people there were beautiful.
Each one, as was appropriate,
Made sacrifice in his own way.
Some forty thousand full-grown cows
And thirty thousand untamed does,
Which had been caught in many ways,
Were sacrificed upon that day.
A hundred thousand birds then followed
And wondrous flocks of table fowl.
And when they made their sacrifice
And eaten very many things,
Since it was fitting for the day,
As was the custom of the time,
They turned the day to one of pleasure.
The knights then jousted with their lances;
The squires squared off with one another,
Casting stones and dice and jumping.
But as the games came to an end,
A fighting match commenced between
Hirelgas, nephew of the king,
A youth of great nobility,
And Evelin, Androgeus' nephew,
Who was a very good opponent.
Their match went on a good long time
Both out of pride and out of hatred,
For they had turned the game to anger
And started trading foolish words.
The words would grow so out of hand
That they would come to naked swords.
Without a moment passing, dead
By great misfortune lay Hirelgas.
All of the court was in confusion.
And when the king had heard the news,
He was in anguish for his nephew,

And he was very fierce and angry.
He'd brought him up and held him dear;
He wished that he could get revenge.
He demanded of Androgeus
And asked according to his rights
That he make come and send to him
His nephew Evelin directly
To sit for judgment in his court
Without delay or be in wrong.
Androgeus thought to himself
That if he did, the king would kill him.
He knew the king was very violent
And feared the judgment of the court.
He said the king was not his lord,
For he was free and had a court;
And he who had a claim against him
Should seek redress in his own court.
The king, who had a swollen heart,
Renounced his oath to Androgeus.
He said he'd strip him of his fiefs
And said he'd kill him if he could.
They were estranged by these bad things
And fell into a mutual hatred.
The king wasted the other's lands,
Burning, destroying, and robbing them.
Androgeus saw his massive losses:
He knew the culprit was the king.
He sent his messengers to him
And asked him and requested him
Not to lay his lands to waste.
He should relent for his own nephew.
The king was cruel and filled with ire;
He would not grant a truce or peace.
Androgeus did not have options;
He knew the king was very cruel,
So he gave up his open lands
And loaded up his fortresses.
He found no one who'd dare to help
Or who could save him from the king.
He did not wish to flee in silence
Or lose what he had strength to keep.

He'd have, he said, great misery
If the king's pride did not abate.
That doing bad could head off worse
Was what the villain thought was wise
And that one ought to suffer evil
To save himself from even worse.
And to destroy his enemy
A man should sometimes harm himself.
Androgeus concluded then
That he would sadly have to wound
The land that he shared with the king
Before he would be saved from him.
He'd be a fool to ever think
That the king's pride would ever lessen.
Privately and on the sly,
He had a letter made and sealed;
He had it sent across to Caesar.
These are the words of that same letter:
"To Caesar, the valiant and the strong:
Close to a death that he desires,
Androgeus, the lord and duke
Of London, sends his salutations.
Caesar, often one has seen
That people have had such great hatred,
Who afterwards have loved each other
And then become the best of friends.
After great anger there's great love;
After great shame there is great honor—
This often happens to the people
Who used to have a mutual hate.
Now we two wished each other dead
When you and I fought with each other.
I only know it can be said
That each desired to kill the other.
But here it's come to pass for us
That I have not been killed—nor you.
I now believe that I need you
And that you can provide me aid.
Two times you've come to battle us,
And two times you have been defeated.
But now you ought to know for sure—

And I will tell you as the truth—
Our ports would have been left to you
If not for me and for my forces.
You could have come in perfect safety
Without defeat from the king's hands.
But with myself and with my aid,
Cassibellan had victory.
Cassibellan beat you through me;
He took the land from you through me.
You lost our land because of me;
You ran away because of me.
But I repent of all this now
That I have been of harm to you;
And I will love you in return,
And I will give the land to you.
I'm sad that I have caused you pain
And that I was there with the king,
For he has since lost moderation
And his excessive pride has grown.
Never again will he love me;
He'll never let me be in peace.
He's set the torch to all my land,
Robbed my people, and chased them off.
He wants to throw me from my land
And take my legacy away.
I swear to God and tell you truly
That I have not deserved all this,
Unless one claims I have desert,
For saving the life of my own nephew,
Whom he'd have judged to suffer death
If I'd permitted him to do so.
The reason for our disagreement
And explanation for its cause
I wish to tell for you to judge,
And so you'll know the truth about it.
For the great honor that we received
From you by gaining victory,
We sent word to our friends and people,
And we assembled there in London.
We made our vows to all our gods
And made our sacrifices to them.

When we had finished all our rites,
Rendered our vows and sacrificed,
For different games in different ways
There was a general gathering
Of serving boys and of young squires.
And so there came to play together
My nephew, who was there with me,
And the nephew of the king himself.
They sparred and played around a bit
Until my nephew beat the other.
The nephew of the king got mad
And made to hit him with a sword.
He drew a sword and tried to strike him;
My nephew ran to hold him back.
He grabbed the hand that held the sword;
He wished to keep from being slashed.
I don't know how, but he stopped him,
And on the sword the other stumbled.
He fell upon it, wounding himself.
The boy was dead; he never moved.
There was no other weapon present;
He was not wounded otherwise.
The king found out and summoned me
And by my fief commanded me
To give my nephew up to him
And to deliver him for judgment.
I knew well what the king would do:
For the one killed, he'd kill the other.
So I told him I had a court
And in my court I would do justice.
Because I contradicted him
And did not follow his command,
He wrecks my land and chases me
And does his best to murder me.
Lord Caesar, thus I ask you now
To come to me, with the agreement
That you will have Britain from me,
And I will be your aid and comfort.
You should not be a bit suspicious
That I speak now with treachery.
I would not do so for my life,

But come soon, sir, and be my aid.
Help me, and I will give you help,
And to you I'll deliver Britain.
The one who's vanquished at the first
Will rise up at the very last."
Caesar listened to the letter,
And then some straight talk was begun.
When he had spoken to his men,
He answered by his messenger
That he would not believe mere words
And would not come there for mere words;
But if he sent him hostages,
He'd come just as he asked him to.
Androgeus dreaded the king,
Who wished to lay a siege on London.
He took his son, whose name was Scena
And had him sent off as a hostage
With thirty very noble youths
Who all were born of his close kin;
And Caesar had them all led off
To Odre, his tower, under guard.
As soon as he could, he boarded ship;
He crossed the sea and came to shore.
He came to Dover secretly
And very unexpectedly.
Androgeus came there to him,
And so they both together spoke
And so affirmed their covenant
And talked about all the details.
Cassibellan gathered his army;
He wished to lay a siege on London.
Rumor, who flies in every place
And who creates great talk from little,
Came to the king and let him know
That Romans had returned to him
And had set up their camp at Dover;
Already they had killed and burned—
So lively was the counsel given.
The king considered it a marvel
That they'd returned to this domain;
He never expected their return.

He summoned his host and called his lords;
He made a hasty trip to Dover.
Caesar, who awaited at Dover,
When he learned that the king was coming,
With the advice of Androgeus,
Issued from the town of Dover.
Close enough within a valley,
He had his men completely armed.
He had his companies prepared
And had his troops arranged for battle
And given orders what to do
First and then second and then last.
When Caesar had arranged all this,
He spoke to all; and he forbade
That, no matter what they might see,
They should not let their ranks get mixed.
No brave man should break up the lines,
And neither should a coward either.
They should remain completely hidden
Until the others came upon them.
But he who ventured close to them
Or he who dashed forth up against them
Might be received by points of lances
Upon the face, the chest, or belly.
Androgeus, in secrecy,
Then set an ambush up himself
With five thousand within the woods
Who all desired to take the king.
And when the king came close to Dover,
He looked down to the valley below:
He saw the Romans with helmets laced,
With all prepared to fight a battle.
He rearranged his companies
And got them ready for a fight.
He moved to close the distance then
And made them draw and lower lances.
For a long time they had been shouting,
Drawing out swords, lancing and throwing

4583-94 Speech and tactic added by Wace (Weiss, *Roman de Brut*, 117, n. 2).

Before Androgeus cried out,
Who issued from his hiding place.
The king then heard the noise arise
And saw the clouds of dust come up.
He could not drive right at the Romans
Or dare to wait on those behind.
He made a turn to cut across;
He wished to go up on a hill.
They all despised him wondrously
And all desired to have him dead.
He held himself betrayed and doomed,
And all the Britons with himself.
Each one thought to save himself
By going fast and running off.
Fleeing was better than foolish staying;
Fleeing fast was their intention.
I know no other remedy
For people who have no defense.
There was a hill that lay close by,
And some of them ran to its top.
The hill was topped with bushy growth,
With boulders and with hazel trees.
They fled and spurred with so much haste
That they came up to the hill's summit.
But in the climb and scramble up,
You could have seen a lot fall down.
But after they were on the top
And were inside the hazel trees,
They were as safe as they would be
If they'd been closed within a wall.
The Roman power then was nothing,
With Britons all so well protected.
Caesar moved around them then,
From time to time assailing them;
And when he saw they were so high
He could not take them by assault,
He laid a siege around them all.
They would not leave except through him.
On the descents and on the paths,
He placed great troops of cavalry
And had great tree trunks laid across them,

Which they could never get around.
He never once forgot a bit—
Indeed he often brought it up—
That they had caused him lots of trouble
And chased him from the country twice.
The British men were proven warriors,
Courageous, strong, and battle-hardened,
Who'd fought the wars against the Romans
And who had beaten this man twice
Who'd won and owned all of the world.
And still there where they were besieged
And where they waited for no help,
They made resistance and defense,
For they disdained to give advantage
To those they used to beat and chase.
But Fortune has a different color:
Her wheel had made its revolution,
And those who'd turned up on the top
Were those who'd been down at the bottom.
The Britons who had been besieged,
Surrounded by their enemies,
Had naught to drink and naught to eat
And did not have a way to get them.
They feared no weapon or assault
Or war machine but that which burned
When thirst and hunger took control,
Attacking without arms or steel.
You'll never see such strength in arms,
For these were men of bravery
Who were so strong and hard to take
That famine could not weaken them.
When all their food had disappeared,
Nothing else assaulted them.
Cassibellan was miserable;
He did not know how to escape.
He saw the Romans everywhere
Who wished to have him in their hands.
He had no means to fight a battle,

4665-68 Wace added the details about Fortune (Weiss, *Roman de Brut*, 119, n. 1).

And rampant hunger killed his men.
They hollered out for Caesar's mercy,
And great hunger distressed them fiercely.
They'd make peace with the emperor
Or die of hunger on the hill.
They suffered for two days, then three;
They sought no peace or offered none.
The king then took a messenger
(A servant or a knight, I guess)
And put a message in his charge
And sent him with it to his nephew
Androgeus, there in the siege,
There to him, strong anger's victim.
He asked him not to dishonor him;
If he could save him, he should do so.
He never had done such a wrong
That he should hate him mortally—
Even if he had warred against him.
One ought not mortally despise
A relative for one small wrong.
They still could come to an agreement
And make amends for their misdeeds.
But when one loses one's own kin,
There isn't any remedy.
Among mankind there had been wars,
Possessions seized and also land,
But in exchange for what they lost,
One group would not then kill the other.
One should be courteous, when able.
No one knows where such was done.
He should report his words to Caesar
And, if he could, make peace between them
As long as he'd not lose his land
Or have his person violated.
The nephew would not there have honor
Where the uncle had dishonor.
Androgeus had this response:
"What happened to the king, my lord?
He's quickly had a change of heart!
It's hardly been much time at all
Since he desired to burn me out

And chase me out of all the land
And threatened me with my own death.
He's calmed his anger very quickly.
When one stays in too great a fortress,
It turns him to great cruelty.
A lord does nothing to get praise
Who's bold and fierce in time of peace.
When he goes out to war or battle,
He seems to be weighed down with fear.
When a king beats a certain lord,
Say, someone like an emperor,
He ought not think and ought not say
That by himself alone he conquered.
He did not battle by himself
Nor win the battle by himself.
Through me and through the other men,
Who many times were thereby wounded,
Cassibellan won victory,
From which he then derived such glory.
The barons and the knights in arms
Are also partners in the glory.
To the extent that each has conquered
Or shown his force or shown his fierceness,
Then each one ought to have his share
Of the rewards of chivalry.
One should indeed inform the king
That he could not have victory
Through his own efforts all alone:
Only a fool would think he could.
But I have gotten fine revenge
When he is so humiliated
That he asks me and he begs me
To get some mercy and some pity.
I will not give him bad for bad,
As if he were a mortal foe.
He is my uncle; I will not slight him.
I am his nephew; I'll save his honor."
Androgeus, talking like this,
Went on his way to Caesar then.
He humbly fell upon his knees
And spoke to him with ample sweetness:

“Caesar, you’ve conquered and you’ve vanquished
Cassibellan and all his land.
Lord, in your mercy he will come,
And from the Romans take his fief.
Accept his truce, accept his homage,
For he holds Britain as an heir.
Grant him mercy; let him be.
What more should you demand of him
Than that he should become your man
And from the Romans hold his land?
Pity is valued in a lord,
More than any other good.”
Caesar walked away from him;
He would not hear him and he left.
Androgeus then went and caught him.
He acted angry, so he said:
“Stay here, Caesar, don’t go away!
Well I’ve kept your covenant.
I have placed Britain in your hands;
You can now be its overlord.
I promised you no other thing;
I made no other covenant
Except that I would do my best
To put Britain into your hands.
It’s yours—just what more do you want?
It would not please the God on high
For my uncle by any right
To be in prison or in shackles.
He will not easily be killed
As long as I’m alive and well.
He is the uncle who raised me.
When he desires for me to aid him,
I am his man; I cannot fail him.
And if you do not wish to hear me
And do the things that I direct,
I’ll leave you and defy you too.”
Caesar then stopped walking away
And authorized what he requested.
They both demanded hostages,
And they were given on both sides.
The Romans then detailed the tribute;

The Britons granted it to them:
Three thousand pounds for every year.
Then forward came Cassibellan
And Caesar, who then met each other,
Exchanged kisses and made their peace.
But I have never found in texts
Or ever heard in any tale
That England ever paid the tribute
After Caesar conquered it.
When all the talk came to an end
And when the peace was orchestrated,
Each one went to his own country,
And this assembly took its leave.
People say, and it could be,
That Caesar founded Exeter.
Exeter is named as such,
Because it lies upon the Exe.
Caesar spent the winter there.
When summer came, he went away.
Out of friendship and of love,
He took Androgeus along
And also English hostages
From all the highest families.
 After Caesar went away,
Cassibellan lived for six years
And rendered tribute for the same;
I'm ignorant of his wife and children.
At Everwic, where he passed on,
The corpse was laid within a tomb.
Tenuancius, who was from Cornwall,
Held the kingdom after him.
He was his nephew, so he took it,
This brother of Androgeus.
The kingdom fell when he had died
To his first-born son Kimbelin,
A brave knight and a courteous man.
He had been made a knight in Rome
By Caesar Augustus the Emperor.
In his time the Savior was born,
Jesus, God's Son, who came from heaven;
Thus God became a man for us,

And for redemption of us all,
He suffered pain upon the cross.
There was in Britain a divine
Who had the name of Teleusin.
He was regarded a good prophet
And was believed by many people.
During a feast they were observing,
Where Britons sat there all together,
The king requested and he asked
That Teleusin would tell him something
About the times that would be coming.
And Teleusin went on to say:
"Man, you should not be in sadness.
We have awaited night and day,
And to the earth from heaven descended
Is the long-awaited One,
The one who'll save us, Jesus Christ."
The prophecy that this man uttered
Was in the memory of the Britons.
For a long time it wasn't forgotten.
He spoke the truth; he did not lie.
For in that time Jesus was born.
The Britons thus believed the quicker
When they heard preaching about the Christ.
Kimbelin was very honored
And very intimate with Romans.
He could have kept the tribute back,
For it was not demanded then,
But nonetheless he paid it all
And kept back nothing of the payments.
He had two sons: Wider the first
And Arviragus the second born.
For ten years king, he then passed on;
Wider his son succeeded him.
He was a marvelous knight in arms,
But he was fierce and full of pride;
He had no love for Roman people
And did not want to do them service.
He took Britain away from them
And took away their tribute too.
He did not want to wait on them

And did not want to pay their tribute.
Now Claudius resented this.
As emperor, he pledged his head
That he would get the tribute back
And disinherit Wider too.
With the consensus of the Senate,
He rode so much and marched so much
With the great host that he assembled
That he crossed over into England.
At Portchester he thus came to land,
Upon a day he came to hate.
Portchester was the city's name,
But it was later burned and wasted.
The emperor besieged the city,
But he had pain before he took it.
He ordered rocks and mortar brought;
Before the gates he built a wall
So no one outside could go in
And no one inside could go out.
He thought he'd starve them out this way;
He had no other means to harm them.
But Wider came to rescue them.
He came with over a thousand shields,
And Arviragus was with him.
Claudius could not resist them.
He drew back to the ships with men
But left a number on the field.
Nevertheless, they often fought,
And well they often were defeated.
Claudius had Hamun with him,
Who was his counselor and baron.
In him was all his confidence,
For he was very valiant.
This Hamun saw Wider in battle,
Slashing at Romans, knocking them down,
Wisely arranging his battle lines,
Leading them forth in orderly fashion.
As long as this man lived, he said,
Britain never would succumb.
He thought about the many means
That he could use to kill the man.

He came upon a British corpse;
He secretly removed its armor.
He dressed himself in British armor
And got mixed up among the Britons.
He was among the British troops;
He fought beside the British troops;
He marched beside the British troops;
He talked among the British troops.
The arms he wore deceived them all,
And he knew how to speak their tongue,
Since from the Roman hostages,
He'd learned a lot of languages.
Hamun knew British rather well
And knew the names of many Britons.
Hamun went so far across
And so far back and so far forward
That he came close to Wider the king
And was then face to face with him.
Upon a turn that the king made,
Hamun drew his sword and killed him.
From here to there he moved around,
And he returned among his people.
Arviragus, who observed
The king was dead upon the ground,
Was the first one to find this out,
But he stopped there for little time;
There was not space at all to stay
Or time to cry or to complain.
The armor and the decorations
Of the king, he took right then.
In secrecy he armed himself
And got back on his horse again.
Then you'd have seen the fighting knights,
Turning often and joining often,
Shouting the king's rallying cry,
Encouraging the British men.
Not a man could figure out
That this was not Wider the king.
The Romans fled in disarray.
They did not dare to hold their lines.
He made them split into two halves;

They could not give each other help.
One half turned toward the ships,
And he who could entered them first.
Now Claudius had turned with these,
And with these men he boarded ship.
The other half turned to the woods,
The half that could not make the ships.
Hamun fled among this group,
And Arviragus followed him.
Hamun was told and he believed
That Claudius was taking leave.
They ran through woods and across the plains
Until they came to ships in port.
Hamun descended from his horse;
He wished to get upon a ship
That merchants there had in possession,
Who were in port to do some trading.
Arviragus followed him
And cut his head right off his body.
Since Hamun died in this location,
Was killed there and was beaten there,
Later in that land it was
And is still called the town of Hampton,
This is to say, it seems to me,
The town where Hamun was destroyed.
In just this way names often come
From little things in the beginning;
By many little accidents
Many names come to endure.
Arviragus slew this Hamun
And left the body lying there.
Meanwhile it came to happen that
This Claudius returned to land.
He reassembled all his ships;
To Portchester he made his return.
He broke the walls and tore them down,
And all the men he set afire
And burned the city to the ground.
It never afterward enjoyed
The good, the worth, or the esteem
That it enjoyed before this day.

When he had Portchester leveled flat,
He went to Winchester fast as he could.
He set a siege on Arviragus
And almost all his relatives.
He made machines and set them up
To smash the walls and tear them down.
Arviragus was very concerned,
For it seemed quite unfortunate
That he was shut up in a siege.
Out of the town he issued forth.
He set his knights into formation
And split his archers in two groups.
The infantry was in the rear,
Completely armed in normal fashion.
They were already in formation,
Ready to stab, ready to throw,
When a group of wise and ancient men
Made their approach in one direction.
They were afraid of all the loss,
And so they sought the emperor
To ask what he desired to do,
To ask if he wished peace or war.
He answered them in a good way
That he had no desire for war
But much preferred both peace and love
As long as Rome had honor there.
He had no other care at all
As long as Rome retained its rights.
He would do good for Arviragus:
He had a daughter he would give him
If he desired to be his man
And hold his fief from Roman hands.
Arviragus granted such,
And they became then reconciled.
In Winchester they took up lodging,
Where they became each other's friends.
From there to Rome some men were sent
Who were prepared on this occasion
To go and lead back Genoïs,
Whom Claudius would give away.
Meanwhile he seized the Orkney Islands

With Arviragus and his help,
And other islands surrounding them
Whose names I happen not to know.
The messengers went on their way,
Returning at the start of summer.
And so they led back Genoïs,
Noble in body, pretty in face.
To see the marriage of the girl
And to affirm their covenant,
The barons of the land came there
Between the lands of Wales and England
Over the Severn in a valley
That was abundant and quite rich.
To keep this act in memory
They did such honor to the place
That they established a town there,
And Gloucester was the name they gave it.
The city got this name because
Of Claudius who founded it.
But others cite another reason
That seems to have validity:
Claudius engendered there
A son who got the name of Glois.
Now Glois was both the Lord of Gloucester
And Duke of Wales, as I've heard told.
Because the birth of Glois was there
And he was noted as its lord,
It was then named for him as Gloucester;
I've found this explanation written.
Gloucester is thus the City of Glois;
There cannot be a better account.
At the wedding of Genoïs,
During the service, she was crowned.
At the conclusion of the wedding,
Claudius returned to Rome.
Around this time, I've learned by reading,
Saint Peter preached and made his travels.
He once had been in Antioch;
He'd there brought Christianity.
He went to Rome for the first time,
Performing wonders and good works.

When Claudius had taken leave,
Arviragus was the ruler.
Surprisingly his self-worth grew;
Surprisingly he grew quite proud.
He held back tribute from the Romans
And wanted not a thing with them.
The Romans lost to greediness
What they by right should have received.
They sent Vespasian up to Britain
With I don't know how many knights.
Vespasian came upon the sea;
He wanted to make land at Dover;
The king, who knew about his coming,
Protected the land against the man,
And this one had his sails unfurled
When he could not make land at Dover.
He sailed a long space on the sea,
And he approached the country's coast.
He came ashore at Totnes then
And found that it was not defended.
He rode to Exeter at a gallop;
He wished to enter by surprise.
But there the people were prepared,
And for six days he made assault.
He never once could get inside.
Arviragus, who soon learned,
Both with his knights and with his host,
Came to the rescue fast as able.
From morning when the sun came up
Until the dusk when it went down,
They gave each other such a fight,
But neither side emerged on top.
At night they had to separate,
But they were very tired and wounded.
When they were armed again at morning
And were engaged again in battle,
The queen got them to come to peace,
For Genoïs was pained by this.
Her background was a useful thing,
For she was born of noble Romans.
For honor of her relatives,

She gave both parties such advice
That the lords came into accord,
Accepting peace and giving peace.
Vespasian sojourned the while
In Britain till the summer came.
He then set out for Rome again,
Completely joyful, fully happy.
For all his life, King Arviragus
Observed the Roman covenant.
He never tried to lie to them,
But gave them service and respect
Out of friendship with the queen,
Who had been born as one of them.

VI. Life Under Roman Influence

Now Marius, his lawful son,
Then ruled the kingdom after him.
This man was quite intelligent
And also very eloquent.
In his father's time he was brought up
In Rome by mother's relatives.
He pampered himself with elegance
And learned to live with grace and beauty.
During the reign of Marius,
In Scotland Rodric came ashore;
The King of Picts, he came from Scythia.
This man was very full of malice
And loved to pillage very much.
He came to lay Scotland to waste
And had already wasted much
When Marius, who learned of this
And had no care for evil neighbors,
Encountered him and brought his end.
In the place where he'd smashed the Picts,
Killed Rodric, and taken his head,
He had a giant stone erected
(Which one can still now go and see)
To show off his ability
And to commemorate the deed.
There was a legend on the stone
That to my knowledge still endures
To testify to the adventure
And to recount the stunning loss
When Marius gave Rodric death
And set this stone up for this reason.
And it's still there, or so I've heard,
And it is called the Vestinaire.

The Picts the king brought to defeat,
He then retained within his land.
He had them given a big part
Of Caithness as a place to live
Since it was lying still in waste
And always had been wilderness.
The Picts went off to settle there;
They plowed the land and started farms.
They sought women among the Britons,
But they would not give them a one.
And so to Ireland these men went
And brought some women home from there.
They settled down across the land,
And soon they grew and multiplied.
    Marius lived for a long time,
And after he had passed away,
King Coïl reigned, who was his son;
He was brought up among the Romans.
He was quite intimate with them;
They found that he was very faithful.
He learned about the Roman laws,
Their ways of thinking and their arts.
Coïl behaved in noble ways
And had himself served very richly.
Then Luces, Coïl's son, was king,
And he had very courtly ways.
Luces had great honesty;
Through him came Christianity
To England for the first time ever,
And I will tell you how it happened:
He heard some talk of Jesus Christ
And of the wonders he performed
And of the signs he made appear
That brought the people to conversion.

5202-08 According to Pickens, Coil embodies a romantic type of *courtoisie* ("*Vassalage,*" 171).

5209-13 According to Pickens, Luces (because of his establishment of British Christianity) has a *courtoisie* that is completely moral in sense ("*Vassalage,*" 170-71).

The king sent word to Eleutere,
Who was the pope, and so he asked
For someone who would baptize him
And teach him all about the faith.
After the pope had heard this news,
He rendered thanks and praise to God.
He sent Dunian to the king
And Fagan his companion too.
They both were wondrous clergymen
And bishops who were very holy.
They came to Luces and baptized him
And taught the law of God to him.
After the king, the royal household
And all his folk were baptized too.
As the king did, the people did
And followed the king's good example.
The pair of bishops did their preaching
And went about the countryside.
With the authority of the king,
As it is right and customary,
They had their dioceses established
And over these archdioceses.
Bishops got the dioceses;
Archbishops, the archdioceses.
They then split up the dioceses
And set up parishes within them.
The temples where the gods were kept,
The gods the heathen folks believed in,
They sanctified and purified
And consecrated to God's service.
The fiefs, the rents, and the estates
And other chattels of that kind
That were reserved for temple use
By those who had to serve the temples—

5219-20ff. The legend of Pope Eleutherius (A.D. 175-189) comes from the *Liber Pontificalis*, 14 (ed. Duchesne, 1:136).

5231 Wace omits many of Geoffrey's details concerning the organization of the church (Weiss, *Roman de Brut*, 133, n. 4).

The king soon authorized their use
By all the bishops and the clergy.
Now after Britain was converted
And had received the law of God,
Luces the king was very happy
To see all of the people baptized
And turned toward serving the Lord God.
He granted franchise to the churches
And gave them fiefs from his estates
And showered them with property.
He served the Lord God willingly;
He ruled in peace; he died in peace.
His body was interred in Gloucester.
He died one hundred fifty-six
Years beyond the Incarnation
That God assumed for our redemption.
Now at the time he left this life,
The king did not have wife or child
Or anyone of close relation
Who could inherit his estate.

When it was noticed by the Romans
That Luces died without an heir,
They got two legions set to go
And ordered them to go to Britain
With Sever, one of their senators,
To guard the land for Roman use.
Sever came with his two legions,
But found the Britons very felons.
Nevertheless, he warred so much,
Promised so much, and gave so much
That he made part submit to him
Through which he conquered many others.
Still others, who disdained his presence,
Withdrew beyond the Humber River;
And Sever followed in their tracks
Until he chased them into Scotland.
The ones in question swore their oaths
To Fulgenius, a proven vassal.
He joined his forces with the Picts,
And they became allied together.
Then they engaged in many attacks

Both openly and secretly
In Scotland in a certain region
That used to have the name *Deïra.*
When Sever had withdrawn from there
And down to London had gone back,
Fulgenius, who had the Picts,
The Scots, and British fugitives,
Took booty and some prisoners,
For whom he got great ransom payments.
When Sever heard the news of this
And went off thinking he could find them,
They'd fled already into Scotland
And were dispersed in many places.
Fulgenius often pulled this off,
And this went on such a long time
That Sever had a moat dug up
That stretched across the country's width.
Over the moat he built a wall,
High and thick, of well-joined stakes,
From sea to sea across the land
To close it off and keep it safe.
He shut his foes completely out.
For a long time none was so brave
To dare to go across the wall
Either to plunder or to rob.
After Deïra was shut off,
Fulgenius dared not enter it
And with his Picts and men consented
To go to Scythia; and he did so.
He spoke to Picts still living there;
He pledged so much and asked so much
That he led off a massive fleet
And brought it back ashore in England.
At Everwic he laid a siege
And seized the land that lay around it.
He then sent word to relatives

5307ff The defense described here is Hadrian's Wall (Weiss, *Roman de Brut*, 135, n. 3).

That he'd great forces in the land.
These men and others for his love
Took their leave of the emperor,
So fully were they taken in—
For he had promised them enough.
Sever employed the other Britons,
And so he called his legions up.
He went to rescue Everwic
And save the people of the city.
He launched attack on the besiegers;
Fulgenius again was armed.
They strongly fought against each other,
And each man did the best he could.
The battle was a brutal one,
For many souls flew from their bodies.
Fulgenius was fatally wounded;
He did not have much time to live.
Sever was also killed in this,
Along with many of his friends.
But through requests made by the Romans,
Among whom he had many kinsmen,
He was brought into Everwic
And with great honor buried there.

He had two sons: one Bassian,
And then another called Getan.
The mother of Getan was Roman,
A relative of senators.
A Briton bore this Bassian,
But she was also well connected.
The Romans made Getan come forth;
They chose him king and raised him up.
The Britons took up Bassian
And promised to give him the realm.
Each one was cherished by his kin
And by the closest of his people.
The Romans loved their Roman man;
The Britons loved their British kinsman.
Because of these elections, there
Was then a war between the brothers;
Getan was quickly killed, however—
I cannot say just how it happened.

The war was then brought to an end,
And Bassian had won the land.
There was a squire who was from Britain;
I heard that Carais was his name.
He was quite clever and quite brave;
He was a man with lots of strength,
Who tested it in many fights;
He was quite brave and very good.
He was, however, low by birth,
And his inheritance quite poor.
But he behaved himself so well
That he did not request his income.
He knew how to endure hard work,
And he loved war better than peace.
Around his time there went by sea
A group of men who pillaged others.
Nobody dared stay on the coasts
What with the outlaws and the pirates.
I do not know what Carais thought,
But he went to the Roman senate
And said that if he had its leave
To set a guard along the sea
And to protect the coastal regions
So that the pirates couldn't pass,
He would restore the tribute money
So that it would be paid completely.
The Romans missed their money badly,
And what he asked they authorized.
They gave him documents and letters.
Then you'd have seen this Carais turn.
Throughout the land he showed his papers
And purchased things in lively fashion.
He got together ships and sailors;
He sought out soldiers and good archers.
The dispossessed, the fugitives,
The robbers and the malcontents,

5373ff "Carausias, who held Britain 286-93. Wace expands on his portrait, on his felonious band . . . , and stresses the wickedness of gamekeeper turned poacher" (Weiss, *Roman de Brut*, 137, n. 2).

And those who had no land to claim
And wished to live some other way,
The brave and valiant knights-to-be,
The outlaws—he sought out such men.
He had a mob of many men,
Born and bred in felony.
When Carais had his fleet together,
He sailed around to many lands.
He went sailing from isle to isle,
Taking men and wasting lands.
From the knights and from the peasants,
From people near and people far,
He took away what he could take.
He knew nothing of moderation.
If pirates had done evil deeds,
Carais did worse, for he left nothing.
The man in charge of the defense
Left nothing he could take away.
The designated guard did evil.
His company grew all the time.
There was no thief, there was no robber,
There was no felon or no traitor
Who did not wish to run with Carais.
No one came who was refused.
The greater the crowd, the greater his pride;
The more he had, the more he wanted.
Castles and towns he set on fire,
Seizing all and robbing all.
He had great measures of presumption
And slavered for a lordly title.
He spoke in Britain to the Britons
Where he had sent his messengers.
His promises were generous,
And he informed them privately
That their advice was bad and foolish
When they did not make him their king.
For he would chase the Romans out
And win their freedom with a war.
He spoke in counsel with the Picts,
Who had great numbers in the land
And who were friendly with the king.

The Picts made him an affirmation
That if he fought against the king
That they would make him win for sure,
For they would leave the king afield
And make him suffer a defeat.
Carais defied King Bassian;
He threatened to make war on him.
They traded threats then back and forth
Until they came to actual war.
There where the best men were combating,
The best were jousting and were falling,
The Picts, who were disloyal traitors,
Took their leave of their liege lord.
The king had placed more faith in them
Than he had placed in all his men.
The more he believed, the more he trusted,
The more he gave them openly.
They dropped him in his time of need;
In times of need one sees one's friends.
They left their lord in time of need;
These men were traitors to their lord.
And Carais killed King Bassian
And later conquered all the kingdom.
He sent the Picts back up to Scotland;
He gave them towns and countryside.
From this time on, the Picts have been
Completely mixed up with the Scots.
When men of Rome had heard the news
Of how this Carais carried on,
They moved three of their legions there
And also two of their best lords.
Allec was one, a very smart
And very brave and valiant man;
Livius Gallus was with him;
Both of them were excellent knights.
They fought a battle with this Carais,
Defeated him, and conquered him.

5459-60 Weiss notes Wace's emphasis on the treachery of the Picts (*Roman de Brut*, 139, n. 1).

The man was killed and so were many
Of those who were in his protection.
Afterwards Allec waged a war
And often afflicted pain on those
Who had rejected Roman rule
And followed the advice of Carais.
The Britons tried to counter them;
They did not want to render tribute.
So they elected as their king
A baron, Asclepiodot,
Who was the baron of the Cornish.
There was no Briton in dissent.
The Britons were assembled then
And sent out word to one another.
They came together in assembly,
With each one summoning the other,
Until they found Allec in London,
The day of a religious feast.
He was at service in a temple
And wished to make a sacrifice.
After he heard the hue and cry,
He went with armies to the field
And entered battle with the Britons.
But many of his people left,
And Allec tried to flee away.
But he could not run off to safety,
For Britons took him in his flight.
He could not save himself; they killed him.
Gallus had a different end:
He forced his entry into London
And made his Romans enter too
And close and bar the city gates.
He put his armies on the walls
To throw things down and make defense.

5493ff "*HRB* and Wace have curiously transformed [Asclepiodotus the Prefect of the Praetorian Guard who restored Britain to the Roman Empire] into a patriotic Briton who wins a great victory over the Romans" (Weiss, *Roman de Brut*, 139, n. 3).

5501-04 Weiss notes the pagan activity in a now Christianized Britain (*Roman de Brut*, 139, n. 4).

Asclepiodot laid the siege
And sent his runners everywhere
To tell the barons and request
That they come help him in the siege.
If they could help, they'd be delivered
From the Romans and their trouble.
He wished to purify the land
So they could not take root again.
At Asclepiodot's command,
The Welshmen came, the Scotsmen came—
They came from every part of Britain,
And so did all their kin and subjects.
They then had arbalests deployed,
Towers erected, catapults built.
They breached the wall and knocked it down;
And by sheer force, they went inside.
Then you'd have see the Romans dying,
The wounded bleeding, lying flat.
You've never been the witness of
A greater slaughter of so many.
Some who saw the wall fall down
Withdrew to fortified recesses,
And Britons charged at these recesses,
Besieging Romans in the towers.
They had this Gallus so hemmed in
That he declared that he'd give up
If they let him leave there alive
And lead away his men alive
And let them leave England alive
Without their losing lives and limbs.
There was just one remaining legion
That would require such leave to go.
They were then granted such permission;
A truce was offered and accepted.
The Romans had surrendered then
And come down from their fortresses
When Welsh and Scottish barons came
Upon them with a massive force.
They found them in the city center
And took them and cut off their heads.
Over some water in the city,

They captured and beheaded Gallus.
They cut the head off from the body
And threw them both into the fountain.
The water Gallus fell and lay in
Was named the *Galli* after him.
The Britons called it *Nentgallin*;
The Anglo-Saxons, *Gualëbroc*.
The names are different in their sounds
But signify a single thing.
    Then Asclepiodot was king;
He was not bad or stupid either.
He held a feast when he was crowned;
He reigned ten years, a time of peace.
He rid the land of thieves and robbers
And greatly hated every felon.
In this man's time a massacre
And a great persecution fell
Upon the servants of our Lord,
Who had belief in Jesus Christ.
This all occurred through Diocletian,
The man who sent Maximian,
Through cruelty and injury,
To wipe out every single Christian
Who made his home in any place
Beyond Montjoie and in the west.
In nearly every single land,
Wars were waged against the Christians:
Satan had enormous power.
St. Alban was a martyr then,
And the saints Jules and Aaron too,
Two citizens of Kaerleon.
All of the bishops and the clergy
Were seized and suffered martyrdom.
There was no priest or cleric left.
The Count of Gloucester, named Choël,
Who was of noble lineage
And who possessed a hardy heart,
Made war on Asclepiodot.
The war increased and got so big
That they together came to battle
And did each other massive harm.

Choël was stronger, and he won;
He killed the king and took the crown.
Some did not like it, and some did;
But England's king was then Choël.
He raised a daughter, called Eleine,
Quite learned in both faith and art.
She was the only royal heir,
Since he'd no other son or daughter.
The lady was well educated
And praised enough for her good looks.
Choël promoted all her learning
And made her listen to her teachers
So that upon his own demise
She would know how to rule a kingdom.

When senators in Rome had learned
King Asclepiodot was dead,
There was no Roman left unhappy,
For he'd opposed them very much
And took away their knights and rights
And tribute money frequently.
They sent a senator to Britain;
They valued this man Constance highly.
He had already conquered Spain
And put it in the Roman Empire.
There was no man known in his day
Who had his value or his valor.
When Constance entered into Britain,
He had great numbers in his troop.
He and his people both were feared.
Choël, who heard of Constance's coming,
Dared not to fight against the man.
He was so good, the other feared him.
This other sent him messengers
And offered him and promised him
That he would tender Britain to him
And render tribute as he'd name it.
He said he'd done him nothing wrong

5605-14 Wace "expands . . . on the education and learning of Helena, making her suitable to be the mother of Constantine" (Weiss, *Roman de Brut*, 143, n. 1).

And had killed Asclepiodot,
Who'd held their tribute back for years
And vilely killed the Roman people
And then just like a felon took
Over their lands through an invasion.
They ought to feel appreciative
That he had given up the land.
Constance knew that he was right
And that he wanted only good.
The other'd offered him the kingdom,
And so they entered into friendship.
After this, one month had passed;
The second one had then arrived—
Choël felt bad and then grew sick
And at the end of eight days died.
And Constance took Eleine the daughter
And ruled the kingdom for himself.
There was no person in that time
Who knew a better, wiser woman
Or girl with better reputation.
Constance took and made her queen.
They both desired to have a son,
And God endowed them with a son
Called Constantine; they loved him much
And pained themselves to raise him right.
He was eleven—not much more—
Quite developed and quite grown—
When Constance fell to failing health
And medicine could not improve him.
Such was his end—he passed away.

Constantine matured and grew;
The barons raised him up as king,
Whom they so loved with righteous faith.
His mother educated him:
She loved him most; she taught him most.
When he had such maturity
That he could lead the baronage,
He had great love for knights in arms
And gave them much with ready will.
If Constance was a gifted man,
Constantine completely beat

Constance in terms of praise and gifts.
The son could never stop to rest
Until he had the men around him
Completely under his command.
Constantine was very wise
And had great love for what was just.
In his young days he was just like
Others are when they are old.
He loved the Britons for his mother
And loved the Romans for his father,
For he was born of these two folks,
Well connected on both sides;
And he loved all his relatives.
There was in Rome then at this time
The prideful Emperor Maxenz,
Who was quite evil and malicious.
He wasted all the Roman wealth,
And he debased the noble people.
He had the senate rank debased
And took away its dignity.
Some people hated him so much
They left their fiefs and their estates,
For they would not remain with him.
To Constantine they went complaining
Because he was, of their own blood,
The strongest and the wisest one.
Through him they sought recovery,
If he'd vouchsafe to share their pain.
They spoke to him and asked so much
And honored him with so much praise
He made great haste to go to Rome
And led his archers and his knights.
Three uncles that his mother had,
Whom he loved much and trusted in,
He took to Rome out of affection
And put them in the Roman Senate.
Joëlin was the name of one;
Trahern was next; the third Marin.
He took the fierceness out of Maxenz,
And he waged war against his power.
Then Constantine was emperor;

And his good mother Eleine went
Across the sea to Jerusalem
And summoned all of the old Jews;
And so the Cross was found by her,
Which had been hidden a long time.
To Joëlin Eleine's own uncle,
A very noble wife was given,
A Roman woman of great worth,
Who was thus married to her equal.
They had a son they raised up well;
Maximian was what they called him.
Octavius arrested those
Whom Constantine had guarding Britain
And had them all beheaded then.
Octavius was crowned the king;
He was from Wales and was a count
And there in Britain made his claim.
He killed the provosts and the counts
And killed the bailiffs and the viscounts.
Constantine remained in Rome
And gave attention to great works.
He took an uncle of Eleine,
Trahern by name, in whom he trusted;
He made him lead a pair of legions
To bring England its liberation.
At Porchester, this Trahern arrived,
And he besieged it two whole days.
The city was then given up;
It could no longer be retained.
To Winchester he went from there;
He wished to take the town by force;
Octavius, though, got there first,
Drawing up there with little effort.
Within Maisure, an open place,

5720-24 The legend of the cross was added by Wace (Weiss, *Roman de Brut*, 145, n. 2; Houck, *Sources*, 246-47). St. Helena was famous for this discovery, the story of which would have been familiar to Wace's audience. Tatlock, who notes that Geoffrey made no mention of Helena's sainthood or her discovery of the True Cross, argues that Geoffrey got the story of St. Helena as the daughter of King Coel from Henry of Huntington (*Legendary History*, 34, 236).

The battle of the two was hard.
The Britons had the greater force;
The Romans could not counter them.
They had to go back to the port;
Trahern then had the vessels loaded.
He made his way upon the sea
And sailed around from place to place
Until he came ashore in Scotland.
He did great harm and damage there.
All of the cities there he pillaged,
Set on fire, destroyed, and wasted.
Octavius heard of these things
And heard their truth confirmed again:
Trahern was laying Scotland waste
And wasn't sparing anything.
He called his men; he wanted to
Be able to provide protection.
This man believed, and so he said,
Trahern would never turn toward him.
Trahern, however, did not leave
Before he countered him and beat him.
The one who conquered at the first
Would be reconquered at the last.
Octavius, who conquered first,
To Norway went away in flight
To King Compert, who would protect him
Against Trahern if he were able.
In secrecy he had requested
All the friends he left behind
To bring together their resources
And kill Trahern on his behalf.
Trahern was feeling all secure
And was proclaimed the king by all.
One day he was on route from London,
A route, though, that was too well known.
While passing through a wooded valley
All secure, he had no fear,
When out of ambush ran a count
Who for Octavius hated him.
He had a hundred knights with him;
He killed Trahern among his men.

He had Octavius return
And had him take the kingdom back.
There was no Roman that the latter
Did not chase off or put to death.
He ruled in peace for a long time
And lived in peace for a long time.
    When he had spent his time right well
And passed the limits of his time,
He thought about what he would do,
To whom he would leave England then,
So there'd be peace when he had died,
So discord would not there increase.
He had a daughter that he wished
Would rule the kingdom after him.
He spoke to friends about this matter,
And some of them requested that
He find some Roman nobleman
To give his daughter and his crown.
There were some men who favored Conan,
The king's nephew, and so they argued
That Conan should inherit all
And wed his daughter afterward.
He would thus give him all his goods,
And he would name him as his heir.
He had a noble count there present,
Caradoc, the Count of Cornwall,
Who said that he would not permit
And would not ever recommend
That he should make this Conan heir.
He ought to get Maximian,
Joëlin's son, who was in Rome,
The kin of Eleine and Constantine,
A Briton on his father's side
And Roman on his mother's side.
He was quite noble on both sides,
And he was held as brave and wise.
The king should wed him to his daughter
And make him heir of his dominion;
And so his daughter would be queen
And all the land would bow to him.
For if this Conan was the heir

And wed his daughter afterward,
He would make trouble for this pair,
Since he by right should be the heir.
"If you," he said, "go through with this,
We'll have no peace while we're alive."
The king was taken by this counsel;
But there was trouble in the court,
For Conan got a bit enraged
At Caradoc for this advice.
He spoke contrary and harsh words
And, if he dared, he would do more.
But Caradoc gave little thought
To all his anger and his words.
For the king's sake and with his leave,
He sent an envoy, his son Mauric,
To parley with Maximian
And bring him back with him to Britain.
Mauric discovered a troubled Rome:
A great disturbance had arisen
In Rome between Maximian
And Valentine and Gratian,
Two brothers with a lot of power
Who wanted to possess the empire
So that Maximian and friends
Could not have any power there.
Mauric found Maximian
And showed him in a secret manner
Who he was and from where he came,
What his name was and what he wanted.
Maximian was overjoyed
About the message that he heard.
I'm not surprised that he was happy.
He spent no time in getting ready.
He found the king who sent for him
And who did much to honor him.
He gave his daughter as his wife
And named him as the heir of England.
Conan departed, turned by evil,
And he was staying with the Scots.
Defying his uncle and his cronies,
He warred against Maximian.

Maximian put up defense,
And so the king seized everything:
And many times he gave it up
And many times he won it back.
They had such labor in this effort
That what was lost was later won.
They got together at the end;
The wise men put them in accord.
Maximian made him a promise
To make him rich, and so he did.

In three years' time, they gathered treasure
And great possessions; then they boasted
That they would cross the sea to France
And take up battle with the French
And wage a war against the Romans
For hatred of the pair of brothers,
Who ruled in Rome as enemies,
And who desired to make no peace.
Maximian prepared himself;
He led great forces and provisions
And carried on with arrogance.
Up in the north and west of France,
He came ashore within a place
That had the name Armorica.
Humbauz, who was the local lord,
Summoned his people and his friends.
He wished to force them from his land
And wished to chase them from his fief.
However, the Britons were the stronger,
And they killed many of his men.
They could not take a profit here
And turned around and took to flight.
Maximian pursued these men
And slaughtered them in wondrous ways.
He killed about some fifty thousand,
Who could not find a fort or town.
Maximian returned from this

5913ff "There is no real evidence for large-scale movements from Britain to Brittany till the 6th century" (Weiss, *Roman de Brut*, 151, n. 1).

And went back to the main encampment.
He took aside Conan and laughed
And, laughing, gave him this advice:
"Conan," he said, while giving a smile,
"This land is very valuable
And seems to be quite good for farming,
And full of bounty and delight.
Look at the land, look at the rivers,
Look at the woods—how thick they are!
The fish are very plentiful;
The deer are very plentiful.
I've never seen a prettier place.
I wanted it for your own use.
Britain was ordained for you
And would have been your own possession,
But you have lost it for my sake,
And you should bear me ill, I think.
But grant me pardon now for this;
I'll give you your reward for this.
Take for yourself all of this land;
Keep what I have conquered of it,
And I will get the rest for you
And make you king and master of it.
We'll empty it of native folk
And populate it with some Britons;
And when it is filled up with people,
It will be known as Little Britain.
We do not want some others here;
It will be Britain with our Britons."
Conan accepted this endowment
And gave him many thanks for it.
He bowed before him very lowly
And humbly asked him for his mercy
And promised him his fealty

5917 ff. H.-E. Keller, "Wace et les Bretons," in *Actes du 14e Congrès International Arthurien* (Rennes: Presses Universitaires de Rennes, 1984), 1: 354-70, here 367, argues that the generally sympathetic view of the Bretons in the *Roman de Rou* and in the *Roman de Brut* indicates that Wace was sensitive to the prejudices of Henry II. Keller concludes that Wace wrote the *Roman de Brut* under orders from the court of London.

And swore to never bear him hate.
So at this time and for this reason,
Armorica thus lost its name
And got the name of Brittany,
Which it will never lose, I think.
From Brittany they went to Rennes
And then besieged the city there.
It was surrendered to them quickly;
There was no other remedy.
The people there were put to flight;
They left the city all unguarded.
It has been said enough of them
That never was a person found
Who was not put to death with pain
Or tortured in a shameful way.
For such a cause they fled away,
The folks who always had lived there.
In just this way the land was emptied
And left completely to the Britons.
Maximian seized all of it
And put his guards into the castles.
There was no one to farm the land
And not a one to till the soil.
Maximian, who knew a lot,
And wished to populate the land,
From England ordered to be led,
Especially chosen to do labor,
One hundred thousand peasant workers.
He ordered thirty thousand knights
To keep the people organized
And to defend the other people.
He then had Conan take the crown
And gave him all the fortresses.
He did not wish to stay there longer;
He passed ahead and moved toward France.
He conquered France and then Lorraine,
And he made Troyes his capital.
He could no longer tolerate
His lack of lordship over Rome.
He took the road that led to Rome
Toward Gratian and Valentine.

He conquered Lombardy and Rome;
He chased off one and killed the other.
  To Dionot, one of his vassals,
A noble and a loyal man,
He transferred power over England
And ordered him to be the regent.
The man was Caradoc's younger brother;
But Caradoc had passed away,
And so his son, who was an envoy,
And Dionot controlled the land.
The latter's daughter was a beauty;
The name she had was Ursula.
The French, who had become emboldened,
Started a war with Conan then.
But Conan put up good resistance.
They did not ever conquer him.
To better cultivate his land,
To get it settled with some people,
And to insure his people's future,
He wished to give his men some wives.
He did not wish to give them French—
Not for power or for riches
To intertwine their ethnic lines
And make their countries unified.
He thus requested Dionot,
Who held the regency of England,
To give him Ursula, his daughter,
Whom he would send across to him.
He also asked that vassal's daughters
Who did not yet have lords and masters
And daughters of the peasantry

6013ff "The fate of Ursula and her companions is described with many more details and pathos than in *HRB*. Wace is fond of portraying storms at sea and always shows sympathy for innocent victims. He adds the name of their place of slaughter—Cologne—and that they fall into the hands of heathen; by so doing, he firmly identifies this story with that of St. Ursula, martyred by the Huns" (Weiss, *Roman de Brut*, 153, n. 3). The story was as popular in Wace's day as it seems to be among feminist medieval scholars today, perhaps for the same reasons: it is the story of women who are given without their consent to one set of men and then stolen and raped *en masse* by yet another set of men. For indications of the story's popularity in the twelfth century, see Houck, *Sources*, 247-50.

And of the poor and of the rich
Be sent to him as soon as possible—
And he would find good mates for them.
Each one of them would have a mate
According to her family's rank.
The other granted him his daughter
And sent her off with rich possessions.
He had the women requisitioned
Who would be going to be married.
He had eleven thousand meet,
All of them born of noble people;
From citizens he took in turn
Sixty thousand all together,
Both very young and fully grown,
Well arranged and decked out nicely.
To ships at London they were sent
Along with those who would conduct them.
Down the River Thames they sailed
And came into the ocean then.
They sailed upon the ocean depths;
They hoped to find both joy and good.
A wondrous storm came into view,
And a cloud rose up full of rain,
Which made the wind then turn around,
The air turn black, the day turn dark.
Great was the wind; the ocean churned;
Waves began to swell in mass
And pile up one upon the other.
In very little time the ships
Were shattered, drowned, soaked, and destroyed.
The helmsmen there could not give aid,
And neither could the other men.
You then could hear the women crying,
The female voices screaming loudly,
The hands slapping, the hair pulling,
The parents crying out their loss,
Great shouts and complaints ringing out,
Prayers to God and to His saints.
You would have seen how they were dying
And how they held themselves together.
You could not have a heart so hard

That you would not have pitied them.
You've never heard in any case
Of women suffering greater outrage.
On every hand the ships were lost,
And women drowned in painful ways.
The few who made escape from this
Came ashore among the heathens,
Where they were killed or they were sold
Or they were kept in servitude.
Eleven thousand were led off
To be beheaded in Cologne.
Ursula was taken there,
And with these women she was killed.

Many of the lost were found
By Wanis and Melga in the sea.
Wanis, the King of Hungary,
Then sailed the sea with a great fleet.
Melga was Lord of Scythia.
They killed a number of the women
Whom they had wished to violate
But who would not give their consent.
They did not kill them otherwise;
They were such cruel pagan men.
They stayed with them as their companions.
These men were told and knew right well
That England had been rendered weak
And had been emptied of good knights.
A lot of them had gone to Rome,
The ones Maximian had led.
Conan had the other half,
And so the land was left unguarded.
Now these two kings desired to have it,
So they invaded it through Scotland.
They burned and wasted everything
And did not spare a single man.
They crossed the Humber afterwards;
They laid the flatlands all to waste.
No one remained except the peasants,
Who had no care to fight a battle;
And so the pirates slaughtered them,
And captives made their cries and moans.

How could a country be defended
That was devoid of its good knights!
Wherever there were any barons,
They held the towers and the keeps.
They sent off for Maximian,
And he sent Gratian up to them,
A knight quite able to give help,
Who was commander of two legions.
This Gratian rescued the besieged
And brought defeat to all the pirates.
He drove them fully out of England
And chased them over into Ireland.
Meanwhile there came the relatives
And the good kin of Valentine.
With Theodosien of the East,
A king of power and of might,
They took Maximian by force.
They killed him in Aquilia.
The Britains who had cried for him—
Some were dead and some had fled;
And Valentine had taken back
The things Maximian had taken.
Gratian himself did nothing else,
The man who subjugated England.
He made himself the chief and king
And led a great nobility.
He was a very deadly tyrant,
Doing evil to the poor.
He honored the nobility
And made the natives leave the country.
The peasants got themselves together.
In a great mob they got revenge;
They tore him up in little pieces,
Just like a mastiff-wolf enraged.
And so the people took their leave
And made their way back to their lands.

When Wanis and Melga heard about
What serfs had done to Gratian,
They put a horde of men together
From Gotland, Norway, and from Denmark,
From Scotland and from Ireland too.

And then they took Northumberland.
They crossed the Humber with their horde
And laid the forts and towns to waste.
The Britons saw the misery
And the destruction done to them.
By messenger and by a letter,
They asked the Senate with its power
To help them in their time of need
Since they were very faithful people
Who never wavered from their counsel
But did their bidding all the time.
The Romans never had forgotten
The treason and the treachery
That they had often perpetrated.
Just one sole legion of their people
Was what they would send up to them,
And it came then without delay
And liberated England soon
And threw the outlaws from the land.
They put them into flight in Scotland,
Killing some and chopping them up.
They mixed together stone and mortar;
They made a wall along a ditch.
There was no opening at all
Between the Scottish and Deïrans,
For often through that place had come
The ones who had destroyed the land.
They set up guards in many places,
Who got great fiefs for being guards.
When they had totally completed
The wall that they had undertaken,
The men of power in the country
Were brought to London for a meeting.
The Romans said that they would leave
And that they'd go back to their lands.
The Britons had to bravely fight
And make their own defense with vigor.

6167 The Antonine Wall, "built between 140 and 142/3, from the Firth of Forth to the Clyde" (Weiss, *Roman de Brut*, 157, n. 1).

The Romans could no longer bear
The cost of going and of coming.
There was a sage who spoke to them
And made the argument to them:
"Lords," he said, "many great losses
And much great pain has been endured
By many of our noble fathers
And by us too, for love of you.
You have made tribute payments to us,
But they have cost us very much.
You've never shown us any love,
And we have settled your affairs.
If we had tribute for one year,
We lost it two years afterward.
For always when you took the dare,
You did not bear us faith or love.
You often have concocted reasons
For why we ought to lose our rights.
Many of our men have died;
Many bad things have been done.
You make requests when you're in need
And promise us both faith and peace,
And when you have made your escape
And all your need has gone away,
Then you are scarcely men of ours
Before we find you very proud.
You take our tribute money back
Or render it begrudgingly.
We'd rather throw away the tribute
Than earn it in this way for long.
It costs a lot to stay abroad,

6185ff Wace replaces the speech of Geoffrey's Archbishop Guithelin with its claims that every peasant is a fighting man with this speech by a wise old Roman. According to Mathey ("De l'*Historia* au *Roman*"), the change reflects a difference in social values. Geoffrey still espouses the values of the the eleventh century while Wace has adopted the chivalric ideals of the court of Henry II Plantagenet: society has three rigidly separate classes—knights, clerics, and peasants. In this view of society, peasants do not fight. Other changes are noted by Weiss (*Roman de Brut*, 159, n. 1). In general, "Wace focuses more on this [section] as the nadir of British fortunes" and looks ahead at the "coming of the house of Constantine (and ultimately Arthur)" (159, n. 2).

And often you have need of us.
We cannot come so many times.
Do the best that you can do.
If we can get back down to Rome,
We won't return for any man.
Before, we gave you guarantees;
We do not wish to help you further;
You must provide your own support;
Defend yourselves if you are able.
We know about your ancestors,
Who were both strong and proud.
They did not fail to conquer all
The lands from here on down to Rome.
These men were very fierce in action;
But you are very different.
I don't know why or how it's happened
That you have not been overcome
By those who might destroy your land
And chase you from it into flight.
You have become so decadent,
I think, because of your own badness.
You'd put some courage in yourselves
If you'd regard the bravery
The British barons used to have,
The ones who conquered the great lands.
When you do not defend your fiefs,
You'll do a poor job beating others.
Defend yourselves from hateful people,
Who come through here quite frequently.
We've closed a section off for you,
So you have what the wall protects.
Erect great towers and strong castles
On riverbanks and in the ports,
The places where the pirates land
Who conquer you so frequently.
You must maintain your freedom well
If you disdain to serve another.
You'll have to fight to have your will."
Upon these words there was great pain
And great chagrin and great lament,
Both for pity and for fear.

They then saluted one another,
And then the Romans went away:
And well they said on their departure
That they did not want to come back.
   Wanis and Melga heard the news
Through the agency of their spies
That finally at last the Romans
Had indeed made their departure.
Then with the Picts and with the Danes
And with the Scots and with the Norse,
They moved on through Northumberland.
They burned; they pillaged; they destroyed.
Up to the wall they left no thing,
For they had burned up everything.
The Britons garrisoned the wall,
And those outside it made assault.
Then you'd have seen on every hand
The hurtling spears and javelins,
The flying quarrels and the arrows,
The stones launched off with catapults.
The men who kept the wall's defense
Fought the battle with great fear.
They all had just been given arms
And had been thrown right into battle.
They did not dare to raise their heads;
Their foes there kept them squatting low.
Never before had there been rain
That fell with more intensity
Than fell the arrows and the spears
With stones that they were catapulting.
The Britons left their battle stations
And clambered down for better comfort.
The men outside climbed up the wall;
They penetrated many places;
They later flattened everything,
And wall and ditch were leveled out.
They then passed through without a hitch,
For there was no defensive work.
They captured castles and took towns
And slaughtered Britons by the lot.
They went about in total freedom,

For they encountered no resistance.
I've never found and do not find
At any time, before or since,
Where there was such a heap of corpses:
How many knights, how many peasants!
God, what destruction and what burning
Of good land and of people too.
The Britons had been very high,
But now they were put very low,
And they would not themselves recover
Without some help from somewhere else.
For knights in arms and for some help,
They sent off to the Roman Senate,
But it said that it would do nothing:
The Britons must do what they can;
The Romans cannot every year
Suffer such pain and effort for them;
Elsewhere they had enough to do.
They could no longer deal with Britons.
The bishops came to an assembly;
They were upset, for much they feared
That through the agency of foreigners
The Christian faith would perish there.
If such a thing were to survive,
The Lord himself would have to come.

6315-20 Wace adds the fears of the bishops (Weiss, *Roman de Brut*, 161, n. 1).

VII. The House of Constantine: Vortigern and the Saxons

There was in London at this time
An archbishop with eloquence,
Guencelin, a learned man
Who lived a very holy life.
For a long time before and after,
London was the archbishop's see,
But afterwards, I know not why,
Canterbury became the see.
The good archbishop Guencelin,
With the approval of his bishops,
Went over to Armorica,
Which Conan filled with British folks,
A place we know as Brittany
(It lost its name Armorica).
Aldroën, who ruled the land,
Was the fourth king to follow Conan.
The people had well multiplied
And made the land inhabited.
The archbishop traveled around
Until he found King Aldroën.
The king received him with great honor,
For he had often heard him praised.
He asked him what he came there seeking,
Since he had come so far to find him.
"Sir," he said, "You can well note,
And you should have no doubt in this,
That I did come across the sea,
Led as I am by urgent need.
You were not born so recently
And do not live so far away

That you have never heard reports
Of the great pain and the great trials 6352
The Britons often have endured
Since the time of Maximian,
Who won the kingdom that you rule
And who made Conan lord of it. 6356
To get the people for the host
That occupied these lands of ours,
Our people went into decline.
We've had no neighbor ever since 6360
Who hasn't taken us to war
And hasn't wished to conquer us.
The Britons were accustomed once
To conquering a lot of lands. 6364
Now by themselves they are not able
To guard their own from other people.
The Romans used to give us help;
They'd succor us in direst need; 6368
Living too far away, they've left us,
Complaining of the cost and journey.
We're great enough and good enough
And have great companies of men, 6372
But we don't have a prince or king.
And thus a group of lawless men
Has trampled down our countryside
And taken all the people captive. 6376
We will, I think, never recover
Without the help of other people.
I'm hardly able to report this;
It grieves me much to bring to mind 6380
The pain and the misfortune that
We've gone through and that still endures.
For this, my lord, I've come to you,
Since you are known for your great bounty 6384
And since you're one of us by birth
And since your kinfolk come from us.
You are British; we are British,
And we are kin, I do believe, 6388
And we should be completely one
And have in common everything.
The one should be the other's rescue,

Both you for us and we for you.
We suffer need; now rescue us;
And so you will receive great honor.
And you should do this naturally
Because we're kin and it is right."
Aldroën, who felt great pity,
Became all sad and teary-eyed
About the tragedy he heard.
Completely crying, he responded:
"If I," he said, "can be of service,
I'll serve you the best that I can.
You'll bow to Constantine, my brother,
And you will make him general.
He is a wondrous man with arms
And very skilled in things of war.
I'll give to you two thousand knights
From the most worthy that I have."
Then he summoned Constantine;
To the archbishop he gave him.
The archbishop regarded him
And with his right hand signed the cross.
He made a bow and came toward him
And said to him while he was moving,
"*Christus vincit, Christus regnat,*
Christus vincit et imperat."
The king summoned his knights to come,
And then he gave two thousand to him.
With very costly things, he sent
Them to the ships when there was wind.
He himself would have gone with them
If he had dared or he'd been able,
But he was warring with the French.

Constantine then came to Totnes;
Many good knights he had with him,
And each one wished to serve a king.
They took a route that led toward London;
They summoned Britons everywhere.
Not a one appeared at first,

6415-16 "Christ conquers; Christ reigns; / Christ conquers and holds sway."

But then they came just like the rain.
From out of woods and out of mountains,
They came in massive companies.
Why should I tell you a long tale?
They marched so much and did so much
They brought the evil folk defeat,
The ones who had destroyed the land.
At Silchester they held a council;
All the lords had to attend.
Constantine was chosen king;
Without a nay, without delay,
They crowned him king with lots of joy,
And so to him they made their pledges.
They gave a woman to him then
Who was of noble Roman stock.
He had three sons by her; the oldest
One the king called Constant.
At Winchester he had him raised,
And there he had him made a monk.
Aurelius was second born;
His surname was Ambrosius.
The last one to be born was Uther,
And of them he survived the longest.
Then the archbishop Guencelin
Took custody of these two children.
If Constantine had ruled for long,
He'd have subdued the land entirely,
But he passed on just way too soon.
He ruled for no more than just twelve years.
He had a Pict within his household,
A traitor and an evil felon,
Who had been serving him for years
And hated him—I don't know why.
This man went with him to an orchard,
As if he wished to give him counsel;
There where the Pict advised the king,
Where no one guarded him from evil,
He had a knife, and so he stabbed him
And killed the king and ran away.
The people of the land assembled;
They wished to crown a king but wondered

Which of the boys to make a king,
For they were small and knew but little.
They still depended on a nurse;
They did not know of any evil.
Constance, the oldest, was of age,
But dared not take his habit off.
It seemed to be both vile and foolish
To have him leave the monastery.
They had selected from the two,
When Vortigern stepped to the front.
This man of power lived in Wales;
He was a very wealthy count.
He had his power from his family
And was quite bright and very wily.
A good long time before, he saw
Just what he wanted to arrange:
"Why go on wondering?" he said.
"Make a king of Constance the monk.
He is the heir; just take his habit;
The other boys are way too small.
I will approve of no one else;
Let all the blame come down on me.
I'll take him from the monastery
And give him to you as your king."
There was no baron who desired
Constance the monk to be the king:
It seemed to them an awful thing.
But Vortigern, with evil mind,
To Winchester spurred on his way;
He asked for Constance there so much
That with the very prior's leave
He spoke to Constance in the parlor.
"Constance," he said, "your father's dead;
The crown is destined for your brothers;
But you by primogeniture
Ought to have the kingdom first.
If you want me to raise my power
And if you love me and believe me,
I'll take you out of these black robes
And dress you in some royal ones.
If you will leave the monastery,

I'll give your legacy to you."
This man desired to wear the crown
And did not love the monastery.
Monasticism had grown boring;
Eager he was to get away.
He promised and affirmed whatever
Vortigern requested of him.
And Vortigern took him at once
And got him from the monastery.
There was no one who dared object—
Of those who cared—when he left thus.
He took away his monkish robes
And dressed him up in costly ones.
From there he led him right to London;
There were not many people gathered;
The archbishop had passed away,
Who should anoint the king by right.
No one else dared to anoint him
Or wished to have a hand in this.
Vortigern picked up the crown
And placed it then atop his head.
There was no benediction given
Except from the hand of Vortigern.
Constance received the crown and threw
Away the clothes he should have worn.
In evil he threw down God's habit,
And so he came to evil end.
One ought not come to a good ending
By doing what he ought not do.
The king and his administration
Were in the grasp of Vortigern.
The king complied with his advice
And did whatever he requested.
Soon enough in many things,
He noted that the king knew nothing
Since he was brought up in a cloister.
He noted the two infant brothers;

6525ff D'Alessandro notes that Wace changes the order of events from that in Geoffrey ("*Historia* et *Roman*," 49).

He noted the land's lords were dead;
He noted he was strongest living;
He noted people were quite restless;
He noted place and time were right;
He wished to seize the crown himself.
Now listen to this crafty scoundrel:
"Sire," he said, "I know for certain,
And I should make you be aware,
That Danes have been called up in armies
And so have Norsemen there in Norway.
Because of you, who aren't a knight,
Because of weakness found in us,
They wish to come upon this land
And capture and destroy your castles—
Unless an army is assigned
By you to guard you and your land.
Provision towers; have them guarded.
I have great fear of treacherous men,
So you should turn your castles over
To those who well know how to guard them."
The king said, "All is in your hands.
Do whatever you want with it.
I will not worry then about you,
For you know better than I do.
Take all the land under your guard
So no one takes and burns it up.
I place myself beneath your guidance,
So do the best that you can do.
Take my cities, take my estates,
Take my treasure, take my possessions."
Vortigern dissembled well;
He well knew how to hide his greed.
When he had seized the fortifications,
The treasures, and the rich possessions,
"Lord," he said, "if it pleases you,
My counsel and advice would be
That you enlist as knights in arms
Some Pictish soldiers up in Scotland
To be with you here in your court
Just in case our war turns bad.
You could send off these Pictish men

Wherever you'd have need of them.
Through the Picts and their relatives
We'll know the ways of foreign people.
They'll speak to us and speak to them;
They'll go between both us and them."
"Do," said the king, "what pleases you;
Have come as many as you'd like;
Give them as much as you would like.
Do the best that you know how."
When Vortigern had taken all
And had the treasure in his hands,
He sought as many Picts as pleased him,
And they came down just as he wanted.
Vortigern gave them great honors
And gave them much to eat and drink.
He had them living in great joy;
Often enough they all got drunk.
So much did Vortigern give them
And honor each and every one,
There was not even one who'd say—
Hearing what he wished to hear—
That Vortigern was not more courtly
And more important than the king.
He was quite fit to have the crown
That the king wore—or even fitter.
Vortigern was thus delighted,
And more and more he honored them.
One day when he had wined them well
And had them all inebriated,
He came to them and gave a speech,
Acting like a man in sadness:
"Much have I cherished you," he said,
"And I have served you willingly
And so still would if I had means.
But all this country is the king's,
And I can't give or spend a thing
Without my giving an account.
My income in this land is small;
Thus I must go abroad for more.
I did my best to serve the king,
But from him I don't get much money

With which I might maintain in honor
A minimum of forty servants.
If I succeed, you can come back;
But now I go and say goodbye.
It saddens me to leave you so,
But I'm so poor I have no choice.
If you get word that I've improved,
Surely then you'll come to me."
Vortigern turned away at that;
False he was and falsely spoke.
The Picts, who'd gotten very drunk,
Believed the evil man completely.
They took as total verity
Whatever he pronounced with falseness.
They spoke together thus: "What will
We do if we lose this good lord?
This king's a fool; let's kill this monk
And raise up Vortigern as king.
He's fit to have the crown and throne,
And we should choose him for these things.
How does this foolish monk serve us?
Why have we suffered so much from him?"
With that they came into the chamber,
Took the king, and beheaded him.
They cut the head off from the body;
They showed it then to Vortigern.
They cried to him: "Have you observed
How we have acted in your service?
The king is dead; now keep us servants;
Take the crown; become the king!"
He recognized his own lord's head.
Acting as if he felt great pain,
He was rejoicing in his heart;
But he was smart and hid his joy.
To cover up his felony,
He had the Londoners assemble
And had the traitors' heads cut off—
He did not let a one escape.
There were some people who believed
(But privately they said such things)
The Picts would not have touched the king

And never looked on him with evil
And never even thought of him,
If Vortigern did not command them.
Those who were raising the two brothers,
When they learned of the king's demise,
Feared that those who killed the king
Would do the same thing to the brothers.
Because of fear of Vortigern,
They took Aurelius and Uther;
They went across to Brittany
And handed them to King Budiz.
Budiz the King received them well;
He was their kin, and so he raised them.
He set them up quite honorably
And dressed them up expensively.
Vortigern had the fortresses;
He had the castles and the cities.
Quite proud, he made himself the king.
But he was bothered by two things:
On the one hand, the Picts were warring
Against him as a constant menace;
The kinsmen wished to get revenge
For those whose heads he had removed.
It also grieved him very much
That everybody was assured
That the two brothers had an army
And would return in little time
And that the barons would receive them
And recognize their fiefs from them.
They'd get revenge for brother Constance,
For they were thought to be great men:
And many people said these things.
In the meantime, three ships arrived;
They landed at a Kentish port;
They bore inside a foreign people
With handsome looks and noble bodies.
Their lord was Hengist, along with Hors,
A pair of brothers of great stature
Who spoke a foreign kind of tongue.
To Vortigern, who at this time
Made his sojourn at Canterbury,

This news was told without delay:
Three ships belonging to a group
Of people from a foreign land
Had come together to his shores.
The king desired—whoever they were—
That they be granted peace and truce
And that they speak to him in peace
And that they turn back home in peace.
They listened to the king's request,
And so they went to him securely.
The king observed the well-made bodies
And handsome looks of the two brothers,
Who were much bigger and more striking
Than all the other youthful men.
"From what land do you come?" he said.
"Where were you born? What do you seek?"
Hengist, the older and first born,
Responded for the lot of them:
"From Saxony," he said, "we come,
Where we were born and where we live.
If you desire to hear the reason
Why we come searching on the sea,
I will relate to you the truth,
If we have your protection here."
"Tell," said the king, "all of your reasons,
For you should fear no bad from us."
"Good king," said Hengist, "noble sire,
I do not know if you've heard tell,
But our homeland is full of people
And more abundant and more fertile
Than any other that you know
Or that you may have heard about.
Our people are quite fertile too,
And babies multiply too much;
There are too many men and women—
This fact distresses us here now.
Whenever people have increased
So that the land is much too crowded,
The princes who possess the land
Make all the young folks come together,
The ones who are at least fifteen;

This is our custom and our habit.
All the best and all the strongest
Are sent outside the land by lot,
And so they go to other regions,
Seeking lands and seeking homes
To cut the overpopulation,
Something the land cannot endure.
For babies there are born more thickly
Than beasts who feed upon the fields.
What with the lot that fell to us,
We've left behind our native land.
Mercury takes good care of us,
A god who has us here conducted."
When the king heard him say the name
Of whom he had protecting him,
He asked about which god they had
And in which god they had belief.
"We have," he said, "a lot of gods
For whom we have to set up altars,
That is to say, Phoebus and Saturn,
Jupiter and also Mercury.
We have a lot of other gods
According to our ancient rite,
But over all the other gods,
We honor Mercury the most,
Who in our language has the name
Woden in very sacred contexts.
Our forebears honored him so much
That they gave to him the fourth day.
For Woden, the god that they so loved,
They named the fourth day, Woden's Day,
And Wednesday's still the name it has.
Besides the god that I have mentioned,
We have the cult of goddess Freya,

6771-92 The conflation of the names of the Roman and Germanic gods goes back at least as far as the Roman historian Tacitus. To the medieval way of thinking, however, all gods other than the true God were demons. Consequently, the thinking went, all non-Christians followed the same religion: they worshipped the devil and his consorts. Little importance was thus attached to keeping all of the deities and the religions straight. For full details, see Glowka, "Laȝamon's Heathens."

Who is revered by everyone.
The ancient ones, to do her honor,
Made hers the sixth day of the week,
And so with great authority,
They called it Friday after Freya."
"Evil," he said, "is your belief,
And you possess an evil god.
This bothers me, but nonetheless
Your coming here seems good to me.
Valiant men and wise you seem;
And, if you wish to give me service,
I will retain the lot of you,
And I will make you wealthy men.
Thieves from Scotland war against me;
They burn my lands and take my towns.
If you desire (if it please God
To render such great good to me),
Destroy the Picts and the Scots too
With help from God and from your gods.
For to and from that place they come
And go, these Picts destroy my land.
Through you I wish to be avenged
Through death or exile of them all.
You will have plenty of supplies,
Plenty of money and of gifts."
And so the Saxons stayed around
And drew their boats upon the shore.
Immediately, the court was filled
With young men fit for doing battle.

There was no long delay at all
Before the Picts with massive force
Came down upon the king's own land,
Burning, laying to waste, and robbing.
When they were set to cross the Humber,
The king, who heard reports of them,
Went there to meet them with his barons,
With his Saxons and his Britons.
Then you'd have seen a fierce encounter;
There were a lot of men thrown down.
The Picts did not feel any fear,
For they were used to winning fights.

Their conduct was quite good at first,
And they laid on ferociously.
They fought the battle wondrously
And made resistance wondrously.
Because they had been used to winning,
They wanted to maintain the custom.
But they put down the custom then,
And Saxons won the field of battle.
With them and with their help and aid,
The victory went to Vortigern.
He paid these Saxons off in gold
And made improvements in their rations.
He gave to Hengist good estates
In Lindsey and great treasures too.
They were like this for a long time,
And their relationship endured.
Hengist saw that there was need
To make his case before the king.
He set about to gain preferment,
Just as every man should do.
He knew how to befriend the king
Beneath the guise of telling lies.
He found the king in joy one day,
And so he gave him this advice:
"You have," he said, "honored me much,
And you have given me enough,
And I serve you and will serve you.
I have done well; I will do better.
But, since I have been in your court
And since I have made your acquaintance,
I've learned enough by observation,
I've heard enough and seen enough,
That not a single lord loves you.
Everyone hates you and complains.
They speak of children I don't know
Who take your people's love from you.
They are their lords by right of birth,
Sons of the people's lawful lord.
Not long from now they'll cross the sea
And take away this land from you.
The people all put bad on you,

Wish bad on you, see bad for you.
They hate you much, threaten you much,
Want bad for you, seek bad for you.
I have considered how to help you,
And in my land I wish to send
Word for my wife and for my children
And for some other relatives.
You then can put more trust in me,
And I will serve you better then.
You will not find a man in war
Who'll take a foot of earth from you.
I have already served so long
That I have many foes for you.
I cannot be secure at night
Outside a castle or a wall.
Therefore, sire, if it please you,
It would be for your fame and glory
If you would give a town to me
Or little castle or a fort
Where I could settle into bed
And sleep at night with confidence.
Your enemies will fear me then
And leave off doing harm to you."
"Send for your people," said the king.
"Receive them well and keep them well,
And I will give you greater rations.
But you are not of our religion:
You are heathen; we are Christian.
And no one will regard it well
That I have given you a fort.
Think of something else you'd have."
"Sire," said Hengist, "You ought to let me—
At one of the houses that I own—
Enclose and fortify a refuge
Of as much earth—I don't want more—
As I could stretch a hide across
Or make a circle with a hide—
Just a bull's hide, nothing else.
And so I'd sleep in greater safety."
Vortigern gave him permission,
And Hengist gave him thanks for it.

He had his messengers prepared
And sent off for his relatives.
He took a bull hide and he cut it
And stretched it out into a circle
That went around a massive mound.
Good workers sought, he made a castle.
Thongchester was the name he gave
It in the language of his country.
Thongchester's name comes from the hide,
But one can call it otherwise
Chastel de cureie in Norman French
And *Kaërcarreï* in British
Because it was thus measured out
Within the compass of a circle.
    When Thongchester was all enclosed,
The people for whom Hengist sent
Arrived in eighteen ships all full
Of knights in arms with their whole families.
They sent along to him his daughter,
Who had not yet been married off.
Rowena was this young girl's name;
Her beauty and her grace were wondrous.
And on a day that he arranged,
Hengist invited Vortigern
To come and spend some time with him
And have some joy and drink and eat
And take a look at his new people
And his brand-new accommodations.
The king arrived with few companions,
For he desired to be discreet.
He saw the castle and the work.
It was well made; he praised it much.
The knights who had just newly come
He kept as salaried retainers.
They ate all day and drank so much—
All and several—that all were drunk.
Out from her chamber issued then
Rowena, gorgeous, dressed to kill.
She bore a cup replete with wine.
Before the king she bent her knee;
She bowed before him very humbly

And greeted him in her own custom:
"*Laverd king, wes heil,*" she said.
The king had questions and he asked,
Since he knew nothing of the language,
Just what it was the woman said.
Keredic at once responded.
This British man was good at tongues;
He was the first among the Britons
Who learned the language of the Saxons.
"Rowena," he said, "has greeted you,
And she has called you king and lord.
It is the custom in their land, sir,
When friends are drinking with their friends
For one to toast and say "*wes heil,*"
And "*drinche heil*" is the response.
The first drinks all or half the cup.
And for the joy and for the friendship
And for the right to get the cup,
The custom is for both to kiss."
The king, just as the other taught him,
Said "*drinche heil*" and gave a smile.
Rowena drank and passed the cup
And as she passed it kissed the king.
So from these people first we get
The custom and the origin
Of saying "*wassail*" in this country
And "*drinche heil*" as the response
And drinking all or half a cup
And giving kisses to each other.
The woman's body was quite nice;
Her face was very beautiful.
She was quite fair and well proportioned,
Of a nice size and a nice height.
She was half dressed before the king,
Who looked at her in wonderment.
He felt great joy and had drunk much,
And he had great desire for her.
The Devil egged him on so much,
The Devil who's turned many bad;
He burned in love and lechery
To have his way with Hengist's daughter.

God, what a shame! God, what a sin!
The Devil had perverted him
So he did not reject this urge
For her a heathen by her birth.
He quickly asked for her from Hengist,
And Hengist granted him his wish,
But first required advice in this
From both his brothers and his friends.
They wanted this arrangement too,
And they advised and recommended
That they should freely give her over
And as a bride price ask for Kent.
Hengist gave her, not wanting more,
And as her bride price asked for Kent.
The king was keen to have the woman;
He loved her, so he made her queen.
She was a heathen, so he wed her
According to the heathen custom.
No priest pronounced a blessing there;
There was no mass; there was no prayer.
That day he fell; that night he got her
And had Kent given up to Hengist,
Who took Kent both to have and hold.
No word was given to Gerangon,
Who held it through inheritance
Before he had been kicked right out.

The king trusted the heathens more
And loved them more than he did Christians;
The Christians therefore hated him,
Rejecting him and his advice.
Even his sons despised him now
And left him, owing to the heathens.
He had a wife whom he had married,
But she was dead and gone already.
He'd gotten three sons from that woman,
And they were fully grown already.
Vortimer was the oldest's name,
And then Paschent and Katiger.
"Sire," said Hengist to the king,
"For me you're hated everywhere,
And I am hated too for you.

I am your father; you're my son:
You have and you enjoy my daughter,
Because Your Grace has asked for her.
I should advise you truthfully,
And you should trust and give me aid.
If you desire to reign secure
And trouble those who hate your guts,
Send for Octa, who is my son,
And for his cousin Ebissa,
A pair of wondrous fighting men,
Yes, wondrous men in war and combat.
Give them land up north in Scotland,
For always war comes down from there.
Protect yourself from adverse foes
Who will take nothing then from you.
Thus all your life you will be able
To live in peace from here to the Humber."
"Do," said the king, "whatever you want.
Send for the good ones that you know."
And Hengist sent for them at once,
Inviting both his son and nephew;
And they came with three hundred ships.
There was no able knight rejected
Who wished to serve to gain possessions—
Who wasn't made to come with them.
Later others often came
In smaller groups of ships each day:
In groups of four or five or six,
Of seven, eight, or nine or ten.
Soon the heathens had increased
And got so mixed up with the Christians
That one could hardly recognize
Just who was Christian and who not.
The Britons were annoyed so much
That they requested and they prayed
The king not to believe these foreigners,
For he had broken his own vow.
He was too friendly with these heathens;
In shame and villainy he acted:
"Get rid of them some way or other;
Send all or most of them away."

The king replied that he would not:
They served him well; he sent for them.
The Britons then came to assembly;
They went together into London.
They raised up Vortimer as king,
The oldest of the king's three sons.
Vortimer defied the Saxons
And sent them packing from the cities.
The king, because he loved his woman,
Held with them and would not leave them.
And so his son pursued them often
And often put them into flight:
He had good help in all the fights.
So open war was set afoot
With Vortimer and with the Britons
Against his father and his Saxons.
He fought with them on four occasions
And conquered them on four occasions.
Above the waters of the Derwent,
He fought them on the first occasion.
Near Epford, at the river crossing,
He came together next with them.
There rushed together man to man
Hors and Katiger, the king's son.
Each hurt the other mortally
As each one had desired to do.
In Kent, along a seaside strand,
Close to their ships, upon a road,
The third great battle came together
As Saxons moved along in flight
From north of the Humber down to Kent.
The route of Saxons there was great.
They fled to Thanet afterwards,
Upon an island in the sea.
The Britons there made their assault
And beat them down the whole long day
With arrows and with crossbow bolts
From little boats and other vessels.
They shot them down from one location;
They died of hunger in another.
When Saxons saw they had no hope

Except in parting from the land,
They asked for Vortigern the King
To beg this Vortimer, his son,
To let them leave in peace from there
Without his doing them more harm.
The king had been with them through this
And had not left them even once.
During the time when he was gone
To get this truce arranged for them,
The Saxons went into their ships
And rowed them hard and sailed them hard
As fast as they could get away,
Leaving their women and their children.
They made escape in their great fear,
Returning to their native lands.
    After these men had thus escaped,
The Britons felt themselves secure,
And Vortimer returned to all
The things that each had lost to them.
To fix the churches up again
And preach about the law of God,
Which had been subject to contempt
By Hengist, who corrupted it,
From Brittany came St. Germanus,
And St. Romanus sent him there,
Who held the jurisdiction of
The apostolic see of Rome.
St. Louis of Troyes accompanied him.
Both of these men were bishops, now,
One from Auxerre, the other from Troyes:
They knew the roads that lead to God.
Through them the law was re-established,
And people were returned to faith:
Through them came many to salvation.
Many signs and many wonders
God performed and showed through them.
All England was in a revival.

7140-42 Here we are in the realm of legend: a Pope Romanus never existed. However, St. Germain of Auxerre was real (d. 448), and is recorded by Prosper of Aquitaine.

When God's own law was re-established
And Britain was again converted,
Hear just what the Devil did:
Out of envy and great hate,
Rowena, like an evil stepdame,
Had poison given to her stepson
Vortimer, whom she despised,
Because of Hengist, whom he'd exiled.
When Vortimer knew that he'd die
And that no surgeon would improve him,
He called together all his lords
And gave them freely of his treasure,
Of which he had collected much.
Just hear what he then asked of them:
"Carry on, good knights," he said.
"Give out gifts and ample rations.
Maintain your country and yourselves;
Protect yourselves against the Saxons
And do not bring them on yourselves.
Get vengeance for my trials and yours.
To terrify these Saxons have
My body buried on the shore
And raise a funeral monument
That will endure for a long time
And can be seen for a long way
Over the sea toward their approach.
There where they know my body lies
They will not turn for death or life."
And so the noble brave one spoke,
And so he died and met his end.
To London was his body borne,
And there in London it was buried.
The body never was interred
There in the place where he had ordered.

Then Vortigern was king again
As he had been before this time.
Because his wife had begged him so,
He sent for Hengist, his wife's father.
He asked him to come back again
But to bring only a few people
So that the Britons would not fear

And start another power struggle.
Vortimer, his son, was dead;
There was no need for a great force.
Hengist came back willingly
But with him brought three hundred thousand
Men of arms: he scared the Britons,
For he would do what he'd not done.
When the king learned that he'd returned
And that he led so many men,
He had great fear and could not speak.
The Britons, though, were very angry
And said that they would go to war
And chase the Saxons from the land.
Hengist, who had an evil heart,
Asked the king in treachery
To give them peace and make a truce
And meanwhile come to speak with them.
They worked for peace and wanted peace;
They longed for peace and looked for peace.
They'd no desire for war at all
Or to remain there using force.
They could retain the ones they picked
And all the rest would go away.
The Britons granted them a truce,
And on both halves it was affirmed.
Now who'd suspect some treachery?
They set a day on which to talk.
The king made a request of Hengist
That he attend with few retainers,
And Hengist granted him those terms.
But he requested in return
That no one there bear any arms
For fear of starting any fight.
In Salisbury, there upon the plains,
Close to the Cloister of Ambrius,
They came to talk from two directions,
On the first day of the month of May.
Hengist had instructed well
And well told all of his companions
To carry knives inside their shoes
So they could slash on every hand.

When they were talking with the Britons
And were completely mingled with them,
He would cry out "Take out your *saxes*!"
And Britons would not understand.
Then all the Saxons would draw knives
And stab the Britons next to them.
When all of them were at the talks
And all together were mixed up
With Britons being there among them,
All unarmed and with no weapons,
"Take out your saxes" was cried out.
Then each of them drew out his knife
And each one stabbed behind himself.
Hengist, who was near the king,
By the mantle drew him close
And let the butchery take place.
And those who had the knives in hand—
Through hooded cloaks and overcoats
Into chests and into guts—
Made the blades of knives to pass.
Men fell down on their sides and faces.
Of them at once there were four hundred
Sixty murdered in that place,
Some of the richest and the strongest.
Some of them ran off in flight
Protecting flesh with things like rocks.
Aldolf, who was a count of Gloucester,
Had a big stick in his right hand;
He found it lying at his feet—
I do not know who brought it there.
With the big stick he defended himself;
He killed and beat up many with it.
With it he killed some seventy;
This count was brave and skilled in battle.
The onslaught made him take his leave,
For none can fight with naked flesh.
Many a knife had stabbed at him,
But not a one had touched his flesh.
He rode across upon his horse,
For it was good and very fast.
To Gloucester he ran off in flight

And readied tower and town for war.
The Saxons wished to kill the king,
But Hengist hollered out at them:
"Spare the king; he's done much good
And has performed much work for me.
You should protect my son-in-law.
But make him give us all his towns
And give up all his fortresses,
If he desires to save his life."
He gave up Winchester and London,
Chichester, Everwic, and Lincoln.
And as a means of paying ransom
And as a means of leaving prison,
He gave them Sussex as their fief
And all of Middlesex and Essex
Because they were so close to Kent,
Which Hengist owned since he first came.
To keep in mind the treachery
Of knives, these places got their names:
Saxes, as the English say,
Is the French plural word *couteaux*,
But now the names have changed so much
That people don't know what they mean.
The English hear reproach in them
For treachery they perpetrated:
The endings of the words display it;
The names of knives are their impeachment
For the dishonor long forgotten
That their ancestors once committed.

Vortigern gave up all to them
And fled across the Severn River.
He traveled way off into Wales:
There he remained and there he lived.
He made his wizards come to him
And all the best among his men.
He sought advice on what to do,
On how he should maintain himself:
If stronger people should invade him,
Just how he could defend himself.
They offered as their counsel to him
That he should build a kind of tower

That would not fall to any force
Or be defeated by machine.
Inside he'd be when it was ready,
And enemies could not then kill him.
He then selected and had guarded
A perfect place to build the tower.
It came to please him and delight him
To build it upon Erir Mountain.
He sought out masons, the best he knew,
And got them working when he could.
These men began to do their work,
To put the stones and mortar down;
But after all their work by day,
At night it all fell to the ground.
When they would work to build it higher,
The bottom crumbled that much more.
Whole days of work were just like this,
With all the work spilled on the ground.
So when the king became aware
There was no other building progress,
He asked advice from his diviners.
"By faith," he said, "I am amazed
That this is how the work is going.
The earth just can't support the thing.
Examine it and learn why not
And also how the ground could hold it."
The men divined and cast their lots
But—can this be?—they told a lie:
If he could find a certain man
Who had been born without a father,
He ought to kill him and take his blood
And put it in the mortar mix.
His building could endure this way,
And he could safely work on it.
The king then had his men sent out
To search around through all of Wales
To see if there was such a man
Who could be brought into his presence.
The searchers traveled all around
Through many regions many times.
Two who went along a road

Arrived together in Kaërmerdin.
Before the village, at the entrance,
There was a gathering of children;
They had come there to play together.
The two men took to watching them.
Among the other children playing,
There were two boys having a fight:
The two were Dinabuz and Merlin;
The one was angry at the other,
And one provoked the other one
And said bad words about his birth:
"Shut up, Merlin," said Dinabuz.
"I come from a good line of people,
But you do not—there's no denial.
You don't know who you are, you bastard.
You have no right to mess with me
And say bad things about my family.
I come from lines of kings and counts,
But if you try to list your kin,
You will not say your father's name,
For you don't know it and never will.
You will not ever know your father,
For you will never have a father."
The men who listened to these children
And who'd gone seeking such a man,
When they had heard this argument,
Went around the neighborhood
Inquiring who this boy might be
Who never, ever had a father.
And neighbors said in answer to them
That he had never had a father
And that the mother who had borne him
Did not know who had fathered him.
Nothing was known about his father;
The mother, whom they knew quite well,
Was princess of Demetia,
Which was an area in Wales.
She was a nun of holy life
There in an abbey in the town.
The men then went to see the provost;
On behalf of the king they asked

That Merlin, who was fatherless,
Go with his mother to the king.
The provost wished not to refuse them:
He had both led before the king.
The king received them graciously
And spoke to them in friendly terms:
"Lady," he said, "tell me the truth:
If not on your own, and you are certain,
Who was the man who fathered Merlin?"
The nun continued facing down;
When she had thought a little while,
She said, "So help me God, I swear
I never knew and never saw
The man who fathered this boy here.
I never heard, I never saw
If it was a man from whom I got him.
But I did and do know certainly—
And I confess it as the truth—
That when I was not quite yet grown—
I don't know if it was a phantom—
A thing would often come to me,
Which kissed me in an intimate way.
I heard him speak just like man,
And like a man he felt to touch;
And many times he talked with me
And did not show himself to me.
He came to me like this so often
And came to kiss me so oft too
He slept with me and I conceived:
I never knew another man.
This boy I had; this boy I have;
There was no more; I'll say no more."
The king then made Magant appear,
A very brilliant man of letters,
And asked him whether things could be,
Such as the nun had told him of.
He said, "We have found written tales

7439-56 *Incubi daemones* were variously condemned by medieval authorities as the consorts of Satan, but some ancient notions of less-than-malevolent creatures who lived in the air (and thus in the sublunary realm) obviously survived in medieval literature.

Concerning certain kinds of spirits 7440
That live between the Moon and Earth.
One wants to ask about their nature?
In part they have a human nature,
In part a higher kind of nature. 7444
Incubi daemones they're called.
Through all the air they have domain,
And they have homes upon the Earth.
They cannot do much bad at all: 7448
They cannot do much harm at all
Outside of tricks and mockery.
They well can take on human form,
And they like doing so by nature. 7452
They have deceived many young women
And in this guise had sex with them.
Merlin could've come this way
And in this way could have been fathered." 7456
"King," said Merlin, "You sent for me.
What did you want? Why was I sought?"
The king said, "Merlin, now you'll know.
You wished to hear and you will hear. 7460
I have begun to build a tower
And have had stones and mortar set,
But all the work done in a day
Sinks in the earth and goes right down. 7464
I do not know if you've heard talk,
But what one builds when it is day
Goes sinking down when it is night.
I've wasted much of my resources. 7468
The wizards that I have, have said
I'll never get the tower built
Unless your blood is put inside it
Because you did not have a father." 7472
"Your tower standing on my blood
Would not please God," Merlin replied.

According to these myths, these airy demons could take on different shapes. The female form was called a succubus. In this form, the demon would seduce a human male and then refine his semen; this refined semen would then be deposited in a human female seduced by the male form of the demon, the incubus. The result of such a union is a person like Merlin with superhuman powers.

"I'll make these men become mere liars
If you have them come in my presence,
All who would with my blood divine:
They would be liars if they lied."
The king had orders sent to them
And had them led in front of Merlin.
When Merlin had examined them,
He said, "You lords of divination,
Say why and how it comes to pass
That this construction does not hold.
If you can't give an explanation
Of why the tower falls right down,
How can you say through divination
That with my blood it ought to stand?
Say what's wrong with the foundation
That makes the tower fall so often
And then say how it could stay standing
And what could make it hold together.
If you cannot give us an answer
About what makes the tower fall,
How can the reasoning be believed
That through my blood it will be stable?
Tell the king the trouble's cause;
Then say what remedy is needed."
All the wizards turned away;
They could not say a thing to Merlin.
Merlin said, "Listen, Lord King:
Under the bottom of the tower,
There is a pool, both large and deep,
That makes the tower fall to earth.
And you will certainly believe me
If you remove the earth and look."
The king had it removed and found
The pool that Merlin spoke about.
"Listen, Your Highness," Merlin said.
"You who ordered I be sought
To mix my blood up in the mortar,
Tell us what this pool contains."
All of these men were mute and silent
And said no word, not good or bad.
Merlin turned to face the king;

Before his men he spoke to him:
"Empty out this pool," he said,
"And drain the water with some channels.
Two dragons sleep upon the bottom,
Lying in separate rocky chambers.
One of the dragons is all white;
The other one is red as blood."
And when the water was drawn off
And was completely drained by channels,
Two dragons came out from the bottom
And fiercely moved against each other;
They fought with great ferocity
While all the barons looked at them.
Well could you have seen them foaming
And spewing flames out of their mouths.
The king sat right next to the pool;
He asked for Merlin to interpet
What the dragons signified,
Which came together with such ire.
Then Merlin said the prophecies,
Which I believe you've heard before,
About the kings who were to come,
Who rightfully possessed the land.
I don't want to translate his book
Since I cannot interpret it;
I do not wish to say a thing
If it were not as I would say it.
The king gave Merlin lots of praise
And thought he was a good divine;
He asked when he himself would die
And by what kind of death he'd end,
For he was scared of his demise.

7535-42 Blacker-Knight has argued that Wace's omission of the prophecies of Merlin "is the most dramatic example of Wace's draining of political import from the material associated with Arthur" ("Transformations of a Theme," 70). She expands these observations in later articles, concluding (1) that Wace, who was dependent on royal favor, omitted the ambiguous prophecies because they were read as anti-Norman (Blacker, "Where Wace Feared to Tread") and (2) that he failed to translate them not because he was not savvy enough to do so but was politically savvy enough not to do so (Blacker, "'Ne vuil sun livre translater'"). Wace thus "depoliticizes the *Brut*" (Blacker, *Faces of Time*, 98-99).

“Protect,” he said, “protect yourself
From fire from Constantine’s own children,
For by their fire, you’ll meet your end.
They come now from Armorica,
Sailing by sea with massive strength.
Of this you can yourself be certain:
To Totnes they will come tomorrow.
You’ve done them harm; they’ll do you harm:
They will get tough revenge on you.
To your harm you betrayed their brother
And to your harm became the king
And to your harm into this land
You brought the heathens and the Saxons.
You have two problems, on two sides;
I don’t know which needs guarding first:
On one hand Saxons war against you,
Who’d willingly bring your destruction.
And on the other come the heirs,
Who wish to take this kingdom over,
Who wish to get their hands on Britain
And get revenge for brother Constance.
If you can flee now, you should flee,
For both the brothers now are coming.
Aurelius will be king first,
And he will die by poison first.
Uther, his brother, called Pendragon
Will hold the kingdom afterwards;
But he will be interred too soon
And will be poisoned by your heirs.
His son, who’ll be from out of Cornwall,
Like a ferocious boar in battle,
Will gobble all the traitors up
And will destroy all of your kin,
And will be very brave and valiant;
He’ll conquer all his enemies.”

VIII. The House of Constantine: Aurelius Ambrosius

Merlin stopped his prophecy,
And Vortigern went off from there.
Not later than the following day,
The fleet belonging to the brothers
Made land at Totnes there in Dartmouth
With cavalry and with equipment.
One saw the happiness of Britons,
One group bucking up the other.
Together they were reunited
Who were before scattered in fear.
Hengist had made them run and hide
And flee into the woods and mountains,
For he'd destroyed the class of lords
With knives employed in treachery.
The Britons were united then;
They made Aurelius king and lord.
Vortigern, who heard this news,
Fled to Wales, prepared for war.
Into a castle called Genoire,
He went seeking his own protection
With the most valiant of his people,
Near the Weye, a flowing river.
The locals called it River Weye,
And Hergrin was the province name.
The castle was on Mount Cloärt;
The local people called it this.
Vortigern prepared quite well
With weapons, people, and provisions.
If this had given him protection,
He would have been prepared enough.

The brothers took the barons then
And sought out Vortigern the King
Till they besieged him in a castle.
They drew and lanced enough at him:
With great desire they wished to take him,
For wondrous was their hate for him.
Now if the brothers hated him,
Vortigern deserved this hate:
He murdered their own brother Constance
Just like their father Constantine
Before, with passive treachery,
But they were certain of his guilt.
Eldulf, who was the Count of Gloucester
And who knew well the land of Wales,
Became a man of Aurelius
And came with him among the host.
Aurelius said, "Eldulf, by God,
Have you forgotten now my father,
Who raised you up and gave you fiefs,
And Constance my brother, who loved you much?
Both honored you with ready will;
They trusted you and loved you much.
Through the devices of this man,
This tyrant, and this perjurer,
The two were killed who yet would live
If they'd not died through his devices.
If you feel sadness over them,
Get revenge on Vortigern."
With only this admonishment,
They armed themselves both one and all.
They made a pile of gathered wood,
Completely filling a great moat.
They then put fire onto the pile.
The flames took hold upon the castle;
From there they spread into the tower
And into the surrounding houses.
Then you'd have seen the castle burning,
The flames flying, the houses falling.
The king was burned, and so were those
Who had sought refuge with the king.
After the brand-new king had conquered

And turned the country to himself,
He said he'd run the heathens out
And bring deliverance to the land.
Hengist knew and was afraid.
Into Scotland he made his way
And left behind all other places.
Beyond the Humber, he went in flight
For the help, aid, and reinforcements
He knew he'd get from men in Scotland.
And his great need increased so much
That into Scotland he would go.
The king on every single day
Received his people as their lord,
And all this time the Britons grew
And came to him in such great masses
That no one there could count them all—
More numerous than grains of sand.
The king found much land lying waste
And saw there was no one to farm it.
He saw the forts and towns destroyed,
The cities burned and cloisters pillaged.
The heathens had set all on fire,
And they spared nothing anywhere.
To all he promised compensation
When he restored stability.
Hengist knew the king was coming
And wouldn't leave without a fight.
He wished to bolster his companions
And wished to give them bravery:
"Barons," he said, "you should not fear
This rag-tag company of men.
You know right well how Britons are:
They'll never hold their own with us.
If you can mount a slight resistance,
You'll see them stop soon afterward.
With little numbers many times,
You've conquered and defeated them.
If they've great numbers, what's the worry?
Their numbers are not worth a thing.
Silly it is to fear a group
That has a weak and foolish leader.

Of sorry men without a lord
A man ought never be afraid.
The one who leads them's just a child;
He cannot carry weapons yet.
We are magnificent men of war
And proven in a lot of fights.
We are defending our own lives,
For there is nothing else to do."
    Hengist stopped inciting them;
He had his warriors arms themselves.
Against the Britons in great haste,
He rode out quickly on his horse.
He thought he'd find them unprepared
And wished to beat them in this way;
The Britons, though, who feared the heathens,
Both day and night were always armed.
When the king knew that they were coming
And wanted to engage in battle,
In a field that seemed quite fair to him,
He led his people and arranged them.
He put on one side with their horses
Three thousand of the cavalry
Whom he had led across the sea,
Retained completely as his vassals.
He had two companies of Welsh:
The one he stationed on the hills
So that the heathens could not mount them
For any need that might befall them.
The others he put in the woods
To guard the entrance to the forest
So heathens could not enter there
If Welshmen did not bring them death.
He had the others on the plain
For good placement, for good defense.
When he had placed his men completely,
Just as he had been advised,
He was, of course, with his own men,
Who were most loyal in his mind.
Near him he had his banner raised
Where his own people could draw up.
Eldulf the count was at his side

And many other barons too.
"Good," said Eldulf, "I'll rejoice
If I can live to see the hour
When I might cross the path of Hengist.
I would remember well right then
That right beside Mount Ambrius
He killed the flower of our knighthood,
Upon the very first of May,
When I escaped there with some trouble."
And with these words that Eldulf spoke,
Who made these charges against Hengist,
Hengist appeared there on the plain
And seized a massive section of it.
They did not waste much time at all
To get the battle into motion.
As soon as they could see each other,
They ran together right away.
Then you'd have seen the vassals fighting:
These against the others slashing;
These attacking, those defending;
Great blows received, great blows delivered;
Some men upsetting other men;
The living stepping on the dead;
Shields being pierced and shafts being shattered;
The wounded falling, the fallen dying.
The heathens fought the battle well,
And even better fought the Christians.
The heathens called on their false gods;
The Christians made their prayers to God.
They made their battle lines fall back
And so they left the field abandoned.
They took the blows both great and large,
And so they had to turn their backs.
When Hengist saw his men turn tail
And leave their backs exposed to blows,
He spurred quite hard to Conisbrough,
For there he wished to find his refuge.
The king, however, followed him,
Urging his men: "Come on, come on!"

When Hengist saw him in pursuit
And saw the castle all surrounded,

He wished instead to fight outside
And put his body into danger
Than let himself be locked inside
Without a hope that he'd get help.
He drew his people back together
And set them up again for battle.
One saw a battle to the death,
A bitter fight and a sharp pain.
The heathens turned themselves around,
And each one gave the other heart.
The Christians then were losing there;
The heathens pressed against them hard;
The former fell in disarray.
But the three thousand in formation,
Who were on horseback, showed up there
And rescued them and held the line.
The heathens fought with hardiness—
No marvel here for well they knew
That they would not escape alive
If they could not defend themselves.
Eldulf saw Hengist, whom he knew;
He hated him and owed him hate.
He saw the time and place right then
To make his deepest wishes real.
With a drawn sword he ran at him;
Hengist was strong and took the blow.
One saw this pair of vassals dueling,
Their swords naked, their shields upraised.
You would have seen them often slashing
And seen the sparks flying from steel.
Gorlois, who was the Count of Cornwall,
Bravely came into the battle.
Eldulf saw him coming near
And gained more confidence and strength.
Just as a hardy vassal should,
He rushed and grabbed at Hengist's nosepiece,
Drew him up close and bent him over,
And led him off with lively force.
"Knights," he said, "give thanks to God.
My fondest wishes have come true.
I've captured and I've vanquished one

Who menaced us with many evils.
Put this rabid dog to death
Who never pitied us at all.
He was a leader in the war
That laid to waste this land of ours.
You'll hold the victory in your hands
When you have put this one to death."
Hengist was then well brought to justice.
Placed into chains and shackled up,
To King Aurelius he was given.
He was well guarded and restrained.
Octa, his son, there in the field,
And Ebissa his relative
Were barely able to escape
And made their way to Everwic.
Inside the city they got ready
With every aid they had on hand.
Many others turned and fled
To woods, to plain, to dale, to hill.
The king was happy in the glory
That God had given him the field.
He entered into Conisbrough;
He there remained for three whole days
To take care of the wounded men
And to give them the chance to rest.
Meanwhile consulting with the barons,
He wanted to know from one and all
What he should do with evil Hengist—
If he should keep or simply kill him.
Eldadus got up on his feet,
The younger brother of Count Eldulf;
He was a consecrated bishop,
A very educated man:
"I wish," he said, "to do with Hengist,
This traitor and this enemy,
What Samuel did quite long ago
With King Agag, when he was taken.
Agag was full of every pride,

7853ff. The Agag story is in 1 Samuel 15, esp. 32-33. Note the rhetorical amplification.

The very glorious Amalek king.
He fought the Jews at every chance;
He did them harm and menaced them;
He raped their lands and burned them up
And very often killed the people.
By his bad luck, he was then taken
As he was sinking in defeat.
He was presented before Saul,
Who then was reigning as the king.
When Saul inquired what he should do
With Agag, who was in his power,
Samuel got up on his feet,
A holy man of Israël.
Never for greater holiness
Was any man known in his time.
Samuel had this Agag seized
And cut him into many pieces.
He had the pieces all cut up
And thrown around the countryside.
And do you know what Samuel said
When he turned Agag into pieces?
'Agag, you've tortured many men,
Put many to death, set many on fire.
You've taken many souls from bodies
And made a lot of mothers sad
And made a lot of infants orphans—
And now you've come unto your end.
I'll make your mother without child
And take your soul out of your body.'
And so you should do such a thing
As Samuel did to such a one."
According with what Eldadus said,
Eldulf advanced and seized on Hengist;
He led him outside of the city
And, sword unsheathed, cut off his head.
The king had men prepare the body,
Entomb and put it in the earth
According with what people did
Who then observed the heathen law.

The king was lively in his actions
And did not stay in one place long.

With a great host he came and closed
His enemies in Everwic.
Inside was Octa, Hengist's son,
And many of his relatives.
He saw that he would get no help
And he could not defend himself.
He figured that he would give up
And put himself in fortune's hands.
In humbleness he'd ask for mercy;
And if he got it, he'd be happy.
He did just what he thought he'd do,
And so his kinfolk praised him for it.
He issued from the town on foot
And soon his men all did the same.
Octa, who first came to the king,
Bore a chain of iron links.
"Sire," he said, "mercy, mercy!
Quickly our gods have failed for us
In whom we used to put our trust.
Your God possesses greater power;
Wonders and deeds of strength he does,
Who totally conquered us through you.
Conquered, I come to seek your mercy.
Accept the chain that I bear here
And do with me what you desire
And also with my men as well.
We're all committed to your pleasure
To take our lives or limbs away.
But if you want us as your servants,
You'll get great services from us.
For we will serve you loyally
And will become men sworn to you."
The king was full of sympathy;
He took a look around himself
To see just what his lords would say
And how they'd counsel him in this.
Eldadus, the good holy man,
Spoke first as if he were in council:
"It's good," he said, " and was and will be
That one have mercy when he seeks it,
For if a man has none on others,

God won't have mercy on that man.
These men now try to get your mercy;
They're seeking it and might yet get it.
Britain, which is long and wide,
In many places is deserted.
Make them take a part of it
And make them plow and work on it,
And so they'll live through their own farming.
But first take their good hostages,
Who loyally will give you service
And loyally conduct themselves.
The Gibeonites requested mercy
From Jews who beat them long ago:
They asked for mercy and they found it;
The Jews then quit their claim on them.
We are obliged to be no worse
Than Jews were on that very day.
They ask for mercy to get mercy—
From here on out they should not die."
The king then granted land to them
(Just as Eldadus counseled him)
Close to Scotland for some farming.
They went there then to take their homes,
But first they gave up hostages,
Children from the best of lines.

Then fifteen days passed in the town;
He called his people to a council.
He summoned there his clerks and lords,
His abbots and his bishops too.
He rendered them their fiefs and rights
And then commanded and established
That churches then would be rebuilt
Which heathen infidels destroyed.
During this time he split his army
And named the viscounts and the provosts
Who would restore the feudal lands
And who would guard his yearly income.
He sought out carpenters and masons
And had the churches built again.
The churches in the areas
That were destroyed in acts of war—

The king had them restored completely
For service in God's adoration.
From there to London he then turned,
Where he was very much desired.
He saw the city in a shambles
And empty of good citizens,
Its houses wasted, churches leveled.
Often enough he moaned in sorrow.
He had the churches all repaired
And called the folks and clergy back
With all their customary laws.
To Winchester the king then went.
The churches, houses, and the towers
He fixed back up as he'd done elsewhere.
To Amesbury then he made his way
To pay a visit to the graves
Where lying in the earth were those
Who suffered death through murdering knives.
Masons and skillful engineers
And carpenters by scores he summoned.
The place where all these deaths occurred
That Hengist brought about through treason
He wished to honor with a work
That would endure forever more.
Tremorius, a man of wisdom,
The archbishop of Kaerleon,
Requested that he call for Merlin
And follow his advice in this.
There was no one with better counsel
Concerning what he wished to do,
For in divining and in building,
One could not find another like him.
The king wished much to see this Merlin
And wished to listen to his wisdom.
To Labanës, which is a fountain
Off in Wales, quite far away
(I don't know where; I've never been there),
The king sent messengers for him.
He came as ordered to the king,
Who honored him in many ways.
He greeted him with lots of honor,

Lots of joy and lots of love.
He begged him much, he asked him much
To teach to him, to speak to him
About the time that was to come—
He wanted much to hear him speak.
"Sire," said Merlin, "I shall not.
My mouth will never work that way
Unless there is a pressing need,
And then in great humility.
If I speak out in vanity
Or mockery or silliness,
The spirits that I have through whom
I have the knowledge that I have
Will draw themselves out of my mouth,
And they will take away my knowledge,
And then my mouth will speak no more
Than any other's mouth might do.
Leave secret prophecies alone;
Think about what you should do.
If you would make a lasting work
That might be very nice and easy
And talked about forever more,
Have the circle carried here
That was in Ireland made by giants,
A work both marvelous and grand
Of stones set up to make a circle,
Some of them placed upon the others.
The stones are of a shape and size,
So very large and very heavy,
That human force before our time
Could never move a single one."
"Merlin," said the king with laughter,
"Granting the stones do weigh so much
That they cannot be moved by man,
Who will be able to bring them here?—
As if we didn't in this kingdom
Have stones with quality enough!"
"King," said Merlin, "don't you know
That cleverness defeats brute strength?
Strength is good, but cleverness better.
Cleverness works where brute strength fails.

Skill and cleverness do a lot
That strength won't even dare to do.
Now cleverness can move the stones;
And cleverness can make them yours.
They were removed from Africa,
Where they were first set in a circle.
Giants, who carried them from there,
In Ireland set them in their place.
They've long been used as medicine,
Beneficial for diseases.
The people used to wash them off
And mix the water with their bath.
The ones who suffered an affliction
Or who were grieved by a disease,
Took baths in certain kinds of basins
And through their baths received a cure.
And never for the ill they had
Did they seek other medicine."
After the king and Britons knew
The stones had such inherent power,
They all had much enthusiasm
And all showed quite an interest
In going off to get the circle
That Merlin spoke about like this.
They all chose Uther with one voice,
And he himself made the proposal
That he would take the trip to Ireland,
Commanding fifteen thousand men
With whom he'd war against the Irish
If they would fight them for the stones.
Merlin too would go with them
To use his skill against the stones.
When Uther called his men together,
To Ireland then he crossed the sea.
Gillomanius, who was king,
Summoned his people and the Irish;
He seized on menacing the British
And wished to chase them from the land.
And when he learned what they were seeking,
That they had come to get the stones,
He started making fun of them:

"They traveled here for foolishness;
These men—to find a bunch of stones—
Had sailed into another land.
They will not have a one," he said,
"And will not take a one away."
He found it easy to disdain them,
But found it hard to overturn them.
He mocked them so and threatened them
And sought them so until he found them.
Soon they came upon each other,
And they laid on each other well.
The Irish were not well equipped
And were not used to doing battle.
They offered insults to the Britons;
The Britons offered them defeat.
The king turned tail and ran away,
Fleeing from one town to another.
After the Britons were disarmed
And had a chance to get some rest,
Merlin, who was there in the group,
Took them up onto a mountain
Where the circle had been set up
By giants, the object of their quest.
The mountain's name was Killomar,
On top of which the circle was.
The men looked closely at the stones
And walked around them very often.
And each one said unto the other
That he had never seen such work:
"How are the stones here held aloft,
And how would they be moved away?"
"Sirs," said Merlin, "let us see
If with the strength that you possess
You're able to pick up the stones
And if you can then bear them off."
The men took hold upon the stones
Behind, in front, and right across.
They strained quite well and pushed quite well
And pulled quite well and shook quite well,
And not the smallest bit with force
Could they get anything to turn.

"Pull yourselves away," said Merlin.
"With strength you'll never get more done.
Look now how skill and cleverness
Are worth much more than physical strength."
He then went up till he was there,
Looked around and moved his lips
Just like a man who said his prayers.
I don't know if he prayed or not.
Again he called the Britons back:
"Come to the front," he said, "Come forward!"
You can now seize upon the stones
And take them to your ships and load them."
Just as Merlin had instructed,
Just as he'd said and planned with skill,
The Britons took the stones in hand,
Carried them to the ships and stowed them.
They took them off to England then
And bore them to Mount Ambrius
Onto the plain quite close to there.
The king came there at Pentecost.
He called together all his bishops
And all his abbots and his barons.
He there assembled many others,
Held a feast, and so was crowned.
Three days he feasted; on the fourth
He gave some decorated crosses
To St. Dubriz of Kaerleon
And St. Samson of Everwic.
Both were great as clergymen,
And both led very holy lives.
And Merlin got the stones prepared
And put them back into their order.
The Britons usually in British
Call the stones the Giants' Ring.
In English *Stonehenge* is their name;
Les Pierres Pendues their name in French.
When the great feast came to an end,
The royal court broke up and left.
Paschent, a son of Vortigern,
Fearing Aurelius and Uther,
Abandoned Wales and Britain too

And took his flight to Germany.
He got his hands on men and ships,
But it was not a massive force.
He came ashore in Britain's north,
Destroying towns and wasting land,
But he dared not stay there for long,
For the king came and chased him off.
When Paschent came back to the sea,
He dared not come back whence he came,
But he so sailed and he so rowed
That he came to the Irish shore.
Speaking to the country's king,
He talked about his needy case.
Paschent begged the king so much
And gave and took advice so much
That they were pledged to cross the sea
To take on combat with the Britons:
Paschent to avenge his father
And stake claim to his heritage;
The king to seek his own revenge
On those who had just recently
Conquered him and robbed his people
And took away the ring from them.
They took each other's sworn allegiance
To seek revenge for each one's cause.
With all the force that they could muster,
They crossed the sea when they'd good wind.
In Wales the whole bunch came ashore,
And to Menevia they then went.
Menevia was a pretty town
That now the people call St. David's.
King Aurelius was in bed;
At Winchester he languished on.
He was quite sick and suffered long;
He got no better; he didn't die.
After he heard the news of Paschent
And of the King of Ireland too,
Who both had come ashore in Wales

8213-14 Detail added by Wace (Weiss, *Roman de Brut*, 207, n. 3).

And wished to lay his land to waste,
He summoned there his brother Uther.
He could not go and he was sad.
He told Uther to hunt them down
And to make war upon these men.
Uther then called upon his barons
And summoned all his mounted knights.
Because he took the long way there
And wished to unify the people,
He often stopped and took much time
Before he actually came to Wales.
During the time that he delayed,
Eäppas had a talk with Paschent.
Eäppas was a heathen Saxon
Who was a very clever speaker.
From youth he worked at being learned,
So he could speak in many tongues—
He was an evil infidel.
"Paschent," he said, "listen to me!
You hate the king without restraint.
What will you give me if I kill him?"
"A thousand pounds," he said, "I'll give you,
And you will never lack a thing
If you accomplish what you say
And kill the king with your own hands."
"I shall," he said, "demand no more."
They made their covenant right then:
Paschent would give a thousand pounds;
And he would kill the king with poison.
Eäppas was ingenious
And eager to acquire some gold.
He dressed himself in monkish clothes
And made a bald spot on his head.
Shaved and tonsured like a monk
And habited just like a monk,
With an expression like a monk's,
He went into the royal court.
This trickster acted like a doctor;
He spoke and made the king a promise
That he would make him well quite soon
If he would let him care for him.

He took his pulse and viewed his urine;
He said he knew about bad piss
And knew just how to make it better.
Now who would doubt a man like this?
The noble king desired a cure
As each one of us would desire.
He had no fear of treachery;
He put himself in evil hands.
This evil man gave him a drink
Mixed up completely with a poison.
He made him warmly cover up
And peacefully recline and sleep.
And when the king had gotten warm
And poison spread throughout the body,
God, what pain! His death was near.
But when he knew he had to die,
He said to those who watched with him
That if they loved him truthfully,
They'd bear his body down to Stonehenge
And bury it inside that place.
Thus he was dead; thus he was finished,
The traitor went away in flight.

IX. The House of Constantine: Uther Pendragon

Uther had come into Wales
And found the Irish at Menevia.
A star appeared then at that time
That was observed by many people.
It was what scholars call a comet,
Which signifies a royal change.
Brilliant it was and marvelous,
For it emitted just one ray.
A flame, which issued from the ray,
Formed the figure of a dragon.
Out of the dragon came two rays,
Which made their exit from its mouth.
One of them stretched out over France
And shone from here down to Montjoie.
Off toward Ireland went the other
And split up into seven rays.
Each of the seven rays shone bright
Both over land and over sea.
The sign that was observed like this
Made all the people get excited.
Uther himself was quite amazed
And frightened by it to great wonder.
He asked for Merlin to explain
What such a sign could signify.
Merlin was very much disturbed,
And his heart hurt; he said no word.
After his spirits settled down,

8289-90 Couplet added by Wace (Weiss, *Roman de Brut*, 209, n.1).

He moaned a lot and sighed a lot:
"O God," he said, "how great the pain,
How great the sadness, great the tears
That on this day have come to Britain!
It's suffered its great leader's loss;
The king is dead, the noble lord
Who brought this land deliverance
From both the pains and the great harms
As they were wrought by heathen hosts."
When Uther heard about his brother,
Of the good lord, who passed away,
He sorrowed much, afraid of much.
But Merlin calmed him down with this:
"Uther," he said, "don't be disturbed.
There was no way to stop his death.
Complete what you have sought to do.
Make war against your enemies.
Tomorrow victory waits for you
Over the Irish king and Paschent.
Tomorrow brings you war and triumph,
And you will be the king of Britain.
The signs appearing with the dragon
For us had great significance
Concerning you, the brave and hardy.
One of the rays concerns a son
That you will have, with massive power,
Who'll conquer France and yet beyond.
The other ray, which turned that way
And split up into seven rays,
Stands for the daughter you will have
Who will be married up near Scotland.
Many good heirs will come from her,
And they will conquer lands and seas."
When Uther had well listened to
The comfort Merlin brought to him,
He made his men rest for the night
And arm themselves upon the morning.
He wished to strike the town straight on;
The Irish, though, who saw him coming
Took up their arms, got into ranks,
And went outside to fight the battle.

They laid on fiercely in the fight,
But soon enough they met defeat.
For Britons finished Paschent off
And killed the Irish king to boot.
Those on the field who were still living
Turned and fled away to ships.
Uther, who followed at their backs,
Made them face death completely vanquished.
There were such ones who did escape,
Who made it to their ships in flight
And got them pushed out in the sea
So Uther could not get to them.
When he had finished this affair,
He turned to Winchester for some rest,
With him the best of all the barons.
Along the way he met a runner
Who told him as the very truth
How by some means the king was dead
And how the bishops with great care
Had made a sepulcher for him
Within the circle of the giants,
Just as he told his serving men
And barons when he was alive.
After Uther heard this news,
He came to Winchester at a gallop;
The people came outside for him,
Crying and shouting with one voice:
"Uther, lord, mercy, by God!
Dead is the one who once sustained us
And did great good on our behalf.
Sustain us now—take the crown
That you inherit and right bestows.
And, happy lord, we ask you this,
For we desire your valor and honor."
Uther saw how he was loved
And how he could do nothing better.
He felt great joy at what they said
And quickly did what they requested.
He took the crown, became the king,
Held honor dear, sustained the people.
For honor and as a reminder

Of how the dragon symbolized
That he was great and would be king
And would have conquerors as heirs,
King Uther made two golden dragons
According with his barons' counsel.
He had the one before him borne
Whenever he went into battle;
To Winchester Cathedral then,
He gave the other as a gift.
From here on out, for just this reason,
Uther Pendragon was his name.
This British name *Pendragon* means
"Chiés de dragon" in our Romance.

Octa, who was Hengist's son,
To whom the king had made a grant
Of large estates and large desmenes—
Both to him and to his friends—
When he had learned that he was dead
Who had maintained the great armed force,
He little praised the brand-new king
And owed him thus no loyalty.
He got his friends and kin together,
Including Eosa, his cousin.
These two were masters over all,
And these two were the bravest ones.
The people who were led by Paschent,
The ones who fled away from Uther—
The two put these into their force:
Their company was big enough.
All the land they took completely
And split it up along the Humber
By length, by width from there to Scotland;
And then they went to Everwic.
They made attacks around the town,
And those inside made their defense
So that the heathens captured nothing.
But they besieged them with their numbers.
Uther wished to save the town

8406 "Head of the dragon." See Norris J. Lacy, "Pendragon," in *The New Arthurian Encyclopedia*, ed. idem, 354-55; and "Pendragon" in *Arthurian Handbook*, 2nd ed.

And give help to his friends inside.
He quickly went to Everwic,
Calling his men from everywhere.
He wished to break the heathen siege,
And so he moved to strike at once.
Bitter and painful was the fight;
Many a soul tore from the flesh.
The heathens had a massive force,
And so they held together well.
The Britons could not damage them
Enough to breach their ranks with force.
The Britons had to turn around,
And when they wanted to withdraw,
The siege force then gave them pursuit
And brought amazing harm to them.
They went on giving them pursuit
Attacking time and time again,
Until they chased them up a hill
And darkness finally parted them.
The hill was called Mount Danien;
The top of it was somewhat pointed.
There were large boulders and recesses
And all around thick hazel trees.
The Britons went right up the hill,
Some on the top, some on the sides.
They occupied the hill completely;
The heathens placed a siege on them.
The ones below upon the plain
Placed a siege around the hill.
The king was very much afraid,
Both for his men and for himself.
He did not know what he would do
Or how they would defend themselves.
The Count of Cornwall, Gorloïs—
Quite brave, quite wise, quite courteous,
And quite older—was with the king.
He was regarded for his wisdom;
They sought the counsel of this man

8465-72 Pickens argues that Gorlois is *courteis* according to the values of *vassalage* found in a work like the *Chanson de Roland* ("*Vassalage*," 169).

And put this business in his hands,
For he would do no coward's deed
For loss of limb or loss of life. 8472
"Advice," he said, "you ask of me.
My advice, if you want it, is
That secretly we arm ourselves
And get ourselves down off this hill. 8476
Let's go and strike our enemies
Who think that they can sleep secure.
They have no fear and have no worries
That we will ever lance at them. 8480
They think they'll take us in the morning
If we desire to wait here for them.
Let's go to them in secrecy,
So we can strike at once in mass! 8484
Order must be kept in this,
No horn blowing, no hue and cry.
Before they might gain consciousness,
We will thus have them quite chopped up. 8488
Any of them who might escape us
Will never turn again against us.
But first let's promise to our God
That we will make amends with him 8492
And for the sins that we've committed,
We'll do our penance and seek pardon
And cast aside the evil deeds
That we have done throughout our lives 8496
And let us pray then to the Savior
To guard us and to give us strength
Against those with no faith in Him
Who war against His Christian people. 8500
Therefore God will be with us,
And so by Him we will be rescued—
And when our God is there with us,
Who is there who can defeat us?" 8504
According with his wise advice
And as he said and recommended,
They promised God in humbleness

8503-4 Romans 8:31.

To live their lives in better ways.
They then were armed, and secretly
They then descended from the hill.
They found the heathens all stretched out,
All disarmed and all asleep.
Then you'd have witnessed massive killing
And wonderful calamity:
Bellies were pierced and chests run through;
Heads and feet and hands were flying.
Just like a lion full of pride
That has gone hungry a long time
And murders sheep and murders goats
And murders lambs both large and small—
All the Britons quickly acted:
They killed the rich; they killed the poor.
Around the fields they were asleep
And were so taken by surprise
That they did not make plays of arms
And could not run away from there.
For Britons made a massacre
Of those they found stretched out unarmed:
They punctured chests; they punctured hearts;
They drew out bowels and drew out guts.
The lords who started up this war,
Octa and Eosa, were captured.
(To London they were sent with guards
And put in prison and in shackles.)
If anyone escaped the field,
The deep black night was his salvation.
He who could flee certainly did so,
Never waiting for his friend.
But many more there met their deaths
Than made escape there with their lives.

When Uther turned away from there,
He passed up through Northumberland,
And from Northumberland to Scotland,
With many men and massive force.
He went around the land completely,
As far as it is long and wide;
He drew completely to his service
The men who lived in lawless places.

Through all the reign he brought such peace—
Never before had king brought more.
When in the north he'd done his work,
To London he repaired in haste,
For Eastertide was on its way,
When he desired to be crowned king.
Dukes and counts and castellans,
All the ones from far and near,
And nearly all the other barons,
He called by letter and by runner
To come in company with their wives
And with their private entourages
To London for the feast he'd give,
For he desired to have a big one.
They all showed up as he requested,
And men with wives brought them indeed.
The feast was celebrated well,
And when the mass came to an end,
The king sat down to eat a meal
Before the room, upon a dais.
The barons took their seats around him,
Each one in order of his rank.
Right in his sight in front of him,
The Count of Cornwall took his seat,
And his wife, Ygerne, next to him—
There was none fairer in the realm.
She was fine-mannered, fair, and wise
And came from very noble people.
The king had heard men speak of her,
And he had heard men praise her highly.
Before he took a single look,
Seeing enough before he saw her,
He wanted her and fell in love,
For she was praised as a great wonder.

8565ff "Note that here men and women eat together, though later [10437ff.] we are told that on feast days British men and women eat separately" (Weiss, *Roman de Brut*, 217, n. 1).

8580ff Light ("Arthurian Portion") notes that Uther's love for Ygerne before he even saw her "gives the first indication of the new spirit of chivalry which suffuses the Arthurian portion" (107) but quotes an earlier scholar's caution that Uther's immediate demand

He gazed at her a lot at dinner;
All his attention was fixed on her.
While he was eating and was drinking,
While he was speaking and was quiet,
He thought about her all the time
And stared at her across the room.
Looking at her, he smiled at her
And to her made some signs of love.
He greeted her through trusted friends
And had some presents sent to her.
He smiled and winked at her a lot
And gave her many friendly looks.
Now Ygerne held herself in check
And neither welcomed nor refused him.
The silliness, the smiles, the signs,
The salutations and the greetings—
The count picked up on these and knew
The king was taken by his wife,
And he would never bear him faith
If he once had her for his pleasure.
He left the table where he sat,
He took his wife, and he went out.
He called to his companions then,
Came to his horse, and mounted up.
The king then reprimanded him
For doing shame and villainy
By leaving court without permission.
He must do right and turn around.
And if he failed to do these things,
He would defy him; despite his rank,
He would no longer hold his trust.

for her is not exactly courtly love (108). See Philippe Ménard, "La déclaration amoureuse dans la littérature arthurienne au xiie siècle," *Cahiers de civilisation médiévale* 13 (1970): 33-42, on flirtatious looks in courtship (33-34), and Keller on the dynastic justification for the passion ("De l'amour," 75). Pickens points out that Uther illustrates the qualities of *fin' amors* and that by having Ygerne closed up (a change from Geoffrey), Wace makes her a victim to be saved from an old husband ("*Vassalage*," 180-82). We might also add that Uther is suffering from a condition considered to be an effeminate disease among the adherents of celibacy in Wace's day. After falling in love with Ygerne and fathering Arthur, Uther loses considerable physical strength (and thus much of his manliness); see Glowka, "Masculinity," 420–25.

The count did not want to go back;
He left the court without permission.
The king had made a lot of threats,
But they were trifles to the count:
He did not know then what was coming.
Back to Cornwall he returned;
He had two castles; he prepared them.
He put his wife inside Tintagel
(His grandfather's and father's once).
Tintagel now was easy to guard:
There was no means to breach its walls;
It was enclosed by cliff and sea.
He who could guard the door alone
Would have no worry and no fear
Of any other entrance there.
The count locked Ygerne up in there;
He dared to put her nowhere else
Where she might be borne off and seized.
He put her therefore in Tintagel.
He led away his infantry
And a good portion of his knights
Into the other of his castles,
Which guarded most of his estates.
The king knew that he would prepare
And that he'd mount defense against him.
As much to war against the count
As get his hands upon the countess,
From everywhere he called his men
And crossed the waters of the Thames.
He went to where the count was staying;
He wished to take him; the count held firm.
Uther put a siege in place.
He sat there for a week like this,
And he could not yet take the castle.
The count did not want to surrender;
He waited for the Irish king,
Who was to come and give him help.
The king despised this waiting game,
And so he fell into depression.
The love of Ygerne afflicted him;
He loved her more than anything.

He summoned to him secretly
Ulfin, who was a household lord:
"Ulfin," he said, "give me advice;
I take advice from only you.
The love of Ygerne has surprised me:
It's vanquished me; it's conquered me.
I cannot go; I cannot come—
I cannot wake; I cannot sleep—
I can't get up; I can't lie down—
I cannot drink; I cannot eat—
Without a memory of Ygerne.
But I don't know how I might get her.
I'll die if you don't counsel me."
"I've heard a marvel," Ulfin said.
"You have harassed the count with war
And you have put his land on fire
And have him closed up in his castle.
Do you believe his wife likes this?
You love his wife; you war on him.
I can't advise you how to get her;
I do not have advice to give you.
But have these questions put to Merlin,
Who's skilled in many kinds of arts;
And he has come into this host.
If he cannot give you advice,
No one can guide you in this case."
The king, through the advice of Ulfin,
Had Merlin ordered to appear.
He told him all about his need;
He begged the man and cried for mercy
That he'd advise him, if he could,
For he would die without relief
Unless he got his way with Ygerne.
He begged and pleaded for his help.
He would give him what he desired,
For he was sick and in much pain.
"Sire," said Merlin, "you will have her;
You'll never die for Ygerne's sake.
I'll fix things so you'll have your pleasure,
But you will give me nothing back.
But Ygerne's under heavy guard:

She is enclosed within Tintagel,
Which never has by any force
Been seized or conquered, it's so strong.
The entrance and the exit can
Be held quite well by two good men.
But I will put you well inside
With novel methods of enchantment.
I can remove a man's appearance
And turn one man into another,
The one face looking like the other,
The one face equal to the other.
The body, face, and countenance,
The speech, and also the appearance
Belonging to the Count of Cornwall
I'll make you have without a fault.
Why do I make the story long?
I'll make you like the count this way,
And I, since I will go with you,
Will then assume Bretel's appearance;
And Ulfin, who will be with us,
Will totally resemble Jurdan.
The count has these two closest friends
As his most intimate advisors.
You can thus go inside the castle
And satisfy all your desires.
You'll never be discovered there
Or be mistaken for another."
The king put lots of trust in Merlin
And thought his counsel was quite good.
In privacy he handed over
Charge of his people to a baron.
Merlin performed all his enchantments
And changed their faces and their clothes.
At night they came into Tintagel.
The ones who thought they knew these men
Rejoiced and let them come right in
And served them in a joyful manner.
The king and Ygerne went to bed,
And Ygerne on that night conceived
The good, the strong, protective king,
Whose name you hear pronounced as Arthur.

The people of the king soon knew
The king was nowhere in the host.
There was no baron who was scared
Or who just wanted to do nothing.
For the delay that made them worry,
They took up arms and put them on.
Without formation into ranks,
They charged the castle in confusion,
Assaulting it from every side.
Strongly the count put up a fight,
But he was killed in the defense,
And so the castle was soon taken.
Some of the men who fled from there
Went to Tintagel to announce
How misadventure had befallen
Upon their lord, whom they had lost.
Hearing the news that was announced
By men who mourned the count's demise,
The king got up and went out front:
"Be still," he said; "It's just not so.
I am alive and well, thank God,
As you can see right here yourselves.
This news is just not true at all:
Don't trust or mistrust everything.
But I will tell you why it is
My people are afraid for me.
I left the castle without a word,
And I did not speak to a soul.
I did not say that I would leave
Or that I would come here to you,
For I had fear of treachery.
But now they fear that I have died
Because they have not seen my face
Since Uther has been at the castle.
For those who have been killed in this
And for the castle that they've lost,
We ought to feel somewhat distraught.
But things stand well, and I'm alive.
To meet the king, I'll go out there;
I'll sue for peace and make accord
Before he may besiege this castle

And things much worse may happen to us.
For if he captures us in here,
We'll plead our case more poorly then."
Ygerne agreed with this advice,
For all along she feared the king.
And then the king gave her a hug
And also kissed her as he left.
With that he went out of the castle;
For he'd fulfilled all his desires.
When they were out upon their way,
The king, Ulfin, and Merlin too
Again were just as they should be,
And each one got his own appearance.
They came back to the host in secret.
The king desired to know just how
The castle was so quickly conquered
And if the count was really killed.
There were enough to tell the tale
Of all the truth of this and that.
He said that he was quite upset
And did not want the count to die.
He mourned him much; he missed him much;
He got enraged at his own barons.
He made a show of being sad,
But there were few who fell for this.
He made his way back to Tintagel;
He called the people of the castle.
He asked them why they made defense:
The count was dead; they should give up.
They could not count on any help
From in the land or elsewhere either.
These people knew the king spoke truth
And that they had no hope of rescue.
They opened up the castle gates
And gave the castle up to him.
The king loved Ygerne very much;
Without delay he married her.
That night he had conceived a son,
And in good time he had a son,
Whose name was Arthur; of his goodness
Many words were later said.

After Arthur Anna came,
A daughter, who was given to
A baron who was brave and courtly,
Whose name was Lot, from Lodonesia.
Uther reigned a good long time,
Healthy and safe and peacefully.
His vigor later was impaired,
And so he fell into bad health.
He languished with a great disease;
Long in bed, he weakened much.
The servants who were there in London,
Whose duty was to guard the prison,
Grew bored of standing guard so long
And, mollified by promises,
They set free Octa, Hengist's son,
And threw him from his prison cell—
And also Eosa, his friend.
For promises and for rewards,
They quit their posts as prison guards
And with the prisoners ran away.
When these men were in their own lands
And reassembled their own men,
They threatened Uther well enough
And put together a great fleet.
With a great mass of cavalry
And with their servants and their archers,
They crossed the sea and came to Scotland.
They put the land to torch and waste.
Uther, who lay diseased in bed
And who could not be helped at all,
To defend his country and himself,
Gave all to Lot, his son-in-law,
Who'd take the army in his care
And also take the cavalry.
He spoke to those attending him,
And they would do what he would say,
For he was nice and generous
And brave enough and wise enough.
Octa warred against the Britons.
With many men, he was quite proud.
As much for weakness of the king

As vengeance for his father and self,
He put the Britons in great fear.
He would not grant a truce with pledges.
And Lot encountered him a lot
And often put him into rout.
Many times he vanquished him;
Many times he lost in turn:
For it is usual in such work
That what is lost is later gained.
Lot could have been victorious
And driven him out of the country,
But the Britons were an arrogant lot
And would not listen to his orders
Because they were as free as he
And owned as much and even more.
And so the war dragged on and grew
So much so that the king perceived it
And people of the country said
The barons were just acting lazy.
Hear now about this man's great fierceness!
He did not lounge around infirm.
He did not wish, he said, to stay;
He wished to see his lords in camp.
He had himself borne on a bier,
Upon a litter on a horse.
He'd see now who, he said, would follow
And so he'd see who would remain.
This man demanded reprimands
For those who would before not follow
Either Lot or his commands,
And they came up without delay.
The king went straight to Verolam,
Which was a city at that time.
St. Alban was there made a martyr,
But then the place was set on fire
And all the city was destroyed.
There had Octa led his people
And there he put them in the city.
The king besieged him from the outside.
He built machines to breach the walls,
But they were strong; he could not hurt them.

Octa and his men felt bold,
For they had foiled the siege machines.
One morning they pulled up the door
And went outside to fight their foes.
It seemed a vile, insulting thing
To have a door closed by the king,
Who warred against them on a bier
And went to battle on a bier,
But he believed their pride would hurt them.
And the man won who should have won:
Octa was beaten and was killed
With his good kinsman Eosa.
Some who managed to escape
Made a journey up to Scotland.
They raised up Colgrim as their lord,
A friend and relative of Octa.

For the victory and the honor
That God gave to the king that day,
He was near jumping up for joy,
As if he had his health and cure.
He was picked up with strength and held
Up by his lords to show his joy.
When he was stretched out and immobile,
He said while laughing to his men:
"I'd rather lie here on this bier
And waste away diseased at length,
Than be in health and in my strength
And be defeated in dishonor.
It's worth much more to die in honor
Than live a long time in dishonor.
The Saxons held me in disdain
Because I lay there in my bed.
They joked about me quite enough
And said that I was halfway dead.
But now, as we have heard the news,
The semi-dead has whipped the living.
Let's follow after those who flee,
Those who destroyed my lands and yours."
After the king had lain awhile
And he had spoken to his men,
He went pursuing fugitives

And never stopped for his disease;
The lords, however, did request
That he spend time inside the town
Till God relieved him of his ailment.
For they feared that the travel hurt him.
Here he remained and would not follow.
With him in bed, the host departed.
He sent his people all away
Except for his own private household.
The Saxons, who were chased away,
When they had gotten back together,
Believed—and they were wrong in this—
That if they killed the king himself,
There would not be an heir to harm them
Or take away the land from them.
They wished to murder him through drink,
With poison and with treachery.
For in their arms they did not trust
Themselves enough at least to kill him.
They chose some low-down evil men;
I cannot say which or how many.
They promised them both cash and land.
They sent them to the royal court
Dressed in poor and ragged clothes
To see if they could spy the means
By which they could approach the king
And if they could then murder him.
They put themselves into disguise,
These men who could speak many tongues.
They came close to the royal court
And looked its situation over.
They could not spy around enough
To get within the royal presence,
But they did come and go enough
To hear about and see themselves
The king's dependence on cold water.
He could not stomach other drink;
The water was for his bad health.
He always drank from the same spring,
Which surged up very near his room.
No other pleased him quite as much.

Those who sought to kill the king
And who desired to bring him death,
When they saw they could not approach him
And could not kill him with a weapon,
They put some poison in the spring,
And then they left the land in flight
So that they would not be found out.
They waited and they listened close
For when and how the king would die,
For he would die in little time.
When he was thirsty and he drank,
He then was poisoned and he died.
He drank the water, then swelled up,
Wretched and darkened, and quickly died.
And everyone who drank the water
Later died just like the king,
And so the cause was figured out:
The evil deed was apperceived.
The commons were assembled then,
And they stopped up the welling spring.
They carried so much soil there
That they raised up a little mount.

X. The Rise of Arthur

When King Uther had met his end,
Down to Stonehenge he was borne,
Where he was buried in its midst,
Next to his brother, side by side.
The bishops called themselves together;
The barons held a council too.
They summoned Arthur, Uther's son;
At Silchester they crowned him king.
He was a youth of fifteen years,
Strong and great for one his age.
I'll tell you Arthur's qualities;
I will not lie to you at all.
He was a very forceful knight,
Of great valor and full of glory.
Proud he was against the proud;
Sweet and kind, against the humble.
Hardy and strong and conquering,
Free and liberal with his goods;
If he were asked by those in need,
He did not shun to give them help.
Glory and bravery he loved much;
He wished his deeds to be remembered:
He always served with courtesy
And acted with nobility.
As long as he both lived and reigned,
He was above all other princes

9015-31 With his displays of kindness, mercy, and generosity, Arthur demonstrates the broader values of *courtoisie* (Pickens, "*Vassalage*," 172). According to Blacker, Arthur is a "repository of Christian and lay virtues and above all, of courtesy, that amorphous, quintessential quality without which moral goodness would be incomplete in the society of *Brut*" (*Faces of Time*, 100-1).

In courtesy and nobleness,
In strength and generosity.
As soon as Arthur was the king,
He said it was his will and pledge
That Saxons never would have peace
As long as they were in his realm.
They killed his uncle and his father,
And they had troubled the whole land.
He called his people, asked for soldiers,
Gave them much, promised them much,
And led his people by command
Until they went past Everwic.
Colgrim, who since the death of Octa,
Maintained the Saxons as their leader,
Had Picts and Scots to give him help
And massive companies of Saxons.
Against Arthur he went to fight,
For he desired to smash his pride.
Next to the waters of the Douglas,
They came together at a crossing.
Many fell on either half
From lances, arrows, and javelins.
But beaten at the very end
Was Colgrim, who was put to flight.
Arthur, who was pursuing him,
Chased him into Everwic.
Colgrim locked himself within,
And Arthur placed a siege around him.
Baldulf, who was Colgrim's brother,
Waited at the ocean for
Childric, the king of Germany.
When Baldulf heard that Arthur had
Besieged his brother at Everwic
And that he'd chased him from the field,
He was quite sad and had great pain:
He wished to be beside his brother.
He gave up waiting for King Childric
And moved some five leagues from the host
And set an ambush in the woods.
Both with men from his own line
And with the foreigners he led,

He had with him six thousand armed.
He wished to storm the host at night
And force the siege to break apart,
But some who saw the ambush formed,
Ran to make the king aware.
Arthur learned of Baldulf's ambush;
With some advice he drafted Cador,
Who was the Count of Cornwall then,
Who would not fail if faced with death.
He gave to him six hundred knights
And some three thousand of his troops.
He sent them off in secrecy
Toward Baldulf sitting in his ambush.
The Saxons never heard a word
And never heard a cry or noise
Until Count Cador hollered out,
Who did not dally with his blows.
He killed quite more than half of them
And wouldn't have let them go one foot
If it had not been night and dark
And if the woods had not been there.
Baldulf turned away in flight,
Moving from danger into danger.
He lost one half of his great force,
And that part was the better half.
He did not know how to proceed
In his attempt to help his brother.
He greatly wished to speak to him
If possible and if he dared.
He went like a minstrel to the siege
And acted like he was a harpist.
He'd been a student once of singing
And playing lais and songs with harp.
To get to speak then with his brother,
He shaved himself around his beard
And also all around his head
And only one side of his moustache,
So he looked like a fool or drunkard.

9105-09 A hairdo appropriate for a fool (Weiss, *Roman de Brut*, 229, n. 2).

He hung a harp around his neck.
He went about with this disguise
And no one there suspected him.
He went about harping so close
That he got so near to the city
That from the wall men knew his face
And pulled him up then with a rope.
They were already in despair
About their flight and their escape
When news arrived behind the lines
That Childric with six hundred ships
Had come to Scotland in a port
And was fast coming to the siege.
But he believed, and well he said it,
That Arthur would not wait for him.
And he did not—he did not wait
Because his friends had said to him
That he should never wait for Childric
And that he should not fight with him,
For he had fierce and wondrous men.
He drew his forces back to London;
If Childric followed after him,
He would engage him more securely,
For he would call his common people,
And on each day his strength would grow.
Arthur trusted in his barons;
Along with them he came to London.
Then you'd have seen the earth stirred up,
The castles readied, the people afraid.
Arthur took advice in this
That he should send away for Hoel,
One of his sister's sons, a nephew,
The king of Little Brittany.
His relatives and kin lived there,
And most of the people of his line.
He had his letters sent to Hoel
And had a messenger seek him out.

9141 Arnold rightly points out the impossibility of Hoel's being the son of Arthur's younger sister Anna (*Roman de Brut*, 2:806-07).

He sent him word that without his help
He'd in the end lose all his land.
Great would be his family's shame
If he thus lost his legacy.
Hoel heard of this great need;
He did not try to make excuses,
And so he got his lords and his kin
Prepared in very little time.
Their ships were ready soon to sail,
Loaded up with arms and men.
They had two thousand cavalry,
Not counting servants or the archers.
They had good wind; they crossed the sea
And came ashore at Port Southampton.
Arthur greeted them with joy
And honor, as he should have done.
They did not stand around at all
Or waste much time getting acquainted.
The king called up his commoners
And got his entourage together.
Without noisy and lengthy speeches,
They went together up to Lincoln,
Which evil Childric had besieged,
But which he had not captured yet.
Arthur had his men don arms;
Without sounding a horn or trumpet,
Very unexpectedly,
They ran against the enemy.
There never was before such death
Or ever such heavy destruction
Or such wounding or such great pain
As there was then upon the Saxons.
They threw down arms, abandoned horses,
Fled to the hills, fled to the vales,
And went into the waters tumbling,
Swimming very awkwardly.
The Britons breathing down their backs
Did not allow them any rest.
They laid out massive blows with swords
Upon their bodies, heads, and necks.
From there to the Woods of Calidon

The Saxons went along in flight.
From every side to the woods they drew,
And so the woods became their refuge.
The Britons picketed the woods;
They went around it on all sides.
Arthur feared that they would flee
And that they'd leave the woods at night.
He cut down one part of the woods
And put the trees in massive piles,
Placing trees on other trees,
Crossing trunks with other trunks.
He set up camp across from there,
So no one could go out or in.
Those in the woods were very frightened;
They had no water or no food.
There was no one so strong or wise,
Nor one so rich or powerful
Who there had brought along with him
Some bread or wine or meat or wheat.
There would not be three days before
They'd all be killed because of hunger.
When they perceived they'd starve to death
And that they could not leave by force,
They were advised that they should plead
That they would leave their arms and booty,
That they would keep only their ships
And give the king some hostages,
And that they'd always keep the peace
And pay him tribute every year
If he would let them go alive
And take their ships without their weapons.
Arthur granted them their plea
And gave them leave to go away.
He kept some hostages behind
To hold them to their covenants;
He let them have all of their ships,
And he retained their weaponry.
And they set off upon the sea
And did not take their arms and booty.
Far were they from any view;
They had lost sight of land completely.

I do not know the reasons followed
Nor who the people were who gave them,
But they turned all their ships around
Between England and Normandy.
And so they rowed and so they sailed
And entered into Dartmouth Bay;
At Totnes they came back to land.
One saw the folk destroyed and killed!
Out of their ships they came to land,
And they spread out all through the country,
Seeking arms and taking plunder,
Burning houses and killing men.
All across the land they went,
And they took everything they found.
They took the weapons of the farmers,
And then they killed them with the same.
Devonshire and Somerset
And a big part of Dorsetshire
They set on fire and laid to waste:
They did not leave a soul alone.
The barons who had any power
Were up in Scotland with the king.
As much through fields as down the roads,
The Saxons carried what they'd stolen.
From there to Bath the Saxons came,
But those inside resisted them.

Arthur, who was up in Scotland,
Wrecked havoc on the Scottish people
Because they went to war against him
And they had given Childric aid.
When he learned what the heathens did,
Who had besieged the town of Bath,
He seized the hostages at once,
Not wishing to attend them longer.
He left behind the Breton Hoel,
Who was confined by a disease,
Lying in bed in the town of Aclud.
I don't know what disease it was.
And Arthur, with what men he had,
Came to Bath, as soon as able,
For he desired to lift the siege

And give relief to those inside.
Near some woods, on a great plain,
Arthur had his fellows armed.
He set his people into order,
And he himself re-donned his armor.
He put on shoes made out of steel,
Beautiful and well constructed.
He donned a good and handsome hauberk,
One suitable for such a king.
He strapped on Caliburn, his sword,
Which was quite long and was quite large—
It came from the Isle of Avalon;
The man who held it naked rejoiced.
The shining helmet on his head
Sported a nasal guard of gold;
The rings around it were of gold.
A dragon was portrayed on top;
The helmet shone with many gems.
It had belonged to Uther, his father.
He got upon a horse, quite gorgeous
And strong and swift and good for running.
Pridwen, his shield, hung from his neck.
He did not look like fool or coward.
Inside the shield with artistry
There was the likeness of my Lady
St. Mary painted and portrayed
For honor and remembrance of her.
He flashed his lance; its name was Ron.
Its iron tip was tempered well.
Somewhat long and somewhat large,
It was quite feared in times of need.
    When Arthur had his people armed
And set in order for his battle,
He made them walk with marching steps.
He did not want them to leave rank
Until they came into the fight.
The Saxons could not hold them back
And turned and ran up a big hill.
They raced each other to the top.
They set up their resistance there,
And stoutly they made their defense

As if they were behind a wall.
But there was little safety there,
For Arthur marched there with his men
And cordoned off the area.
He went pursuing after them,
Encouraging his men the while:
"See here," he said, "in front of you
The infidels, the prideful ones
Who have your relatives and kinfolk
And your good friends and your good neighbors
All destroyed and put on fire
And even caused yourselves great harm.
Revenge your friends and relatives;
Revenge the great destruction now;
Revenge the losses and the troubles
That they have caused you many times.
I'll get revenge for the foul deeds;
I'll get revenge for the lost trust;
I'll get revenge for my forebears
And for their pain and suffering;
I'll get revenge for the return
That they have made at Dartmouth's port.
If ever we can get at them
And get them down from off that hill,
They'll not be able to resist;
They will have no defense against us."
With these words spoken, Arthur spurred
And placed his shield before his chest.
I do not know which Saxon he reached;
He struck him dead upon the ground.
Before he moved, he cried aloud:
"Holy Mary, the help of God!
The first of blows is mine," he said.
"I've given this one his just wages."
Then you'd have seen the Britons help,
Felling and battering the Saxons.
On every side they went around them,
Lancing and striking and giving blows.
Arthur was full of hardiness,
Of great strength and of great prowess.
He raised his shield; he drew his sword;

He made his way against the flow.
He made disruption in the crowd,
Killing many right and left.
Alone he killed four hundred men—
More than all his people did.
He made them come to a bad end:
Dead was Baldulf, dead was Colgrim,
And Childric took his leave in flight,
He and others, down a slope.
They wished to get back to their ships
And get in them and save themselves.
Arthur heard that they were fleeing
And wished to get back to the ships.
Cador of Cornwall figured this out;
He put himself on the fleer's trail
With some two thousand mounted knights,
The best and swiftest that there were.
Arthur turned himself toward Scotland,
For a man came and said to him
That Scottish men had laid a siege
On Hoel, and he was almost taken.
Childric fled down to the ships,
But Cador was a man of skill.
Taking a pathway that he knew
Went down to Totnes more directly,
He moved ahead of Childric's army.
He came and filled the ships with men.
He put the serfs and farmers in them
And then set out against the fleers.
By twos, by threes they made their flight,
As if they could thereby flee better.
To travel with a lighter load
And make their flight with greater freedom,
They had abandoned all their armor.
They carried nothing but their swords.
They made great haste to reach the ships,
For they considered them their refuge.
    As they were crossing Thanet's waters,
Cador attacked them, shouting his signal.
One saw the Saxons all confused
And scattered here and there completely!

Upon the top of Thanet's hill,
Childric was caught and put to death.
The others, just as they arrived,
Suffered horrible, painful deaths.
The men who managed to escape
Fled to the ships from everywhere,
And from the ships men shot them down
And tumbled them into the sea.
There were some men who did surrender;
There were some men who killed themselves.
In forests and among the mountains,
They hid in massive companies.
They hid so long that there were many
Who died from hunger and from thirst.
When Cador stopped the slaughtering
And set the country all at peace,
He took the road that led to Arthur
Since he had not yet finished Scotland.
In Aclud he encountered Arthur;
His nephew Hoel had recovered.
He found him wholly safe and well;
He'd gotten over his disease.
The Scots had broken up the siege
When they heard news of Arthur's coming.
In Moray far away they fled;
They readied themselves inside the city.
There they stayed to wait on Arthur,
And there they stayed to give resistance.
Arthur knew they'd reassembled
And met as one to counter him.
He followed them right up to Moray,
But they had fled there in advance.
Throughout the waters of Loch Lomond
They were split up across the islands.
Sixty isles were in the lake,
And there were many flocks of birds.
There was a rock on every isle,
Where eagles used to live in nooks,
Building their nests and taking flight.
And just as I have been informed,
When evil people used to come

Intent on bringing Scots destruction,
The eagles all would get together,
Fighting each other and crying out.
One day or two or three or four,
You would observe them in their fights.
The observation signified
The mass destruction on its way.
The lake was large and very deep,
For there among the hills and valleys,
Sixty waters fell inside
And all of them stayed in that place,
Except the one descending seaward
Through the only exit there.
The Scotsmen moved into the water
And spread themselves out through the isles.
And Arthur hastened after them;
Employing boats, barges, and ships,
He gave attack and worried them;
He pinned them down and made them starve
So by the score, the hundreds, thousands,
They fell down dead along the shore.
Gillomarus, the Irish king,
Who came to help the Scottish people,
Arrived just after Arthur did.
And Arthur went against the man
And fought the Irish king in battle.
He vanquished him with little effort.
He made him and his people flee
And make their way again to Ireland.
Arthur went back to the lake,
Where he had left the Scottish people.

Bishops and abbots then appeared,
And monks and other men of faith,
Bearing holy saints and relics.
They asked for mercy for the Scots.
The women of the land appeared,
Completely barefoot, hair disheveled,

9469 Light observes that in the Arthurian portion "Wace reduces the role of the clergy and increases that of the commonality" ("Arthurian Portion," 126).

Their garments tattered into shreds,
Their faces scored with marks of scratches,
Their little infants in their arms.
With lots of tears and lots of crying,
They groveled down at Arthur's feet,
Sobbing and keening, crying for mercy:
"Mercy, lord!" was what they said.
"Why have you destroyed this land?
Have mercy on the ones you've caught
Whom you now kill with hunger, sire.
If you've no mercy for the fathers,
Look at these infants and these mothers.
Look at their sons; look at their daughters.
Look at their families you destroy!
Give fathers back to little sons,
And give back husbands to their mothers;
Give noble lords back to their ladies,
And give back brothers to their sisters
We paid enough in reparations
By having Saxons pass through here.
It was not through our will at all
That they came passing through this land.
It made us sad that they passed here:
They often hurt and wounded us.
If we have given them some lodging,
So much the more they brought us damage;
They took and ate up our belongings
And sent them off into their land.
We had no one to hold them off
Or to protect us from these men.
If we provided them with service,
We did it for them with displeasure.
The power was theirs; we had to do it,
For we looked forward to no help.
The Saxon men were infidels,
And we were always Christian people.
For that they made us suffer more
And kept us down more heavily.
They did us wrong; you do us worse.
It does not give you praise or honor
To murder men who ask for mercy,

Who die of hunger on the rocks.
You've conquered us, but let us live.
Give us land, wherever it is!
Make us live as slaves, so please you,
Both us and all our relatives.
Have mercy on some Christian people.
We have the faith that you profess.
Christendom will be debased,
If this our country is destroyed,
And will be ever damaged by it."
    Arthur was good, above all else.
He felt moved by these fallen people
And by the relics and the clergy.
He granted them their lives and limbs;
He took their homage and let them be.
    Hoel had observed the lake
And spoke about it to the people.
He marveled at its massive size,
Both at its width and at its length.
He marveled at the many isles
And at the number of the rocks
And at the many nests and eagles
And at their noises and their cries.
He held it all as marvelous
Whenever he looked at that place.
"Hoel," said Arthur, "splendid nephew,
You seem amazed by this lake here.
You will be more than quite amazed
About another lake you'll see
Close to this one, here in this land.
The space inside it is a square,
Twenty feet long, twenty feet wide
And five feet in its deepest part.
In the angles of the corners,
There are four different kinds of fish.
Never do those inside a corner
Move into another corner,
And there is no device at all
Or barrier of any kind
That anyone can there perceive
Or feel with hands or see with eyes.

I do not know if humans built it
Or whether nature formed the thing.
I'll tell you of another pool
About which I will make you wonder.
It sits in Wales close to the Severn.
Upon high tide, its waters fall.
The sea tides never get so high
And pool tides never get so low
That it gets full on rising tides.
However high the tides may get,
It never gives in to the tide
And never overflows its banks.
But when the sea retreats around it
And the tide falls back and makes retreat,
Then you will see the water rise,
The banks covered and overrun,
With great surges flying aloft
And falling down, wetting and soaking.
If there is someone native present
Who comes to watch and faces it,
The water always flies up high
And jumps right on his clothes and person.
And there is no one with such strength
Who doesn't nearly fall right in.
Many there have fallen in
And many there have drowned.
If someone goes with back in front,
With heels turned right around in back,
He can then stand upon the bank
And for as long as he will stay,
He will not be within the water
And won't be touched or won't get wet."
"Great is this marvel," Hoel then said,
"And marvelous was the one who made it."

Then Arthur had his trumpets blown,
His cornets and his bugles sounded.
These were the signs of his return.
He gave his people leave to go
To put their houses back in order,
But not the barons of his household.
The others turned away in joy,

Saying great things about King Arthur.
Never in Britain, so they said,
Was there a leader ever so brave.
Arthur went to Everwic;
He stayed there through the Christmas season.
The day of the Nativity,
He was there for the celebration.
He saw the city much impoverished,
In disrepair and rendered weak.
He saw the churches left in ruins,
The houses fallen and laid to waste.
Piram, who was a clever chaplain,
Who had not served the king in vain,
Was made the metropolitan
So he would keep the churches up
And bring back life to monasteries
That heathen men had laid to waste.
The king had peace cried everywhere
And put the peasants back to work.
The free men who had lost their lands
He called from all over the realm.
He gave them back their legacies,
Granted them fiefs and greater rent.
Three brothers born from noble lines—
From royal lines—were present there,
Urien, Lot, and Angusel,
Who were from the best family lines.
Their ancestors at one time held,
As later they did during peace,
The land that stretched from Humber north
By right, with no wrong done to others.
Arthur gave them back their fiefs
And then increased their legacies.
To Urien, the very first,
He gave back Moray free of charge,
Without the rent that it entailed.
He asked him to be king of it.

9619-20 "Urien is an historical character, ruler of the northern British kingdom of Rheged, who led the Welsh resistance to the English in the second half of the sixth century" (Weiss, *Roman de Brut*, 243, n. 1).

He was named king then at that time,
The man who was the Lord of Moray.
The king gave Scotland to Angusel,
And he accepted it as fief.
To Lot, the man who had his sister
And who had had her a long time,
The king returned all Lodonesia
And gave him other fiefs to boot.
Walwain, his son, was at that time
Still a boy too young for arms.
After Arthur judged the land
And meted justice everywhere
And put his realm back in the order
That it maintained in ancient times,
He took Guinevere as his queen,
A gracious, young, and noble woman,
Beautiful, courtly, aristocratic;
Her parents were some Roman nobles.
Cador had raised her at some cost
In Cornwall for a good long time
As if she were his closest kin.
Her mother was a Roman still.
She was a very polished woman
With noble ways and noble manners.
She spoke quite well on many topics.
Arthur loved and cherished her.
But they produced no heir as two;
They were not able to have children.
  When the winter passed away
And summer came with all its heat
And it was nice to sail the sea,
Arthur got his navy ready.

9645-58 See Wulf: "Wace's description of Guenevere is one of his most original passages, as he not only made important changes from the version in the *Historia*, but also heavily influenced many later authors, beginning with Marie de France and Chrétien de Troyes" ("Wace's Guenevere," 66). Wace's Guinevere looks "like a queen" and "knows how to *act* like a queen" (68); Wace puts emphasis on her acquisition of these abilities (68) and on the failure of Arthur and Guinevere to produce an heir (69). Pickens argues that there is no *fin' amors* between Arthur and Guinevere and no children. While Uther saves a captured Ygerne and their union is fruitful, Guinevere, who is sterile, turns to Modred for a union both sterile and lacking in *courtoisie* ("*Vassalage*," 182).

He'd said that he would go to Ireland
And that he'd conquer all of it.
Arthur made no long delay;
He called the best of his young men
And those who knew the most of war,
The rich and poor men of the land.
When they had crossed the sea to Ireland,
They took provisions from the land.
They took the cows; they took the beeves
And anything of use to eat.
Gillomar, the king of Ireland,
Knew what Arthur'd come to seek.
He heard the noise; he heard the news;
He heard the griping and complaints
That all the peasant folk were making
Who'd lost the food they had to eat.
Against Arthur he went to fight,
But it was not a time to do so,
Because his men did not wear armor.
They had no hauberks and no shields;
They were not cognizant of arrows
And did not know how bows were drawn.
The Britons, though, who did have bows
Drew back those bows a lot on them.
They did not dare to show their eyes
And did not know just where to hide.
You would have seen a lot escaping
And hiding one behind the other,
Turning into woods and forests
And into towns and into houses,
Seeking refuge for their lives.
Conquered they were and beaten down.
The king tried fleeing to the woods,
But he was trapped and couldn't flee.
Arthur pursued him and gave chase
Until he had made him a captive.
But he did Arthur homage then
And took his legacy from him.
He also gave up hostages
To guarantee his annual tribute.
After Arthur conquered Ireland,
He crossed the ocean then to Iceland.

He took the land and conquered it,
Totally subjecting it.
He wanted lordship over all.
Gonvais, the king of the Orkney Islands, 9708
And Doldani, the king of Gotland,
And Rummaret, who was from Wendland,
Very quickly heard the news,
And each of them perceived right then 9712
That Arthur would run over them
And leave their islands in destruction.
He had no equal under heaven:
No man of arms could lead such men. 9716
For fear that he would overrun them
And that he'd lay their lands to waste,
Not with force but with volition,
They went to him in Iceland then. 9720
They brought so many goods for him
And pledged so much and gave so much
That they made peace, became his men,
And gave their legacies to him. 9724
They promised a specific payment;
And each one gave up hostages.
By such a means, they all kept peace,
And Arthur went then to his ships. 9728
He went to England once again
And was received with lots of joy.
For twelve years after this return,
King Arthur governed peacefully, 9732
And no one dared to give him war.
And he did not make war on others.
Alone, without another's urging,
He started such great learning up 9736
And spoke with such nobility

9710 Houck observes that Rummaret is an addition probably from an oral tradition (*Sources*, 257-58); Charles Foulon notes that Rummaret's son is connected with the story of the Round Table in Lawman ("De quelques additions de Wace," *Annales de Bretagne* 80 [1973]: 627-37). Keller identifies Gotlandia/Gotland as the Shetlands and Weneland (which I have rendered as Wendland here) as the Faroes ("Les conquêtes du roi Artur en Thule," *Cahiers de civilisation médiévale* 23 [1980]: 29-35). Ernest C. York argues that Weneland is the Viking Vinland: "Wace's Weneland: Identification and Speculation," *Romance Notes* 22 (1981): 112-18.

So beautifully and courteously
That no one's court had speech like this—
Not even the Roman Emperor's!
He heard no talk of any knight
Who did some deed worthy of praise
Who would not be one of his men,
If he had means to make him be.
If he requested to pay for service,
He would not leave for lack of pay.
Because the noble lords he had
Each believed himself the best,
Each one behaved the best he could;
So none would think himself the worse,
Arthur constructed the Round Table,
Of which the Bretons tell great tales.
The vassals took their places there,
All chivalrous, all equal too.
They sat at dinner equally,
And they were served there equally.
None of these men were able to boast
That he sat higher than his peer;
All were seated equally;
There was not one who was left out.
For courtesy no one stayed home—
No Scot, no Briton, or no Frenchman,
No Norman, Angevin, or Fleming,
Burgundian, Lorrainian,
Or anyone who held his fief
From in the West down to Montjoie,
Who did not go to Arthur's court
And who did not spend time with him
And who was not dressed in the clothes

9759 Laura Hibbard Loomis, "Arthur's Round Table," *PMLA* 41 (1926): 771-84, argues that the idea for the table comes from the iconography of the Last Supper, not an unkown Celtic source. Tatlock adds his weight to this argument and discusses analogous objects, but does not understand how the Round Table works (*Legendary History of Britain*, 472-76). In a review of other attempts to figure out how the knights are seated at the Round Table, Lecoy ("*Meain* et *forain*") argues that everyone at Wace's Round Table sits with someone on both sides and that no one sits outside on an end. See also Lacy, "Round Tables."

And heraldry and ornaments
According with the fashions used
By those who served at Arthur's court.
There they came from many lands
To seek for honor and for fame,
As well as to hear the courtesies,
And gaze upon the things they owned
And make acquaintance of the barons
And take possession of rich gifts.
The king was loved by all the poor
And much respected by the rich.
Foreign kings held him in envy,
For they were scared and very frightened
By one who conquered everyone
And took away each large estate.
As much for love of his largesse,
As for fear of his skill in arms,
In this great land of which I speak,
I do not know if you have heard,
Marvels were experienced,
And there adventures were turned up
That are so often told of Arthur
In stories that have been dressed up—
Not all lies and not all truth,
Not all folly, not all wisdom.
The storytellers tell so much
And the yarnspinners spin so much
Embellishing their story lines
That all they tell does not sound true.

For the goodness of his heart,
The reputation of his nobles,
And the great deeds of chivalry
That he prepared and tended,
It's said that Arthur crossed the sea
And that he conquered all of France.
But first of all he went to Norway
And made his in-law Lot the king.

9789-98 See Langille ("'Mençunge ou folie?'," 26-27) and Blacker (*Faces of Time*, 34-36) for comment on Wace's avoidance of what he considered fictions and lies.

Sichelin, the king, was dead,
Who did not have a son or daughter.
Upon his death he had requested
And in his health he had requested
That Lot would be the King of Norway
And have his fief and have his realm.
He had no other heir; his nephew
Lot should have it all by right.
When Sichelin had set this up
And thought that this was how it was,
The men of Norway thought it folly,
Both this command and will of his.
After they saw the king was dead,
They all denied the realm to Lot.
They did not want an alien
Or foreign man to be their lord.
They would be old and gray-haired men
Before they'd recognize this man
And give to men of other lands
The things they ought to give to them.
They'd make a king of their own race,
A king who'd love them and their sons.
With these considerations, they
Made Riculf king, one of their lords.
When Lot saw that he'd lose his right
If he did not get it through force,
He asked the help of his lord Arthur,
And Arthur then well promised him
That he would give him the whole realm
And Riculf would not then be happy.
He called up many men and ships
And entered Norway forcefully.
He laid a lot of land to waste,
Burning towns and looting houses.
Riculf had no will to flee,
No will to give the country up.
Against Arthur he planned defense:
He counted on the folk of Norway,
But had few people and few friends.
Riculf was conquered and was killed.
There were so many others killed

That there were very few remaining.
As soon as Norway was subjected,
Arthur gave it all to Lot,
But Lot held it from Arthur's hands
And recognized him as his lord.
From St. Sulpicius, the pope,
Whose soul was then reposed in glory,
Walwain recently arrived,
A brave and famous knight in arms.
The pope had dubbed the man a knight,
With arms that were well placed with him.
Valiant he was and moderate;
He cared not for excess or pride.
He wished to do more than he said
And give much more than he had promised.

After Arthur'd taken Norway
And Lot secured it in his power,
The king had picked and summoned all
The best of these brave, valiant men,
The hardiest of these combatants,
And loaded them on ships and barges.
With other people that he led,
With good weather and with good wind,
He crossed the sea to get to Denmark.
He coveted the country's goods.
Aschil, who was the King of Danes,
Saw the Britons, saw the Norse,
Saw Arthur, who had conquered all,
And saw that he could not resist him.
He did not want himself impaired
Or his good country to be damaged,
Or his gold spent or silver either,
Or people killed or towers surrendered.
He said and did and sought so much
And promised and gave gifts so much,
And asked so much and begged so much
That he came to accord with Arthur:

9853 Again, "Pope Sulpicius" is legendary. (One wonders if this name is somehow an error for Pelagius.)

He swore him fealty, became his man;
He kept his kingdom under Arthur.
Arthur rejoiced in these great deeds
And in the conquest that he made.
He could not yet put down these things:
From Denmark he had chosen then
Good knights in arms and also archers
Of unknown hundreds, unknown thousands.
He wished to lead them into France,
And he did so without delay.
He conquered Flanders and Boulogne;
He took the towns and took the castles.
He led his people on with wisdom;
He did not want to waste the land,
To burn the towns or sack and plunder.
He kept his men from pillaging,
Except for things to eat and drink.
And if he found a man who sold them,
They were then purchased with good money
And were not just taken away.
The name of France was Gaul back then;
There was no king; there was no lord.
The Romans had it in their power
And kept it in their power too.
It was delivered to the care
Of Frollo, long its guardian.
He took the tribute and the rent
And sent them down by certain terms
To Leo, the Roman emperor.
Frollo had a lot of strength:
He was a noble man from Rome
Who did not fear a living man.
Frollo learned through many runners
About the seizures and the damage
That Arthur and his people wrought
On those who got their rights from Rome.
All of the men who could bear arms
Belonging to the fief of Rome

9913 The actual emperor Leo I reigned from A.D. 457 to 474.

From whom he thought he could get help
And who were in his territory
Were all then called by him to come,
And he outfitted them quite well.
Against Arthur he went to battle,
But he did so at a bad time.
He was defeated, and he fled;
He lost there many of his men—
To death, to drowning, and to capture—
And some returned to their own lands.
There was no marvel in these things,
For Arthur had a massive army.
For in the lands that he had conquered
And in the cities he had seized,
When possible, he left no man
(Who was a decent knight or soldier
At the right age for combat duty
And who was able to fight wars)
Who was not led away with him
Or who was not then called to him.
He drafted many foreign men,
But not into his private guard,
Which was composed of daring knights
And warriors who had met the test.
The Frenchmen went to him themselves,
The ones who could, the ones who dared,
As much to speak and get to know him,
As to enjoy his generous gifts;
As much for his nobility
As for their fear and need of refuge.
They went to him and made their peace;
They recognized him as their lord.
Frollo, in his sad defeat,
Scurried to Paris in a hurry.
He did not dare to stop right then
Or try his confidence right then.
He sought a fort he could defend
In fear of Arthur and his army.
He had provisions brought to Paris
From towns and cities all around.
In Paris he would wait for Arthur;

In Paris he would make resistance.
Because of the people who had fled there
And all the native people there,
The city was filled up with people.
Each one struggled as he could
To get in wheat and other food
And build up both the walls and gates.
Arthur knew what Frollo did,
Who was in Paris getting ready.
He came behind him and besieged him;
He set up camp around the city.
He had the land and river watched
So food could not get there inside.
The Frenchmen held the city well;
Arthur sat there for a month.
There were great numbers in the city;
There soon was scarcity of food.
All that they had gotten in
In the short time they'd been allowed
Was soon used up and eaten up.
You would have seen great numbers starving!
Great numbers had but little food.
Women and children suffered much.
If the poor men increased in number,
The town would soon be given up.
Many were crying: "Frollo, what gives?
Why don't you ask for peace from Arthur?"
Frollo saw the people ruined
By the provisions that they lacked.
He saw the people starving to death
And saw that they desired to quit.
He saw the city laid to waste.
He much preferred to risk his body
And leave it out where it could die
Than openly abandon Paris.
He trusted in his own strength well.
He sent a message to King Arthur:
The two should meet upon an island
And fight each other man to man.
Whoever could then kill the other
Or could defeat the other alive

Would get the whole land of the other
And would receive the whole of France
If he did not destroy the people
And did not lay the city to waste.
Arthur liked this invitation;
It came to please his fancy well.
The battle would be fought by two
Just as Frollo had requested.
They got their pledges in this way,
And both sides gave up hostages,
The men of both the host and Paris,
According to set covenants.
One saw the pair of fighting men arm
And go inside the island meadow!
Then you'd have seen the people shouting,
Men and women going out,
Climbing out on walls and houses,
And saying in God's Holy Name
That he who won could have their land
As long as no more war could come.
Arthur's men, across the way,
Were listening and looking on,
Praying that the King of Glory
Would give their lord the victory.
Whoever then saw the two lords
Armed and sitting on their horses,
Their battle horses leaping swiftly,
Their shields lifted and lances brandished,
Could say and would say truthfully
He saw two hardy fighters there.
The horses were both good and fast,
The shields, hauberks, and helmets gorgeous.
It was not easy to determine
Either by looking or observing
Who had the edge or who would win,
For each one looked like a great lord.
When they were dressed and set to go,
They separated at some distance.
Spurring with their reins released,
With shields raised up and lances lowered,
They rode to crash against the other,

Both of them with wondrous demeanor.
But Frollo failed to make a hit;
I do not know if his horse flinched.
And Arthur struck a blow on Frollo,
Upon the center of his shield.
He carried him far from his horse,
About the length a lance extends.
He spurred to him with his sword drawn.
The battle came to realization
When Frollo jumped up on his feet.
Against Arthur he lifted his lance.
He struck his horse upon the chest;
He hit it this way in the heart.
He made the horse and made the knight
Tumble together to the ground.
Then you'd have seen the people raging,
The Britons shouting and seizing arms.
They would have violated the truce
And crossed the water to the island
And all have done a shameful thing—
When Arthur leapt up on his feet.
He raised his shield over his head;
Frollo had drawn out his sword.
Frollo was very brave and strong;
He was not slow or stuporous.
He raised his sword defiantly.
He struck the forehead of King Arthur.
Frollo was strong; the blow was great;
The sword was hard and biting.
The helmet cracked and split right open;
The hauberk failed and broke apart;
He wounded Arthur in the forehead;
The blood fell down upon his face.
When Arthur felt the wound he had
And saw himself covered with blood,
He changed his color in his rage
And charged forward with no delay.
He gripped his sword named Caliburn,
Which he had had in many fights.
He struck the top of Frollo's head
And from there split him to the shoulders.

He drooped, he fell, and he crashed down,
With brains and blood all over the place.
There was no valor in that helmet
Or in that hauberk he held dear.
He kicked his feet a little while;
He died right there; he made no sound.
The townsmen and the host cried out:
The one group cried; the other laughed.
The city people cried for Frollo
But nevertheless ran to the gates.
They let King Arthur come inside
With his own knights and with his people.
Then you'd have seen the Frenchmen come
And offer themselves as feudal vassals.
And Arthur took their offered homage
And to keep peace took hostages.
He spent a long time there at Paris;
He sat as judge; he set up peace.

He split his army in two parts
And thus set up two companies.
With Hoel, his nephew, he endowed
One of the halves and asked him then
To conquer Anjou with these men
And Gascony, Auvergne, and Poitou;
And he would conquer Burgundy
And Lorraine too, if he was able.
Hoel followed his directives
According to established plans.
He conquered Berry and Touraine,
Anjou, Auvergne, and Gascony.
Guitard, who was the Duke of Poitou,
Was brave and had good knights in arms.
To keep his land and independence,
He fought against him many times.
He often chased; he often fled.
He often won and often lost.
At last he saw that if he lost
He'd not recover easily.
He made his peace accord with Hoel;
Outside a tower and a castle,
He'd nothing left for him to waste,

No branch or vine left to be stripped.
He pledged his loyalty to Arthur,
And Arthur later loved him much.
All of the other parts of France
Arthur conquered with great force.

XI. Arthur at the Height of Power

When he had peace in all the land
And there was no war anywhere,
To the old men and married men
Who had been with him a long time
He tendered gifts and cash awards
And sent them back into their lands.
The bachelors and the young men,
Who were intent on making conquest,
Who did not have a wife or children,
Remained nine years in France with him.
The nine years that he spent in France
Produced a plethora of marvels.
He brought down many prideful men
And brought in line a lot of felons.
In Paris during Eastertide,
He held a massive feast for friends.
He gave his men their property
And gave them well-deserved rewards.
He rendered service to each one
According to the way he'd served.
To Kay, his master seneschal,
A knight who was both brave and true,
He gave Anjou and all Angers,
And he received them willingly.
To Bedevere, his butler knight,
One of the counselors in his household,
He gave all Normandy in fief,
Whose name was then Neüstria.

10153-60 "The seneschal and cup-bearer (*dapifer* and *pincerna*) were two of five great officers of state in the royal household" (Weiss, *Roman de Brut*, 255, n. 1).

These two indeed were very loyal,
And they were privy to his thoughts.
And he gave Flanders to Holdin,
Le Mans to Borel, a relative. 10164
He gave Boulogne to Ligier
And gave Puntif to Richier.
To many according with their rank,
To many according with their service, 10168
He gave out honors with largesse
And gave out lands to feudal vassals.
When he'd endowed his lords with fiefs
And made his household company rich, 10172
In April when the summer starts,
He went across the sea to England.
You would have seen at his return
Many men and women happy. 10176
The ladies kissed their husbands then,
And mothers gave their sons some kisses.
Sons and daughters kissed their fathers,
And mothers cried a lot from joy. 10180
Cousins gave each other kisses,
And neighbors kissed each other too.
Friends gave kisses to their friends
And took more pleasure at their leisure. 10184
Aunts gave kisses to their nephews.
Great joy was had by one and all.
Upon the roads and at the crossroads,
You would have seen a lot appear 10188
To find out how it was for them
And what they did out on their conquests:
What they did and what they found
And why they'd been away so long. 10192
These men recounted their adventures,
Both the battles strong and hard
And the hard work that they had done
And dangers that they had observed. 10196
Arthur honored all his men;
He loved them much and gave them gifts.

10174ff "The passage of rejoicing is entirely added by Wace" (Weiss, *Roman de Brut*, 257, n. 3).

To make a show of his great wealth
And set the people talking of him,
He took counsel and was advised
That at this summer's Pentecost
He'd have his barons all together
And have himself then crowned as king.
To Glamorgan, to Kaerleon,
He ordered all his lords assembled.
The city had been well constructed
And had been situated well.
Now at this time—or so men say—
It looked like Rome with palaces.
Kaerleon was on the Usk,
A river that flows into the Severn.
People who came from other lands
Could travel there upon this river.
On one half was the river bank
And on the other full-growth forest.
There the fish were plentiful,
And there was also lots of game.
The meadows there were beautiful;
The farm land there was very rich.
There were two churches in the town,
And both were very dignified.
The one, St. Julius the Martyr,
Had nuns in service there to God.
The other was for his companion,
The one that people call St. Aaron.
The latter was the bishop's see;
Great clergymen were in that place
And canons of great scholarship
Who knew about astronomy.
Their studies focused on the stars;
They often spoke to Arthur the King
About what outcomes there would be
For works that he desired to do.
Kaerleon was good back then;
It had not suffered any damage.

Because of its costly construction,
Because of its grand situation,
Because of the beautiful woods and fields,

Because of the beautiful sites you heard of,
Arthur wished to hold court there.
He made his barons all appear;
He called his kings; he called his counts;
He called his dukes and viscounts too;
He called his barons and his vassals;
He called his bishops and his abbots.
And those whom he had called appeared
Just as they should come to a feast.
From Scotland came King Angusel,
Very beautifully attired;
From Moray, Urien the King,
And his son Ywain, the courteous;
Stater, the king from southern Wales;
And Cadwal, from the north of Wales.
Cador of Cornwall was there too,
For whom the king had great regard;
Morvid, who was the Count of Gloucester;
And Mauron, who was Count of Worcester;
Gurguint, who was the Count of Hereford;
And Bos, who was the Count of Oxford;
Urgent of Bath; Cursal of Chester;
And Jonathas of Dorchestershire.
From Salisbury came Sir Arnaud;
From Canterbury came Kimmare.
Baluc came, Silchester's count;
And Jugeïn of Leicester came;
And Argahl, Count of Warwick, too,
Who came to court with many men.
There were some other barons too
Who did not have just minor honors.
There was the son of Apo, Donaud;
And Regeïm, the son of Elaud;
Cheneüs, the son of Coil;
And Cathleüs, the son of Catel;
Edelin, the son of Cledauc;
And Cymbeline, the son of Trunat;

10253-82 See Weiss for detailed notes on this list of names (*Roman de Brut*, 259, n. 2).

Grifu, the son of Nagoïd;
Run FitzNeton; Margoïd,
Glofaud, and Kincar, sons of Aingan;
And then Kimmar and Gorboän,
Kinlint, Neton, and Peredur,
Whom men called sons of Elidur.
About the men who served at court,
Who were the king's own special men,
Who were the Knights of the Round Table,
I do not wish to tell you tales.
Many others of lesser rank
Were there, but I don't know the number.
Many abbots and bishops were there,
And three archbishops of the land:
From London and from Everwic,
And St. Dubric from Kaerleon.
The Roman legate who was there
Was a great and holy clergyman.
For love of him and for his prayers,
Many sick ones came for healing.
London was the see back then
And had the metropolitan
Until the Angles ruled the land,
Who let the churches lie in waste.
There were enough barons at court
Of whom I do not know the names.
King Gillomar was there from Ireland;
And King Malvasius from Iceland;
Doldanïed of Gotland too,
For whom the food was not sufficient.
Aschil was the there, the King of Danes;
And Lot, who was the King of Norway;
And Gonvais, King of the Orkney Islands,
Who had control of many pirates.
From across the sea came Count Ligier,
Who held the fiefdom of Boulogne;
From Flanders there was Count Holdin;
And Guerin, the Count of Chartres, too.
The last in great nobility
Led the twelve peers with him from France.
Guitard came there, the Count of Poitiers;

And Kay, who was Count of Angers;
And Bedevere of Normandy,
Which then was called Neüstria;
Count Borel of Le Mans were there;
And Hoel came from Brittany.
Hoel and all the ones from France
Had very noble looking faces,
Beautiful arms and beautiful clothes,
Beautiful trappings and big horses.
There was no lord left out—from Spain
To the River Rhine in Germany—
Who did not come there to the feast
Because he heard the invitation,
As much for Arthur as his gifts,
As for the chance to meet his lords,
As for a look into his houses,
As for the courteous things he said,
As for the love, as for the order,
As for the honor and the power.
When the king's court was all together,
You would have seen a handsome group;
You would have seen the city moving,
Servants going and servants coming,
Lodging taken and lodging adorned,
Houses emptied and curtains hung,
The marshals opening up the lodges,
The rooms and chambers opened wide,
And (for the ones who had no room)
Lodging made and tents erected.
You often would have seen the squires
Leading palfreys and war-horses,
Making up stables, fixing posts,
Leading horses, tying up horses,
Grooming horses and giving them drink,

10331-36 Arthur's clever, appropriate speech is an example of his *courtoisie* (Pickens, "*Vassalage*," 175). Granting the emphasis on *courtoisie*, Blacker notes that administrative affairs are conspicuously absent in the discussion of life at Arthur's court (*Faces of Time*, 101-2).

10337-58 Added by Wace (Weiss, *Roman de Brut*, 261, n. 1).

Carrying oats and hay and grass.
You would have seen in many ways
Valets and chamberlains running around,
Mantles hung and mantles folded,
Mantles shaken and attached,
Gray and shiny furs brought out,
And portraits painted of your face.
Upon the morning of the feast,
So says the story of these deeds,
The three archbishops all arrived,
And all the abbots and the bishops.
They crowned the king inside the palace
And led him down to the cathedral.
The two archbishops led him there,
Who went along at his two sides.
Each one held up an arm of his
Until he came up to his throne.
There were four swords on hand with gold
Upon the guard, the hilt, and turnings.
Four kings carried these four around,
Going right before the king.
This ritual belonged to them
Whenever the king held feast and court:
One from Scotland, one from North Wales,
The third was from the south of Wales;
Cador of Cornwall was the one
Who got to carry the fourth sword.
He had no lesser dignity
Than anyone who was a king.
Dubric, who was the Roman legate
And was the prelate of Kaerleon,
Began to do the ritual
Since this event was in his church.
In quite another place, the Queen
Was served with care and great regard.
Inviting them before the feast,
She got together at the feast

10385-408 According to Wulf, Wace's expansion of Geoffrey's account of the coronation gives Guinevere a function in the society ("Wace's Guenevere," 69).

The noble ladies of the land.
She had the wives of men she knew,
Her friends and all their relatives,
And pretty noble mesdemoiselles
Come to see her at the feast
And stay with her throughout this time.
Inside her chamber she was crowned
And led into the convent church.
To split apart the massive crowd
That just one place could not contain,
Four ladies walked in front of her,
And each one carried a white dove.
They were the wives of the four men
Who had the charge of the four swords.
After Queen Guinevere then came
Other ladies, who followed her,
With lots of joy and happiness
And wonderful nobility.
They were indeed quite well arrayed,
Nicely dressed and nicely fixed.
You could have seen many a one
Who wished to serve many another.
There were a lot of costly adornments,
Costly clothes and ornaments,
Costly blouses, costly mantles,
Costly buckles, costly rings,
Many gray and shiny furs,
Accessories of many kinds.
There was a crowd at the procession;
Each person tried to press ahead.
After the mass had been commenced,
Because the day was so exalted,
You would have heard the organs sounding
And clerics singing with the organs,
Voices falling and voices rising,
Songs descending, songs ascending.
You would have seen there in the church
Many knights coming and going.
As much to hear the clerics sing
As to observe and see the ladies,
They ran from one church to the other,

With lots of going, lots of coming.
I do not know with certainty
At which they stayed the longer time.
They had no other way to get
Enough of seeing or of hearing.
If every day was just like this,
I think they'd never have been bored.
After the service reached its end
And *Ite missa est* was sung,
The king removed the crown he wore
And had it carried to the church.
He put a smaller crown on then;
The queen did likewise after him.
They took their stately garments off
And put on lighter, less grand clothes.
After the king turned from the church,
He went to dine within his palace.
The queen herself went to another
And took her ladies along with her.
The king ate dinner with his men;
The queen ate dinner with her ladies
With great delight and with great joy.
It used to be a Trojan custom
(And Britons keep it to this day),
That when they have a feast together,
The men eat dinner with the men
And do not bring the women there.
The ladies eat then somewhere else
With no one there except their servants.
After the king sat at the dais,
According to the country's custom
The barons sat in seats around him,
Each one in order of his rank.
The seneschal, whose name was Kay,
Who was attired in ermine furs,
Served the dinner to the king,

10437-58 According to Wulf, Wace implies that the women's celebrations are "not inferior to the men's"; Guinevere "must not be diminished in any way" as the "fitting consort to Arthur in his full glory" (71).

Accompanied by a thousand nobles,
Who all were dressed in ermine furs.
These noblemen served up the food,
Frequently and often going,
Bearing bowls and bearing plates.
Bedevere, on the other hand,
Served as the butler—steward of wine—
Together with a thousand youths,
Dressed in ermine, noble and handsome.
In cups and goblets of fine gold
And chalices they carried wine.
There was no man employed in service
Who was not dressed in ermine furs.
In front of them went Bedevere,
Who bore the goblet of the king.
Right behind this came the youths,
Who served the barons with their wine.
The queen had servants of her own—
I cannot tell you names or numbers.
Richly and beautifully was she served,
Yes, she and all her company.
You would have seen lots of rich ladies,
Quite lovely and quite beautiful.
And lots of food quite richly served
And lots of different kinds of drinks.
I can't, however, name them all
And can't enumerate the riches.
Of men who were both good and rich,
Of bounty and nobility,
Of courtesy and also honor
England bore the flower then
Over all surrounding realms
And over all that we now know.
More courteous and valiant were
Even the impoverished peasants
Than knights in arms in other realms;
The women too were just the same.

10491-516 The *pax Arthuriana* illustrates the romantic qualities of *courtoisie* (Pickens, "*Vassalage*," 174-75).

You never would have seen a knight
Who did a thing that rated praise
And did not have his arms and clothes
And ornaments in just one color.
They made their arms in just one color
And dressed themselves in just one color,
And so the ladies rating praise
Were also dressed in just one color.
There never was a knight in arms,
No matter what his lineage,
Who ever would succeed at love
Or have a courtly female friend
If he had not been tested thrice
In acts and deeds of chivalry.
The more the knights did valiant deeds,
The better they performed in battle;
The better were the ladies too,
Who lived in chastity yet more.
After the king got up from dinner,
They all went out for entertainment.
They left the city for the fields;
They had their fun in many games.
Some of them went to do some jousting
And show their speedy horses off.
The others went to clash in arms
Or launch off stones or jump around.
There were a few who threw their spears,
And there were some engaged at dice.
Each person took a part in games
That he himself knew how to play.
The one who vanquished his companions
And won the prizes in the games
Was led at once up to the king
And shown to all the others there.
The king would give him such a gift
That he would go away all happy.
The ladies climbed upon the walls
To watch the men who played at games.
She who had a friend down there
Would often give him lots of looks.
At court there were lots of jongleurs,

Singers and instrumentalists.
You could have heard a lot of songs,
Old standards and the latest hits,
The sounds of vieles and accompanied songs,
Songs for vieles and songs for rotes,
Songs for harps and songs for flutes,
Lyres and drums and flutes of reeds,
Stringed instruments and psalteries,
Monochords, tambors, and horns.
There were enough magicians too
And dancing girls and balladeers.
Some of them told stories and tales;
Some of them needed dice and tables.
There were some who played games of chance,
Which is a game with evil aspects.
The greater number played at chess
Whether for money or for pleasure.
Two teams of two would play together:
The one would lose; the other win.
They envied those who threw the most;
They told the others to chip in.
They borrowed money for their bets,
Repaying gladly twelve for eleven.
They put down bets; they picked up bets;
They snatched up bets; they pledged their bets.
They often swore and often cursed;
They often drank and often joked;
They strove a lot, got mad a lot;
They often miscounted; they often complained.
Two and two they threw, then fours,
Snake eyes, tierce, and winning threes.
They threw down just as often fives;
They threw down just as often sixes:
Six, five, four, three, two, and ace
Took the shirts from many backs.
They had good hope who held the dice;

10543-52 The details of court music are added by Wace (Weiss, *Roman de Brut*, 265, n. 1).

10561ff The details of the dice game are added by Wace (Weiss, *Roman de Brut*, 267, n. 1).

They cried when their companions did;
Often enough they cried and shouted;
Some would often say to others:
"You're cheating me; throw them out here.
Shake your hand; rattle the dice!
I envy you before you throw!
If you want money, bet—I bet!"
One could sit down there all dressed up
Who would get up to leave quite naked.
The feast went on three days like this.
On Wednesday when the fourth day came,
The king enfeofed his bachelors,
Dividing up the honors freely.
He paid for all the services
Of those who served so they'd get land.
He gave out towns and fortresses
And bishoprics and abbacies.
To those who were from other lands
Who came unto the king for love,
He gave horses and chalices;
He gave the costliest possessions;
He gave adornments; he gave jewels;
He gave out hounds; he gave out birds;
He gave out furs; he gave out clothes;
He gave out cups; he gave out goblets;
He gave out cloaks; he gave out rings;
He gave out shirts; he gave out mantles;
He gave out spears; he gave out swords;
He gave out arrows with barbed points;
He gave out quivers, gave out shields
And bows and lances with mill-ground tips.
He gave out leopards, gave out bears,
Harnesses, saddles, and mounts for the hunt;
He gave out hauberks and mounts for war;
He gave out helmets, gave out coins;
He gave out silver, gave out gold;
He gave the best of his own treasure.
There was no man of any worth
Who came to him from other lands
To whom the king did not give gifts,
The king who honored lords like this.

Arthur sat upon a dais
Surrounded by both counts and kings.
Twelve men appeared, hoary and gray,
Well adorned and well attired;
Two by two in the room they came;
Each set of two was holding hands.
They were a dozen, and they had
Twelve olive branches in their hands.
And in an ordered marching step,
Beautifully and impressively,
They made a pass around the hall.
They came to the king and greeted him:
They said that they had come from Rome
And they were Roman messengers.
They then unrolled a proclamation
That they'd been charged to give to Arthur
By the Emperor of Rome.
Hear the proclamation's gist:
"Lucius, who wields the might of Rome
And has the lordship of the Romans,
Demands the things that he deserves
From King Arthur his enemy.
It is amazingly disdainful
And I'm disdainfully amazed
That through abuse and utter pride
You dare to turn your eye on Rome.
It is disdainful and amazing
That you would entertain advice
On instigating war with Rome
While you know any Roman's living.
You've also done great foolishness,
For you have ventured an invasion
On us who ought to rule the world
And be the head of everyone.
You don't know yet, but you will know;

10639 In Geoffrey, the emperor is Leo and the procurator is Lucius Hiberius; Wace has collapsed the two into Luces the emperor (Weiss, *Roman de Brut*, 267, n. 3). "Wace lengthens the Roman ambassadors' speech and adds the resulting uproar and Arthur's respect for their rights" (268, n. 1).

You have not seen it, but you will;
How great a thing it is to anger
Rome, which should rule everything.
You have exceeded natural bounds
And you have crossed beyond your limits.
Who in the hell do you think you are
To take our tribute and withhold it?
You take our lands and take our tribute.
Why do you have them? Why not pay them?
Why do you keep them? What right is yours?
You'd be a fool to keep them longer.
If you could keep them any longer
Without us forcing you to stop,
You could then say with some amazement
The lion flees before the sheep
And the wolf flees before the goat
And the hound flees before the hare.
These things can never really happen,
For nature would not let them happen.
Our forefather Julius Caesar—
Can your regard for him be low?—
Conquered Britain and left with tribute,
Which afterwards our people got.
From other islands all around,
We've gotten tribute a long time.
One or another, in presumption,
Has taken it in acts of folly.
Yet you are guilty of more shame
In that you do us still more damage:
Our baron Frollo is now dead,
And you by tort hold France and Flanders.
Because you have no fear for this,
In its great dignity, the Roman
Senate now summons you and asks
And in its summons now demands
That you appear sometime in August
In Rome, whatever it may cost you,
Prepared to make us reparations
For that which you have borne away.
You will thus give us satisfaction
For what we will accuse you of.

But if you do not go and thus
Delay in doing what I ask,
I will go past Montjoie in force
And take away Britain and France.
Don't think that you will wait for me
And that you'll keep me out of France.
It is my hope that you will never
Dare to come across that sea.
And if you stay beyond the sea,
You can expect my coming soon.
You will not have a place to hide
From which I cannot make you run.
I'll bring you back to Rome in chains,
And I will give you to the Senate."
There was great noise upon these words,
And everyone got very angry.
You would have heard the Britons shout,
Making oaths and swearing to God
These men would be ignobly punished,
Who had delivered such a message.
To the messengers they said a lot
Of harmful and reproving things.
The king, however, stood right up
And shouted out: "Shut up, shut up!
No harm will come: they're messengers.
These men have lords who wrote the message.
These men can say whatever they like;
No harm will ever come to them."
After the clamor settled down
And those at court were reassured,
The king led all his dukes and counts
And all his private guards with him
Into a tower of stone he had
That people called the Giant Tower.
He wished to hear their counsel there
On how to answer these messengers.
They stood awhile upon the heights,
Barons and counts, side by side,
When Cador said upon a smile
(The king in the front was listening):
"I have," he said, "been much in fear

And many times I've had the thought
That through inaction and through peace
The Britons would become infirm.
Inaction brings infirmity,
And many men have gotten lazy.
Inaction gives men laziness;
Inaction lessens skill in arms;
Inaction stirs up lechery;
Inaction causes love affairs.
Through long repose and through inaction
The youth become too soon attentive
To jokes, to baubles, and to cards
And other entertaining games.
Through long sojourn and through repose,
We can destroy our reputations.
We have been sleeping for a while,
But the Lord God, who's merciful,
Has wakened us a little bit,
And given Romans heart enough
To lay a challenge on our land
And on the others we have conquered.
If Romans trust themselves so much
That they'd do what their letter says,
The Britons still will win the prize
For hardiness and vigor too.
I would not love a lengthy peace;
I've never loved a lengthy peace."
"Sir Count," said Walwain, "by my faith,
You are afraid of nothing real.

10765-72 "The eight-line capsulated definition of chivalry is further evidence that Wace has drained the Brutus story of explicit political import; matters of state are irrelevant to this conception of the advantages of peace, where light conversation and lovemaking are its paramount justification" (Blacker, *Faces of Time*, 100). Weiss notes that Wace adds Walwein's speech (*Roman de Brut*, 271, n. 1). Shichtman ("Gawain") has argued that Walwein, with his espousal of the values of chivalry, represents the new order of the twelfth century while Cador represents the old order. Keller ("De l'amour") has suggested that Walwein's speech demonstrates the arrival of Provençal notions of courtesy and *fin'amor* in the north of France. The exchange may also be seen as representative of the twelfth-century debate about the importance of celibacy to manhood and manly strength and vigor. A love affair (with its expense of semen) could, according to the argument, render a man weak. Such notions survive among athletic coaches today (see Glowka, "Masculinity," 413–16.

Peace is good after a war;
The Earth's better and fairer for it.
Pleasantries are very good,
And love affairs are also good.
For friendship and for female friends,
Knights do deeds of chivalry."
Upon the words that these two spoke,
They went inside the tower and sat.

When Arthur saw that all were seated,
All attentive and all still,
He thought awhile and said no word.
He raised his head then and he spoke:
"Barons," he said, "you all are here,
My good companions and my friends,
Companions in prosperity
And also in adversity;
When major conflict came to me,
You persevered along with me.
When I have lost or I have won,
You've taken either one with me.
You are the partners in my losses
And in my gains when I succeed.
Through you and through the help you give,
I have had many victories.
I've led you often in times of need
On sea, on land, both near and far.
I've found you faithful all the time
In conduct and in counsel matters.
Many times I've tested you,
And I have always found you good.
The countries all around us here
Are subject to my sway through you.
You've listened to the strong demands
And heard the letter of intent
And the excessive ferocity
With which the Romans ordered us.
They have provoked us quite enough
And quite enough have threatened us.
But if God helps both you and me,
We will be rescued from the Romans.
They're rich and they're quite powerful

So there is need for us to plan
What we can say and we can do,
With careful thinking and with reason.
When something is planned out ahead,
The situation's handled better.
The man who sees the arrow coming
Ought to turn aside or hide.
We ought to do the very same.
The Romans wish to drag us down,
And we should get ourselves prepared
So they cannot bring harm to us.
They ordered tribute from the Britons;
It's theirs 'by right'; they make demands
On us for other islands too
And for the power over France.
Concerning Britain first of all,
I will respond with justification:
Caesar, they say, once conquered it.
He was a strong and forceful man.
The Britons couldn't hold him off;
With force he made them render tribute.
But might is not the same as right;
Rather it's pride and gross excess.
A man does not possess with right
What he receives by using force.
This means that we should keep by right
What they by custom take with force.
They blame us for the damages
And losses and humiliations
And tribulations and the fears
That they gave to our ancestors.
They boasted that they conquered them
And took their tribute and their income.
Thus we should give them no more trouble,
And they would have us pay again.
We ought to hate the ones they hate
And show dishonor where they do.
They are quite wrong reproving us;
They once had tribute; they ask it now.
They want to have as legacy
The same we have and tribute too.

They used to get tribute from Britain,
And so they wish to get it now.
Using the reasons that they use
And other kinds of reasons too,
We can ourselves make threats to Rome,
And we can plead our case there well.
Belin, who was a king of Britain,
And Brennës, Duke of Burgundy,
Two brothers who were born in Britain,
Sensible and valiant knights,
Went down to Rome and laid a siege;
They made attack and captured it.
They hanged two dozen hostages
While all their relatives looked on.
When Belin went away from there,
He left Rome in his brother's hands.
I'll let Brennës and Belin be,
And I will talk of Constantine.
He was from Britain, Helen's son;
He had dominion over Rome.
Maximian, the king of Britain,
Conquered France and Germany,
Marched past Montjoie and Lombardy
And held dominion over Rome.
These men were my close relatives,
And each had Rome within his hands.
Now you can hear and you can know
That I ought to possess Rome too
By right, as I do Britain now,
If we consider ancestors.
The Romans got our tribute once;
My kinfolk got it once from them.
As they claim Britain, I claim Rome!
The sum of my advice is this:
The one who can defeat the other
Gets his money and his land.
Concerning France and other lands
We've taken from their hands by force,
They should not have complaint at all
When they did not attempt to save them,
From lack of will or ability,

Or possibly from lack of right.
For forcefully through greediness,
They kept them in their servitude.
Let him have all who can get all.
No other right is necessary.
The emperor has threatened us;
May God not wish the man to hurt us!
He said he'd take away our lands
And take me captured down to Rome.
He thinks us small; they fear me little;
But, God be pleased, if he comes here,
Before he can make his return,
He'll have no taste for making threats.
When he and I meet to dispute,
Let him take all who can take all!"
    After King Arthur spoke his piece
And laid this out before his lords,
There were some men who later spoke
And there were some who listened to them.
Hoel spoke after the king:
"Sire," he said, "it is my creed
That many reasonable words
Cannot improve a single thing.
Call your people; summon your men
And us who are now here at court.
Cross the sea without delay.
Pass through Burgundy; pass through France;
Pass Montjoie; take Lumbardy!
The emperor defying you—
Put him to flight and make him fear
So he won't have the chance to grieve you.
The Romans have stirred up a fight
In which they all will be defeated.
God himself wants to exalt you.
Do not delay; don't fool around.
Put the emperor under your sway
Who wants to be there for his pleasure.
Remember what the Sibyl said

10927 For a discussion of Sibylline and similar prophecies known in the Middle Ages, see Tatlock, *Legendary History of Britain*, 403ff.

In prophecies that she has written:
'Three Britons from Britain there will be
Who'll come to conquer Rome by force.'
Two of these have passed away,
Who had the lordship over Rome:
Belin, who was the first of these;
Constantine, the second one;
You'll be the third who will have Rome
And who will conquer it by force.
The prophecy will be of you
And be fulfilled as Sibyl said.
Why do you wait to seize this thing
That God desires to give to you?
Exalt yourself; exalt us too,
Since we have interests in this thing.
Truly we are able to say
That we fear neither stroke nor strife
Nor death nor prison nor travail
As long as we strive for your honor.
And I will put into your force
As long as this affair goes on
Two thousand knights with all their arms;
And if your funds are insufficient,
I'll get a loan for all my land
And give to you the gold and silver.
I'll never keep a single cent
As long as you have need of it."
After Hoel gave this speech,
The King of Scotland, Angusel,
Lot and Urien's brother, spoke:
"Lord," he said, "Hoel spoke well,
And when you take this matter on,
Just speak to those who are right here,
Here where your best lords are present,
Who heard the message come from Rome.
Know that each will work for you
And that each one will give you aid.
It is the custom to provide
Some help and aid and to give counsel.
All of the people from your land
Who have their fiefs and land from you

Should give you help and strengthen you.
And they'll do so if they are able.
I've never ever heard such news
That seemed so good and nice to me
As making war upon the Romans.
There's little love or praise for them.
Before I even heard a thing,
I hated Romans and their pride.
What shame it is for evil men
Who have no other kind of honor
(And never will get any kind)
To make their threats to such good men.
The emperor did foolishly
And made himself a mockery,
Who ordered you to be provoked.
Still I believe the day will come
When he'll wish he'd not asked for tribute—
Even to have a tower of silver.
The Romans have begun a fight
In which they'll suffer indignation.
And if they had not spoken first,
We should have started it ourselves
And gone to war of our own will
To get revenge for our own kin
And to bring down the pride of those
Who try to say and try to prove
That we should give them tribute money.
They say our ancestors were used
To paying tribute to them once.
I don't believe that they gave tribute
Or that they sent them any either.
They neither gave nor rendered it,
But those men took it off by force.
And now we'll take it off by force!
We'll get revenge for our forebears.
In lots of fights we've been the winners;
In lots of wars we've been the victors.
What value are our victories
If we're not victors over Romans?
I've never heard of such desire
For things to drink or things to eat,

As I now have to see the time
When we are running sure together
Upon our horses, spears in hand,
Shields on shoulders, helmets laced.
God! What possessions! God! What treasures,
If God protects our king from harm,
The men who wish to have will have.
They won't be poor ever again.
There we'll see the nice possessions.
There we'll see the handsome houses.
There we'll see the gorgeous castles
And see the horses strong and swift.
It seems to me I'm there already,
And I already see them conquered.
We go, we go to conquer Rome;
We're taking land away from Romans!
After we have conquered Rome
And killed the men and seized the city,
To Lothringen we'll make our way,
And we'll then conquer Lothringen,
Both Lothringen and Germany
So that no land at all remains
Here to the Alps that won't be yours.
There is no one who will escape us:
We'll take them all, right or wrong.
And so my actions match my words,
I myself will go with you
And lead two thousand knights in arms
And such a lot of infantry
They won't be counted by a soul."
After the king of Scotland spoke,
They all together said and cried:
"May he be shamed who stays behind
And does not put his strength in action!"
After each had said his thoughts
And Arthur listened to them all,

11027-34 "Wace adds Angusel's exhortations to conquer more than Rome" without worrying about right and wrong (Weiss, *Roman de Brut*, 277, n. 1).

11045ff "Wace invents Arthur's generosity, his words to the ambassadors and also their subsequent report to Rome; all enhance the king" (Weiss, *Roman de Brut*, 279, n.1).

He had his letters made and sealed.
He had them given to the Romans
And had them all bestowed with honors
And given gifts from his possessions.
"To Rome," he said, "you can announce
That I am Britain's overlord.
I hold France and I will hold France,
And I'll defend it from the Romans.
And know the truth about this thing:
For soon I will go down to Rome,
Not to carry any tribute,
But to demand tribute from you."

XII. Arthur's Roman Campaign

The messengers then turned from Arthur;
They came to Rome and there they told
Just how they came upon King Arthur
And where and how they spoke to him.
They said he was quite generous;
He was quite brave; he was quite wise;
He was a quite well-mannered man,
Who was quite rich in his demeanor.
No one, they said, could possibly
Maintain the costs that he maintains.
His household men were very rich,
And they were very well attired.
The Britons would not pay them tribute
And said that Rome would pay instead.
After the lords of Rome had heard
What the messengers reported
And heard the letters that they bore,
Their speeches were of one accord
That Arthur would not render service
And that he would request their tribute.
Before the emperor they said
(And their advice was well received)
That he should summon all the empire,
Go past Montjoie and Burgundy,
Engage King Arthur in a fight,
And take away his realm and crown.
Lucius Hiberius did not tarry:

11085ff Springing into existence in the cultural milieu of the *chansons de geste*, the legendary history of Britain cannot avoid the inclusion of anti-Islamic touches. The Roman international army thus includes some Saracens (and some amusing anachronisms like a Muslim ruler in Spain). See Glowka, "Laȝamon's Heathens," for details.

He called his kings and counts and dukes
To come to him by the tenth day.
As each of them so loved his honor,
They were to be in Rome with him,
All set to go where Arthur was.
These men all came without delay,
The ones who heard the call to arms.
Epistrod came, the King of Greece;
And Echion, Duke of Boethia;
There came Hirtacius, King of Turks,
Whose knights were strong and powerful;
There Pandras came, the King of Egypt;
And Ypolitus, the King of Crete.
The last was quite an overlord,
Who had in hand one hundred cities.
King Evander came from Syria;
Duke Teücer came from Phrygia;
Micipsa came from Babylon;
From Spain came Ali Fatima.
From Media there came King Boccus;
Sertorius of Libya;
Politetes the Bithynian;
And Xerxes came, the King of Tyre.
Mustensar, the African lord,
Lived far away and came from far,
Leading Africans and Moors,
And had them bearing his great treasures.
From those within the senate class,
Who held the highest ranks in Rome,
Marcellus and Lucius Catellus came,
And also Cocta and Gaius Metellus.
There were a lot of other barons
Whose names I have not learned about.
After they were all assembled,
Four hundred thousand and one hundred
Four was the total number there,
Not counting low-class men and servants.
When they were ready and prepared,
They moved from Rome at August's coming.

Arthur had his court dismissed;
He asked his barons all for help.

He called all of them out by name,
And by his name he summoned each
To give him help with their armed forces
Just as each desired his love.
Each said how many knights he'd get
According to the fief he had.
Ireland, Gotland, and Iceland too,
Denmark, Norway, and the Orkneys
Each promised twenty thousand armed,
Dressed in customary livery.
They did not have a single horseman
And did not know just how to ride.
All on foot would carry their weapons:
Hatchets, spears, javelins, axes.
The Normans and the Angevins,
The men from Maine and from Poitou,
The Flemish and Burgundians,
With all their arms, without delay,
Promised eighty thousand men.
They said this many ought to serve.
A dozen counts with other forces,
Who were acclaimed as Peers of France,
Who were from Chartres with Sir Guerin,
Increased their number by twelve hundred.
They promised each one hundred knights;
He said this many ought to serve.
Hoel pledged ten thousand more;
Angusel the Scot, two thousand.
From Britain, which was his own land,
Which men call England in these times,
Arthur made a count of knights
With haubergeons at sixty thousand.
Of low-class men and arbelists
And of the servants and the archers,
I know no count, but they made none,
The ones who saw the host together.
When Arthur knew what men he'd have
And just how many knights each had,
He then commanded and requested
Upon the terms that he established
For each to come with his own fleet

To Barfleur there in Normandy.
After the barons took their leave,
They then returned to their own lands.
They got their men prepared to go,
The ones who had to go with them.
To Modred, one of his own nephews,
A marvelous and hardy knight,
Arthur gave his realm to guard—
And to his wife, Queen Guinevere.
Modred had great nobility,
But he was not a loyal man.
He'd been in love with Arthur's queen,
But this had been a hidden thing.
He hid this close; and he desired
To have his uncle's wife in love
And specially to be the lord
Of all the men he had in fief.
Modred loved his uncle's wife—
His whore—and hid the shameful evil.
For Modred and for Guinevere—
God!—this power grab turned bad;
The king gave all except the crown.
To Southampton he came for passage;
The ships were brought into that place
And there the companies were joined.
You would have seen ships being fixed;
Ships being tied; ships being anchored;
Ships being dried; ships being floated;
Ships being pegged; ships being nailed;
Cords being stretched; masts being fitted;
Gangplanks set out; ships being loaded;
Helmets, shields, and hauberks carried;
Lances prepared and horses pulled;
Knights and servants going in;

11173–89 Weiss, of course, notes that the mention of Modred's love of the queen is Wace's addition (*Roman de Brut*, 281, n. 2). According to Pickens, Modred has good qualities but turns *fin' amors* into *putage*; as the enemy of *vassalage*, Modred has *vilainie* ("*Vassalage*," 177–79). Wulf observes that Arthur entrusts his kingdom to both Modred and Guinevere; Guinevere thus has more importance than she would otherwise have had ("Wace's Guenevere," 72).

And one friend calling to the other.
Many went about saluting
Those who stayed and those who left.
After the ships had all been filled
And they had suitable tide and wind,
Then you'd have the seen the anchors lifted,
The chains drawn up; the shrouds rolled up;
Mariners leaving on their ships;
Sails and masts being deployed.
Some were working on the winches;
Others on the luffs and lees.
The steersmen were way in the back;
The master steersmen were the best.
Each one applied himself to steer
The rudder, which guided the ship.
Above the helm it ran to port;
Below the helm it ran to starboard.
To catch the wind inside the sails,
They made the bowsprit face ahead
And pulled the rigging in real tight.
Some there tightened up the brails
And lowered the sails a little bit
To make the ship more smoothly run.
Some pulled in stays and pulled in sheets
And made the ropes all taut and stretched.
They loosened cleats and let down sails;
They pulled and hauled the bowlines in;
They watched the wind and watched the stars;
They carried sails to suit the tide.
They had the sails reefed to the mast
So wind would not be caught in them.
They sailed with double and triple reefings.
He was quite brave, he was quite nice,
The man who made the first of ships

11205 See Arnold's discussion of these technical naval terms (*Roman de Brut*, 2:810–11). Light gives some information in English about the technical terms ("Arthurian Portion," 164).

11235 In some mythological accounts, the first ship was the *Argo*, which carried Jason and the Argonauts to Colchis on the quest for the Golden Fleece. See Mark P. O. Morford and Robert J. Lenardon, *Classical Mythology*, 4th ed. (New York: Longman, 1991), 515ff.

And went to sea before the wind,
Seeking land he did not see
And shores he did not even know.
Arthur's people went with joy.
They had good wind and nicely sailed.
At sea at midnight they were sailing
And they were going to Barfleur
When Arthur felt the call of sleep.
He fell asleep; he could not watch.
It seemed to him, there where he slept,
He saw a bear high in the air,
Flying from the orient,
Quite ugly, strong and gross and large;
Its face was very horrible.
Across from that he saw a dragon
Flying from the occident
And throwing flames out of its eyes.
Because of its bright luminescence,
The land and sea were lit up there.
The dragon fell upon the bear,
Which raised a very strong defense.
They fought together wondrously
And struck each other wondrously,
But the drake took hold of the bear
And smashed it down upon the ground.
After Arthur slept a bit,
He pondered on the dream he saw.
He left his bed and dressed himself
And told the clerics and the barons
About the vision all in order
In which he saw the bear and dragon.
Some of them replied to him
And said the dragon he had seen
Could be interpreted as him
And the great bear was a sure sign
Of some great giant he would kill
That would come from a foreign land.
The others read it other ways;
They read it all as good, however.
"It seems to me," he said, "to be
About the war we have to make

Between the emperor and me.
But the Creator knows all this."
Upon these words the day arrived;
The weather was nice; the sun came up.
They came to port in the late morning
Within Barfleur at Constantine.
As soon as able, they left ship
And spread out in the countryside.
Arthur waited for his men
Who had not made arrival yet.
He had not waited very long
Before he heard and he was told
About a very massive giant
Who had come up from down in Spain.
He'd seized Eleine, the niece of Hoel;
He raped and put her on a mountain
That people call Mont St. Michel.
There was no church or chapel then;
It was closed off by rising tides.
There was no man so daring there,
No nobleman, no peasant either,
So prideful or so brave and hardy
Who dared to fight against the giant
Or go into the place he was.
When the land's men were mustered up
And went to fight upon the mountain,
Often by sea, often by land,
There hardly was a war with him.
Their ship broke up upon the rocks;
Many there died; many there drowned.
They had to let the business be;
They did not dare to be there longer.
You often would have seen the serfs
Running from houses, bearing infants,
Leading women, chasing beasts,

11285ff Pickens observes that in the encounter with the Giant of Mont St. Michel, Wace demonizes the giant: Arthur and Bedevere have "courtesy"; the giant does not. Further, the channel voyage marks the transition from the values of courtesy as practiced in Arthur's kingdom back to the values of feudal vassalage and war ("Arthur's Channel Crossing"). See Finke and Shichtman, "The Mont St. Michel Giant."

Climbing the hills, hiding in forests.
They fled to forests and to wastelands,
And still they feared that they would die.
The land was all abandoned then;
All of the people fled away.
The giant's name was Dinabuc—
May he contract a bad disease!

When Arthur had heard word of him,
He summoned Kay and Bedevere.
The first one was his seneschal;
His butler was the other one.
He wished to speak to no one else.
That night as soon as bedtime came,
He made these two and made their squires
Grab their armor and their horses.
He did not wish to take his army
Or make a public show of this.
He feared that if they knew about it
That they'd be frightened by the giant;
Besides, he was so great a man
That he'd suffice as its destroyer.
All night they rode so long by horse,
Traveled so much and spurred so much
They came at morning to the shore
Where they were sure they'd get across.
They saw a fire burn on the mountain;
A man could see it from afar.
There was another smaller mount,
Which wasn't distant from the larger.
A fire was lit on both the mounts.
Arthur therefore did not know
Upon which mount the giant was
And on which mount he'd find the thing.
There was no one who knew the answer,
At least no one who'd seen the day.
He said that Bedevere should go
And check out one mount or the other.
When he had found what he was seeking,
He would return and make report.
This man got in a little boat
And went across to the closest mount.

There was no other way to go,
For it was high tide on the sea.
When he came to the closest mount
And climbed up to an open place,
Upon the mount he heard great sobbing,
Great lamenting, sighs, and cries.
He was afraid and took to shaking,
For he believed he heard the giant.
But soon he reassured himself;
With his sword drawn he went ahead.
He had recouped his bravery.
He had the thought and the desire
To fight the giant by himself
And put himself into adventure.
Even for fear he'd lose his life,
He would not do a cowardly thing.
But thoughts like these were all in vain,
For when he came upon the plain,
All he saw was just a fire
And a new marker for a grave.
The grave had recently been dug.
The count came there with his sword drawn.
He found an ancient woman there,
Her clothes in rags, her hair messed up.
She was stretched out next to the marker.
She often sighed, often complained,
And often for Eleine spoke sadly.
She made great dole; she launched great cries.
When she had noticed Bedevere,
"Wretch," she said, "just who are you?
What misadventure leads you here?
In dole, in sorrow, and in pain
You'll have to end your life today
If the giant can get sight of you.
Flee, misfortunate, take your way
Before the evil foe can spot you!"
"Good woman," said Sir Bedevere,
"Speak to me and stop your crying.
Tell me your name and why you cry
And why you stay upon this isle
To lie upon this sepulchre?

Tell me about all that has happened."
"I am," she said, "in destitution,
A tired woman cursed by fate.
I cry here for a noble girl
That I gave suck to at my breast.
She was Eleine, the niece of Hoel.
Here lies her body by this marker.
I was commanded to give suck.
Tired girl—why was she given me?
Tired girl—why did I give her milk
To have her ravished by a devil?
A giant ravished me and her
And brought both me and her right here.
He made attempts to rape the girl,
But she was slight and could not take it.
He was too huge; he was too big,
Too ugly, gross, and also heavy.
He made her soul depart her body.
Eleine could not sustain this thing.
Worn-out-one-in-pain, my sweetness,
My joy, my pleasure, and my love
The giant brought to shameful death,
And I put her here in the ground."
"Why," said the count, "why don't you leave
Now that you have lost Eleine?"
"You wish," she said, "to hear just why?
Noble and mannered you seem to me;
There's nothing hidden from your eyes.
After Eleine had passed away,
I thought that I would lose my mind,
For I observed her shameful death.
The giant made me stay right here
To keep me for his lechery.
He's made me stay here with his force,
And he has raped me with his force.
His force requires that I submit
And that I do not push him back.
I never do it for my pleasure—
I call on God to be my witness.
I don't lack much before he kills me,
But I am older and I'm stronger,

And I am larger and I'm tougher
And hardier and more protected
Than a young female like Eleine.
Nevertheless, I have great pain;
My body soon just hurts from this;
And if he comes as is his custom
To satisfy his lechery,
You'll die; from him you can't escape.
He's right there on the smoking mount.
He'll come real soon; such is his custom.
What did you seek here, friend? Flee soon
So that you won't be taken here.
Let me complain and make my dole.
She has been dead awhile, my love.
My friendship with Eleine seems cursed."
Sir Bedevere then pitied her,
He gave her comfort very sweetly,
Then left her there and turned away.
He came to Arthur and reported
What he heard and what he learned
About the old one who made dole;
About Eleine, who was then dead;
About the giant who sojourned
Upon the bigger mount, which smoked.
Arthur mourned about Eleine,
But he was neither scared nor slow.
Upon the ebbing of the tide,
He had his fellows climbing up.
They went up to the bigger mount
Just as soon as the sea exposed it.
Their palfreys and their battle mounts
They left commended with the squires.
The three of them went up the mount,
Arthur, Bedevere, and Kay.
"I'll go," said Arthur, "on ahead,
And so I'll fight against the giant.
You'll follow after at my back
And make quite sure that no one strikes
As long as I can help myself
And I am not in need of it.
It would resemble cowardice

If anyone but me was fighting.
But, nevertheless, if you observe
That I'm in need, come rescue me."
These men agreed to what he asked,
And then the three walked up the mount.
The giant sat beside the fire,
And on the fire he roasted pork.
He cooked a part of it on spits,
And part he roasted on the coals.
He had a moustache and a beard
Smeared with flesh cooked in the coals.
Arthur wanted to surprise him
Before he could pick up his club.
The giant had seen Arthur, though,
Marveled some, got on his feet,
And on his shoulder put his club,
Which was squared off and very large.
Two peasants could not carry it
Or even lift it from the ground.
Arthur saw him standing up
And coming close to smash him well.
He drew his sword, raised up his shield,
Covered his head, and braced himself;
The giant gave him such a blow
That all the mount resounded from it.
It totally astonished Arthur,
But he was strong and did not fall.
Arthur felt the heavy blow;
He held his sword; he raised the blade
And lifted up his arm on high
And hit the forehead of the giant.
Into his two eyebrows he cut;
The blood fell down into his eyes.
He would have had him dead and headless
With no means for recovery,
Except the giant had the club
Held up against the blow on high.
He ducked his head—it stayed attached—
And nevertheless received a blow
That covered all his face with blood
And made it hard for him to see.

Then you'd have seen the giant curse!
When he perceived his eyes were hurt,
He looked around him like a boar
When dogs have chased him for a while
And threw himself against the hunter,
All at once, with lots of anger.
He charged the king and grabbed him so
That he'd not lose him for the sword.
Massive and strong, he hugged his middle
And made him fall upon his knees.
But this one turned himself at once
And stood back up and fixed himself.
Arthur was quite angry then;
Wondrous was his ability.
He was worked up, and he was scared.
He forced himself to do his best.
He struggled to compose himself.
He had great strength; he did not faint.
He ducked across while jumping up;
He was thus free of his opponent.
When he had gotten loose from him
And felt his body gain its freedom,
He was quite fast; he went around:
He now was here; he now was there—
Often striking with the sword.
And that one felt about with hands:
His eyes were all filled up with blood;
He could not tell white things from black.
Arthur ducked around so much—
Often behind, often in front—
That with the blade of Caliburn
He struck the giant in the neck.
He pulled and struggled, and he fell.
He tumbled down and gave a cry.
He made a crash upon his fall
Just like an oak tree felled by wind.
Arthur started laughing then,
For he no longer felt his anger.
He stood from far and looked at him;
He gave an order to his butler
To cut the head from off the giant

And hand it over to a squire.
He wished it borne up to the host
To have it shown off as a marvel.
"I was," said Arthur, "in some fear.
I've never heard of greater giant
Except for Rithon all alone
Who has made many kings feel pain."
Rithon conquered so many kings
And vanquished them alive and dead,
That with the skinned-off beards of kings
He had constructed a fur coat.
He made the coat so he could wear it:
Someone had to kill this Rithon.
With some great pride and fierceness too,
He had demanded that King Arthur
Peel the beard he had right off
And send it to him with good wishes;
And since he was the strongest king
And had more worth than other kings,
He'd give his beard a place of honor
And make the border out of it.
If Arthur said he would not do
The thing that Rithon had requested,
Man to man they'd come together
And man to man they'd have a fight.
The one of them that killed the other
Or who could make the other yield,
Would get his beard and take the coat
And make a border or some tassels.
Arthur fought against this man
And won on Mount Aravia.
He got the coat; he skinned his beard.
Arthur never found again
A giant who had equal strength
Or of whom he had equal fear.
After Arthur killed the monster
And Bedevere removed the head,

11563–65 For some ruminations on the sources and analogues for the story of Rithon, the giant who collects beards, see Tatlock, *Legendary History of Britain*, 388–89, esp. ns. 35–37.

They left the mount joyous and happy,
Rejoined the host and then recounted
Where they'd been and why they'd been there:
Then they showed the head to all.
Hoel sorrowed over his niece:
He was in misery a long time;
He was ashamed of how she died.
In honor of Our Lady Mary,
He built a chapel on the mount
That is now called the Tomb Eleine.
From the gravesite of Eleine
It got its name, the Tomb Eleine.
From the grave where the corpse was laid
The Tomb Eleine received its name.

When the Irish had arrived
And others who were supposed to come,
Arthur, on each and every day,
Made his way through Normandy.
He went by castles and by towns;
His people grew in massive numbers.
They all were going for his sake.
He passed through France to Burgundy.
He wished to go straight to Autun,
For he had heard some scout reports
That Roman men were coming on
And taking up positions there.
Lucius Hiberius was their leader,
Who occupied the throne of Rome.
When Arthur had to cross the river
You hear one call the River Aube,
The peasants gave him information
And scouts of his announced to him
That close to there, if he so wished,
He would encounter the emperor,
Who had his shelters and thatched huts
Set in a place quite close thereby.
The emperor's men, the kings he led,
The companies with which he rode
Were such that he'd be mad to stay.
His people would not prosper there;
He was outnumbered four to one.

He should make peace and leave the battle.
Arthur was not fazed at all.
Brave he was with trust in God.
He had heard many threats before.
Over the Aube, in a strong place,
He put a little fortress up.
With his great numbers, he soon enclosed it.
He closed the fortress off like this
So he could leave equipment there;
And if the battle grew too sharp,
He would recover in the fortress.
He summoned then a pair of counts,
Who were quite wise and eloquent,
Each one a man from noble people.
Gerin of Chartres was one of them;
The other was Sir Bos of Oxford,
Who recognized both right and wrong.
He added Walwain to this pair,
Because he'd spent so long in Rome.
Because they were so well commended
And so well known by coats of arms,
The king put them into a group
And sent them to the emperor.
He ordered him to turn around;
France was his; he should stay out.
If he did not go back from there,
He'd come to battle as a test—
On the first day that he would come—
Of who would have the greater right;
For Arthur, as long as he would live,
Would fight for France against the Romans.
He'd conquered it with violence;
He'd taken it with violence;
And Romans in the olden days
Through violence had had it too.
The battle now would prove again
Which of the two ought to have France.
    The messengers of Arthur turned
And got upon their favorite horses,
Dressed in hauberks with laced helmets,
Shields on shoulders, lances gripped.

Then you'd have seen some knights in arms,
Some bachelors, the ablest men,
Who went to counsel Walwain then;
And they implored him in their counsel
That there in court where he was going
He should do something ere he left
That would then get the war in motion
That had been threatened for so long.
It would turn out to be disastrous
For them to come so close together
And not to have a single joust
And just to turn away in haste.
These men made way across a mountain,
And then a forest and a plain.
They saw the bivouac of the host,
And they arrived there soon enough.
Then you'd have seen the Romans come
And knights emerging from the tents
To see the three ambassadors
And learn about the latest news.
They kept on asking what they sought
And if they came to seek for peace.
But they were silent and unmoved
Till they came to the emperor.
They dismounted before his tent;
They had their horses held outside.
They went before the emperor
And laid out the demands of Arthur.
Each one of them said what he pleased
And what he knew was good to say.
The emperor heard everything,
And when it pleased him, he responded.
Sir Walwain said, "We come from Arthur,
And we are bearing Arthur's message.
We are his men; he is our lord.
All of us must give the message.
Through us he has forbidden you—
And all should know this openly—
To set a single foot in France
Or put yourself inside of France.
He now owns France and will own France

And will defend it as his own.
He orders you to leave it be,
And if you challenge him for it,
It will be challenged in a battle
And be disputed in a battle.
The Romans took it through a battle
And conquered it through battle too;
And they have owned it through a battle
And through a battle held it too.
It will be proved again through battle
Who ought have the power there.
Tomorrow, without other delay,
Come if you wish to fight for France—
Or go away and get on back.
Return! You have no business here!
We have won, and you have lost."
The emperor responded then
That he did not have to return.
France was his; he would go forward.
It saddened him that he had lost it;
He'd conquer it if he was able.
But he expected his success
In winning France and owning France.
Quintillian sat next to him;
He took the floor right after him.
His nephew, he was very proud
And quite contentious as a knight:
"The Britons," he said, "are boastful men
And very good at making threats.
They've made their boasts and made their threats.
They boast a lot and do quite little."
He would have said more, I believe,
And made more insults to these men,
But Walwain, who became incensed,
Drew out his sword, stepped up to him,
And made his head fly off his trunk.
He said to the counts, "Go, mount up!"
And both the counts then mounted up,
Walwain with them and them with him.
Each one of them got back his horse
And turned away in a great rush,

Shields on shoulders, lances in hand:
They took no formal leave of Romans.
One saw the court in total chaos!
The emperor loudly cried out:
"What did you do? You brought us shame!
Kill them for me! They will not go!"
Then you'd have heard the vassals cry:
"Weapons, weapons, horses, horses!
Right now, right now, mount up, mount up!
Spur on, spur on, take care, take care!"
You would have seen this host in motion,
Putting on saddles, grabbing horses,
Picking up lances, buckling spurs,
Spurring hard to catch them quickly.
The counts were going away in flight,
Looking back from time to time.
The Romans followed in disorder,
Some on the road, some in the fields,
Here two, here three, here five, here six,
Here seven, here eight, here nine, here ten.
There was a man who spurred ahead;
His horse was good and very fast.
He passed ahead of his companions,
And as he rode he cried a lot:
"You'd better stop, you knights, now stop!
It's shameful that you will not turn."
Gerin of Chartres turned around.
He gripped his shield, stuck out his lance,
And bore him far from his good horse
To the extent the lance permitted.
He told them then: "It's too bad now.
Your horse has made too great a leap.
You should have stayed back in the tent
Instead of coming way up here."
Bos observed what Guerin did
And heard his words to his opponent.
He wished to do a similar thing.
He pulled his horse's head around
And let the horse run at a knight,
Who ran at him, who did not fear.
Bos then slashed him at the throat,

Across the shoulders to the spine,
And this one fell, his throat wide open,
Having swallowed down the lance.
The count then shouted: "Mister Don,
I'm skilled at feeding bits like this.
Rest in peace; lie down right here.
Wait for those who follow you.
Tell the ones who come by here
The messengers have gone this way."
There was a man of Roman birth,
Of noble Roman lineage;
The Romans called the man Marcellus.
He had a very speedy horse;
He rode this horse behind the rest,
And then he passed all of the leaders.
He did not bear a lance at all;
He had forgotten it in haste.
This man was getting close to Walwain,
Spurring on with loosened reins.
Already he was by his side;
Walwain could not draw away.
The man reached out his hand for Walwain;
He'd promised he'd take him alive.
Walwain saw he came quite fast
And could ride on a horse quite fast.
He grabbed his reins and stopped himself.
This man was close and ran on past.
He passed as Walwain drew his sword
And cut his head off all at once.
He sliced him just above the shoulders;
The helmet gave him no protection.
This man fell down; his life was gone;
And Walwain said for courtesy:
"Marcell, in hell where you are going,
You will inform Quintillian
And make him know yourself and say
That Britons are hardy enough;

11831–38 The *courtoisie* of Walwain in battle may be ironic (Pickens, "*Vassalage*," 175).

They want to fight well for their rights
And do much more than just make threats."
Then Walwain summoned once again
His friends, Guerin and Bos, by name
So that each one would turn around
And joust with one of those pursuers.
And so they did what Walwain said.
They quickly knocked three Romans down.
The messengers then took their leave.
Their battle horses bore them quickly,
And Romans followed after them
And did not turn away a bit.
They often came where they could reach them
And often hit them with their lances.
They often slugged them on the back
Either with lances or with swords.
But they could never hit them so
That they could ever stop or wound
A one or pull one off a horse
Or give one any kind of damage.
One of these, Marcellus' cousin,
Was on a very speedy horse.
He was upset about his cousin
Whom he saw lying on the road.
Across the fields he spurred and reached
The side of the three messengers.
He wished to strike across at them,
But Walwain was aware of him.
He spurred at him and went to strike;
The man had not a chance to turn.
He let his lance fall to the ground;
He was not able to employ it.
He drew his sword, he wished to strike,
He raised his arm, put up his hand—
And Walwain cut completely off
The arm the man had lifted up.
The sword, the arm, and the hand too—
He made them fly off far afield.
He would have hit him once again,
But Roman men were coming fast.
They went on in this chase like this

Until they fled into the woods
That were around them and the fort
That Arthur'd built just recently.

Arthur had six thousand knights
Sent out after the messengers
To look around the woods and valleys
And scout around the countryside.
They might encounter the messengers;
If there was need, they'd rescue them.
They'd made their way across a forest,
And they had stopped right next to it.
Armed, they sat upon their horses.
They looked upon the messengers:
They saw the plains completely filled
With men in arms in massive troops.
They recognized their messengers
And saw the men who followed them.
Right into view they made a leap
With one sole voice and one sole cry.
The Romans quickly made retreat
And spread themselves across the fields.
Some of them were quite upset
That they had given such pursuit,
For Britons were now pressing them
And striking them a lot in turn.
They'd reached and captured quite a few
And killed and hacked up quite few.
Petreius, who was a rich lord,
Possessed in arms no Roman peer.
He had ten thousand men in arms;
He had this many in his region.
This man had heard about the guard
That had been set up by the Britons.
Quickly with ten thousand shields
He brought those Roman men some help.
With sheer force and pressure too,
With the armed men that he conducted,
He forced the Britons back in the woods;
They could not hold him back at all.
Into the woods the chase went on,
For they could not maintain their ground.

They made resistance in the woods
And in the woods made their defense.
Petreius launched attacks on them,
But suffered many losses there
Because the Britons knocked them down
And dragged them back into the woods.
The heavy blows were very thick
Inside the woods and in the bushes.
When Arthur noticed the delay
His messengers were suffering
And saw that those who went for them
Themselves were not then coming back,
He called on Ider, son of Nu,
And gave to him five thousand knights.
He sent them out after the others
And asked this man to look for them.
Walwain and Bos were fighting on
And struck well on the other side.
There were a lot of shouts and yells
When Ider, son of Nu, arrived.
The Britons were then energized,
And they took back the battlefield.
Ider attacked and gave his cry,
And so did those he led with him.
And the attack was well performed,
For many saddles there were emptied,
Many horses seized and taken,
And many knights chopped up in pieces.
The storm did not disturb Petreius:
He stopped his men and turned around.
He knew when it was good to turn
And flee or chase or hold one's ground.
You often would have seen nice chases
And turns aside in many places.
The hardy one found hardy one.
The joust-seeker was jousting soon.
The slash-seeker was slashing soon.
The one who could not last fell down.
The Britons charged in disarray;
They did not want to be in order.
They were quite eager for the jousts

And eager to engage their arms.
They wanted to be chivalrous,
And so they often broke their ranks.
It did not matter how they went
As long as they began the fight.
Petreius was quite obstinate;
He kept his good men close to him.
He well knew fights; he well knew war;
He well knew how to wait or seek.
He often turned; he often charged;
He rescued those who'd fallen down.
Sir Bos of Oxford saw quite well
Petreius was adept at war
And Britons would not turn unscathed
If they did not knock out Petreius,
By killing him or seizing him,
Because he kept the Romans safe.
The Britons way too foolishly
Engaged in combat with these Romans.
Some of the bravest and the best
Bos took in council with some others:
"Barons," he said, "talk to me now,
You who truly love King Arthur.
We have begun this raging fight
Without the presence of our lord.
If well befalls us, well we'll be;
If bad, however, he will hate us.
If we become the less in honor
And do not win upon this field,
We will receive disgrace and harm
And be despised by Arthur himself.
Because of this we need to try
To put some shackles on Petreius.
We can take him dead or alive
And give him to Arthur dead or alive.
We cannot leave here otherwise,
For we might lose a lot for this.
Do everything that I now do
And make attack where I attack."
They said that they would do just that:
Where Bos would go, they would go too.

When Bos had those he wanted with him
And he had spied and he had seen
Just where Petreius kept himself,
Who kept the others all together,
Bos fiercely charged into that section,
And so did all the other Britons.
He never tried to stop or cease
Until he came into the press
Where Sir Petreius rode his horse
And oversaw his companies.
Bos recognized and charged at him.
He joined together their two horses;
He threw his arms around the man.
Bos trusted in his company
And let himself fall willingly.
You would have seen a thing of wonder!
In the great press he tumbled down;
Between his arms was Sir Petreius.
Bos held and dragged on Sir Petreius;
The latter tried to free himself.
The Romans ran to rescue him;
The man who bore a lance soon broke it.
After their lances failed to work,
They slugged like new men with their swords.
They wished to rescue Sir Petreius;
The Britons wished to rescue Bos.
You would have seen them strike together
In a thick storm, in a hard fight,
Splitting helmets, piercing shields,
Hauberks failing, shattering shafts,
Saddles emptied, saddles turned,
Falling men and wounded men.
The Britons cried out for their lord;
The men from Rome cried out for theirs.
The one side struggled so they'd have him;
The other always dragged him back.
One could not ever tell for sure
Just who was Roman, who was British,
Except by speech or battle cries,
So thickly fell the heavy blows.
Walwain went through the great press;

He made a passage with his sword.
He struck and pushed and slugged and butted.
He struck down and he routed many.
The Roman who observed his blows
Made way for him if possible.
Yder turned off somewhere else
And cut great clearings in the Romans.
Gerin of Chartres gave him help.
The one was strengthened by the other.
They made their way past Sir Petreius
And gave no thought to him and Bos.
The Britons gave Sir Bos relief
And put him back upon a horse.
They kept Petreius in their grip,
Who had received a lot of blows.
Around the press they led the man
Inside their army into safety.
They left him under heavy guard
And started back into the fight.
The Romans had no leader then,
Just like a ship without a pilot
With wind pushing it where it likes
When no one's there to steer it straight.
Just such a thing befell the men
Who had just lost their general.
They were not able to resist
Now that they had lost their leader.
The stirred-up Britons went at them
And beat them down in massive numbers.
They went across the fallen ones
And went behind the fleeing ones.
They captured some; they killed off some;
They pillaged some; they tied up some.
The Britons then withdrew their men
Into the woods and to their captives.
They bore Petreius from that place
And made him stand before their lord,
And many other captives with him.
Arthur gave his men his thanks.
He told them then that if he won,
He would increase the fief of each.

Arthur had the prisoners guarded
And had them given to the guards.
After some talk, he was advised
That he should transfer them to Paris.
He'd have them held inside a prison
As long as he was pleased by this,
For if he kept them in the host,
There would be fear of losing them.
He then prepared the ones who'd move them
And set some leaders over them:
Cador and Borel and Richier
And Bedevere, who was the butler,
Four counts from very noble lines.
The king requested that they rise,
Go with the prisoners in the morning,
And take them far enough away
So the conveyors would be safe
And past the place where they should fear.
The emperor by means of spies
Quickly heard about the news
That in the morning they would move,
These men who had to move the captives.
He had ten thousand knights mount up;
He asked for them to ride all night
So that they would come to the captives
And rescue them if they were able.
Sertorius, the lord of Libya,
And King Evander, lord of Syria,
And Sir Caricius of Rome
And Sir Catellus Vulteius too:
Each of these four had lots of land,
And each one was quite skilled in war.
They were selected and called forward
To go and give the captives aid.
They were the leaders of the others.
They moved ten thousand troops at night.
Some natives acted as their guides,
Who knew the ways that were direct.
They rode their horses all the night
And rode them hard in a such a heat
That they came to the Paris road.

They found a spot appropriate
For setting up an ambush trap.
They silently remained in there.
One saw the force of noble Arthur
Riding along somewhat secure;
They feared no ambush in the least.
They rode their horses in two groups.
Cador and Borel with their people
Came along, riding in front.
Counts Richier and Bedevere,
Who were to guard the prisoners,
Followed with five hundred troops
And made the captives go along
With hands tied up behind their backs
And feet tied up beneath the horses.
One saw the trap that lay ahead,
The trap the Romans had set up.
The Romans jumped out all at once:
All of the earth trembled and shook!
They set on them with hardiness;
The others fiercely made defense.
Bedevere and Richier
Heard the great noise and saw the blows.
They forced the prisoners to stop
And turn into a safer place.
They left their squires in charge of them
And ordered them to guard them well.
And then they let their horses run
And did not cease to spur them on
Until they were joined with the others.
They held together with great vigor.
The Romans struck both here and there.
They did not have as much intention
To bring the Britons to defeat
As to bring rescue to the captives.
The Britons struck collectively
And held together as a body.
They came and went with one intent
And as a unit made defense.
The Roman men ran up and down
And sought the captives here and there.

They stayed so focused seeking them
That they lost many of their men.
The British split themselves in groups
And put themselves into four lines.
Cador had the Cornish troops;
And Bedevere had Norman ones.
Sir Richier had his in order,
And Borel had the men of Maine.
King Evander realized
His force and people were decreasing.
He made them keep themselves together
When they could not get to the captives.
He made them hold together then
And do their fighting in their ranks.
The Romans then began to win,
And things got worse then for the Britons.
They hurt them much and captured many
And even killed the four best ones.
Yder's son, Sir Er, was killed,
A valiant and a forceful knight;
And Hyrelgas of Periron—
There was no braver man at all;
And from Tintagel, Aliduc,
For whom his kinfolk had great sorrow;
And Maurice Cador was one too—
If Welsh or British, I don't know.
Borel of Mans, a noble count,
Who was in trouble with his men,
Was holding on with bravery
And often urged his people on.
Evander charged upon him, though,
And struck upon him with his lance,
Running him through around his throat.
Borel fell; he could not stand.
The Britons went on in dismay
Because they'd lost so many people.
The Romans had them seven to one;
They flew at them to gain advantage.
They would have died, been seized or beaten
And might have lost their captives too,
But Guitard, Count of Poitiers,

Who guarded foragers that day,
Had heard about the news at once
That one part of the Roman army
Was there to get the captives freed.
They ran their horses to that place
With some three thousand knights in arms
And foragers and archers too.
The Romans planned to make attack
And finish off the British force
When Guitard came up with his troops,
Spurring hard with lances lowered.
They knocked down more than just one hundred
Who did not put up any fight.
One saw the Romans all dismayed
And feeling that they had been shamed.
They thought that Arthur came himself
And all his people followed him.
When they observed so many falling,
They had no hope of being saved.
The Poitevins attacked them well;
The Britons were not holding back.
The one group gave strength to the other,
And both strove hard to beat the Romans.
The Romans turned their backs to them,
All uncovered and exposed.
They wished to go back to their camps;
They did not know another cure.
The Britons chased them a long time
And took good vengeance for the dead.
They followed close and reached their backs
And did not shrink from striking them.
King Evander and Catellus
And some five hundred others too
Were struck at and were then knocked down,
Some of them killed, some of them taken.
The Britons took the ones they wished,
As many as they could lead off;
And then they went back to the road
Where the battle had been held.
Borel, the doughty count of Mans,
And other dead they sought afield.

They found the count upon the ground,
Covered with blood, expiring his soul.
They had the wounded carried off
And had the dead interred right there.
To those whom Arthur had selected
(And just as Arthur had commanded),
They gave the charge of the first captives
And sent them off to Paris then.
The others who were just now taken
They had tied up in narrow bonds.
They led them to the fort with them,
And there they showed them to their lord.
They told him of the fight and trouble
And all together promised him
That if they fought against the Romans
They'd vanquish them without a doubt.
   The emperor learned what had happened
And also of the great defeat,
About Evander, who was killed,
And all about the others captured.
He saw his people in confusion,
Saw the war begun already,
Saw things that often had gone wrong,
And saw that he would conquer nothing.
He was in anguish and dismay.
He thought and thought, and he was scared.
He was not sure of what to do:
Go ahead and fight with Arthur
Or wait for those still at the rear
Who would be coming after him.
He greatly feared to have the battle
Because he would win nothing there.
He was advised to seek Autun
And cross through Langres on the way.
He had his people called and moved;
They'd come to Langres in the night.
They'd take up lodging in the city
And set up bivouacs in the valleys.
Langres sat upon a mountain,
And valleys lay there all around.

Soon Arthur learned what they would do
And where they wanted to withdraw.
He knew the other would not fight
Until he had much greater force.
He did not want to let them stay
In safety when he was so close.
As soon as he could, in secrecy,
He had his people called together.
Leaving Langres to the left,
He went across it on the right.
He wished to beat the emperor
And cut his way off to Autun.
All of the night until the morning,
He rode with his host through woods and plains
Until he came into a valley,
A valley that was called Saussy.
He made his way then through this valley,
Which went from Langres to Autun.
Arthur had his people armed
And put his companies in order
So when the Romans did arrive,
He would receive them straight away.
All the harnesses and trappings
For which they'd have no use in battle
He had abandoned on a hill
And made to look just like an army,
So that the Romans, when they saw them,
Would be afraid of their great numbers.
Six thousand six hundred sixty-six,
All counted, in one battle line
He put in the woods behind a hill—
I do not know which side it was.
The Count of Gloucester, who was Morvid,
Was made the leader in this place.
The king said to these men: "Stay here!
Do not move for anything.

12302 For some discussion of what this valley may actually be, see William Matthews, "Where Was Siesia-Sessoyne?" *Speculum* 49 (1974): 680-86, and H.-E. Keller, "Two Toponymical Problems in Geoffrey of Monmouth and Wace," *Speculum* 49 (1974): 687–98.

If there is need, I will turn here
And have some others here by you.
And if the Romans, by some fate,
Turn around in their defeat,
Charge after them and get on them:
Kill them off and do not spare them!"
And these men said, "We will do so."
He took another legion then
Of noble men, of vassal lords,
With helmets laced, upon their horses,
And put them in an open place.
Outside of him they had no leader.
This was his household company,
Which he had nourished and raised up.
He had his dragon held up there,
Which he had as his battle flag.
He made eight groups from all the others;
He had two leaders in each one.
Half of the men were cavalry;
The other half were infantry.
To these he gave the same command
And told them this and begged them too
That those who were upon the horses,
When those on foot were in the fight,
Should strike the Romans from the sides
And make their charges from the sides.
Five thousand five hundred fifty-five
Knights, all of whom were well selected,
Composed each battle company,
All of them armed with every weapon.
They were set up in groups of four,
With companies in groups of eight,
With four behind and four in front.
Another massive group of men
Was in the middle, armed like them.
The front of the first company
Was led by Angusel the Scot
And also Cador, Count of Cornwall;
The second group was in the hands
Of Bos and Guerin, Count of Chartres.
The third of these was handed over,

Well arranged and well equipped,
To Aschil, who was King of Denmark,
And Lot, who was the King of Norway.
Hoel took the fourth in hand,
And with him Walwain, fearing nothing.
After these four, there were four others
That he had readied for the battle.
Of one the leaders was Sir Kay;
Another, Bedevere the butler.
Bedevere had Neustrians;
Kay, Angevins and Chinonese.
To Holdin, who was Count of Flanders,
And to Guitard the Poitevin
The next group was commended then;
And willingly they took command.
The Count of Leicester, Jugeïn,
And Count of Dorchester Jonathas
Received the seventh company;
They were its lords and constables.
The Count of Chester, Corsalen,
And Urgen, who was Count of Bath,
Had the eighth group in command,
And Arthur had great faith in them.
The good servants and good archers
And also valiant arbalesters
Were on two sides outside the press
So they could draw into the sides.
All of them were before the king,
Who was behind them in his group.
When Arthur had his companies
And battle-lines set up to go,
Hear what he said to his own men,
To his own lords and to their sons:
"Lords," he said, "you comfort me
When I remember your great goodness,
Your great virtues, your great conquests.
I find you always brave and ready.
Your prowess grows with every day;
It always shines no matter what.
When I remember and perceive
That Britain is in your time now—

Because of you and your companions—
Lady over thirty regions,
I'm very happy; I'm glorified;
I put my trust in God and you
That you will conquer once again
And capture and possess yet more.
Your prowess and your able hands
Have dashed the Romans down two times.
You know my heart divines for me
And it is my clear destiny
That now you'll beat them once again
You'll have thus beat them three times then.
You've brought defeat upon the Norse;
You've brought defeat upon the Danes;
You've brought defeat upon the French,
And you have France below your feet.
Well you ought to vanquish worse
When you've already vanquished better.
They want to make you tributaries
And to extract payments from us
And to recover France from us.
They think they'll find such people here
Like those they're leading from the East.
But one of us is equal to
A hundred of them, without a doubt,
For they are worth as much as women.
We well should put our trust in God;
And we should not turn to despair,
For with a little hardiness,
We will defeat them easily.
You've never failed me for a man
And never turned in flight from one.
I know quite well what each will do,
And well I'll see who'll do the best.
I'll go around and I'll see all,
And I'll watch out for each of you."
After the speech came to an end,
In which the king had made his case,
All of the men who had attended
Unanimously answered him
That they would rather die right there

Than leave the field sans victory.
You would have heard them taking oaths,
Making their pledges one by one,
That they'd not fail for fear of death
And that they'd do whatever he did.
  Lucius had his birth in Spain
And had a noble Roman family.
He still enjoyed a youthful age,
Less than forty, more than thirty.
Hardy he was and quite courageous;
He had already accomplished much.
For his strength and for his valor,
He had been made the emperor.
He turned from Langres in the morning;
He wished to go straight to Autun.
All of his massive host was moved;
The road was very long and wide.
When he was told about the ambush
That Arthur'd set in front of him,
He saw that he would have to fight
Or that he'd have to turn around.
He had no wish to turn around,
For that would look like cowardice
Even if foes would come to him
And make him suffer lots of damage,
For fighting together and taking flight
Cannot be done at the same time.
His kings, his princes, and his dukes,
Of which he had at least two hundred,
And those men who were senators,
He summoned and he spoke to them:
"Fathers," he said, "you noble lords,
Good vassals and good conquerors,
You are the sons of ancient nobles
Who won great honors in their conquests.
Through them Rome's now the head of all
And so will be while Romans live.
They won the great empire through conquest.
To lessen it would shame our age.
They were noble and you are noble:
From valiant fathers valiant sons.

Each of you had a valiant father;
Your valor today is just like theirs.
Each one should try to do his best
To imitate his good old father.
One can be shamed by running off
And losing his father's legacy
And giving up most wrongfully
The things his father won by conquest.
I do not say, you understand,
That I hold you as lesser men.
They were brave and you are brave;
I hold you all as valiant men.
Lords, I see and so do you,
I know quite well and so do you,
The road we had has been removed,
The one that went straight to Autun.
We cannot go or pass on it
Without engaging in a fight.
I do not know what kinds of robbers—
Either robbers or some thieves—
Have just cut off the road ahead,
The road down which I ought to lead you.
They thought that I would flee away
And that I'd leave the land for them,
But I've been going back this way
To make them come up to the front.
And now they're set to fall on us.
Pick up your arms and arm yourselves!
If they await us, we'll attack;
And if they flee, we'll follow them.
Let's put the brakes on their invasion
And let us wreck the power they have!"
They then jumped up to take up arms;
They did not wish to tarry longer.
They made their battle preparations,
And formed their lines and companies.
A lot of pagan kings and dukes
Were mixed in with the Christian people.
These pagans held their fiefs from Rome
And served the Romans for these fiefs.
In groups of thirty and of forty,

In groups of sixty and a hundred,
In larger groups of many thousands,
They made divisions of their knights,
Many on foot, many on horse,
Some on the hill, some in the valley.
When they were all in ranks and files,
They went against the men of Arthur.
From one part of the valley there,
Entered the Roman men in arms;
Within their sight, across the way,
The Britons occupied the field.
Then you'd have heard the battle horns
And trumpets blasting very loudly.
In ordered lines with ordered steps,
They came together, getting closer.
In this approach, you would have seen
A lot of spears and arrows launched.
No one there could open an eye
Or let his face become exposed.
The arrows flew like pelting hail;
Violence and anger rose up soon.
They came to break the lances then
And shatter shields and pierce them through.
They gave their shafts powerful cracks;
The broken pieces flew up high.
After this they came to blows
And great swipes with polished blades.
Then there was a marvelous fight;
I've never seen a deadlier
Or more mixed up or thicker one.
The man who wished to strike soon did.
There was no need for fools or cowards;
A coward knew not what to do there.
One could hardly strike another
In the great thickness of the crowd.
You would have seen the field in action,
One line crashing on another,
One group smashing on another,
Some of them striking, some of them slugging,
Some of them coming, some of them turning,
Some of them falling, some of them standing,

Spear shafts shattering, rocks a-flying,
Swords being drawn, shields being lifted,
The strong ones crushing down the weak,
The living trampling on the dead,
Cinches breaking, chestplates breaking,
Saddles emptied, horses fleeing.
They fought together for some time
And beat each other for some time,
For Roman men did not withdraw,
But did not push the Britons back.
It was not easy to discern
Who would then get the victory
Until deployment of the column
Led by Bedevere and Kay.
They saw that they made little ground
And that the Romans did quite well.
With anger and with pure displeasure,
Directly with their companies,
They fell among the Roman men
Just where they saw the greatest press.
Bedevere and Kay struck well.
God, what lords in a king's court!
What a seneschal! What a butler!
They served quite well with blades of steel:
This pair of lords vanquished a few.
They had done much and would do more.
They went about breaking the press
And went about smashing it up.
Their great company came behind,
Which angrily did not stop striking.
Many blows were taken and given;
Many men were killed and wounded.
Bedevere struck right in the press;
He did not rest and did not cease.
In other places Kay kept on:
He knocked down many on their heads.
If any had made quick resistance
And had then kept their men together
As soon as Britons ran at them
And came upon this other group,
There would have been great bravery

And they'd have saved themselves from death;
But they were much too passionate
And they desired to strike ahead.
They did not know control at all;
They wished to push the battle forward
And put their trust in their own goodness
And in the masses that they led.
But Britons ran into a line
Commanded by the King of Medes.
His name was Boccus; he was pagan;
He was quite brave and had large masses.
The counts got mixed up with these men
And did not fear their massive numbers.
This was a battle with great blows
And a melée conducted well
Between the Saracens and heathens
And the Normans and the Angevins.
King Boccus wielded a great lance:
A body ailed when he came up!
He brought defeat to the two counts
And struck at Bedevere the worst.
Right through the body with the lance,
He made the hit go all the way.
Bedevere fell; his heart departed;
His soul went into Jesus' care.
Kay found the dead Sir Bedevere.
He wished that he could carry him off;
He held him dear and loved him much.
With all the people that he had,
He made the men from Mede go back
And made them cede the place they held.
But while he waited and delayed
To take the corpse of Bedevere,
The King of Libya came up,
Sertor by name, who was quite praised.
He had a mob of heathen men
Whom he had from the land he ruled.
He gave Sir Kay a mortal wound
And killed a lot of Kay's own men.
He wounded lots and struck down lots,
But Kay retained the body well.

A troop of his surviving men
Came around him to protect him.
They bore him to the golden dragon
Without permission of the Romans.
  Bedevere's nephew Hyrelgas
Always loved his uncle much;
He took enough of friends and kin
To come up with three hundred men
With helmets, haubergeons, and swords
On horses that were strong and swift.
He lined them up into formation
And said to them: "Come with me now.
I wish to avenge my uncle's death."
He then took off toward the Romans.
He caught sight of the King of Medes;
He recognized his battle flag.
Out of formation he rode striking,
Often giving Arthur's cry
Just like a man out of his senses
Who cannot act with moderation.
He had no fear that he'd be struck
As long as he could avenge his uncle.
The men with him loosened their reins;
With their shields raised, they lowered lances.
They killed a lot and knocked them down.
They rode across the fallen ones.
They came into the lines of the king,
The king who had killed Bedevere.
Using the strength of the good horses
And showing the anger of good lords,
They went turning both right and left,
And Hyrelgas went leading them.
They kept on going to the banner
Where they encountered Boccas the King.
Hyrelgas had seen him well
And turned his horse in his direction.
He struggled forward through the press
And reached the top of Boccus' head.
Strong was the lord; great was the blow;
The sword was hard and it was biting.
It pierced the helmet and destroyed it;

The throat guard of the hauberk failed:
He cut him right down to the shoulders.
The heart burst open; the soul took leave;
And Hyrelgas stuck out his arm
To keep the corpse from falling down.
He dragged the corpse in back of him;
He held it upside down from horseback;
In back of him he dragged the corpse;
It never cried or shouted out.
The knight was full of ire and anger;
The horse was full of energy.
He then came back among his people
And was not struck by Roman or pagan.
The press departed and broke up;
Companies made way for him.
He bore the corpse up to his uncle
And chopped it up all into pieces
And said to his companions then:
"Come," he said, "you barons' sons!
Let's go and kill these Romans now,
These no-good tramps, these sons of whores.
They've led into this country here
People without belief in God
Who have no faith at all in God,
To kill both us and our good friends.
Let's go, let's kill these heathen men
And let's kill too these Christian men
Who've made alliance with the heathens
To wipe out Christianity.
Come and test your manly strength!"
    One saw them take the field again.
Then you'd have heard the shouts and cries,
And you'd have seen the massive blows,
Swords and helmets flashing brightly,
And fire a-flying from the steel.
Guitard, the Duke of Poitier,
Did not at all ride like a coward.
He held the fief before him well.
He came against the African king.
The one struck fiercely on the other;
The King of Africa fell, however,

And forward passed the count from there,
Killing Africans and Moors.
Holdin, who was the Duke of Flanders
And Lord of Lens and Brussels too,
Turned against the company
Of Ali Fatima, King of Spain.
They fought against each other there,
And each one struck upon the other
Till Ali Fatima and Count Holdin
Were both subjected to their deaths.
Lygier, who was the Count of Boulogne,
Attacked the King of Babylon.
I can't say who struck on the best,
But each one slugged upon the other:
Dead was the count; dead was the king.
Three other counts were also dead:
Balluc and Cursal and Urgent too.
Each of the three led massive forces.
Urgent was the Lord of Bath,
And Balluc was the Count of Wiltshire;
Cursal was the Count of Chester,
Who marched in consort with the Welsh.
These men were killed in little time;
They were run over on both sides.
The people these men had to lead
And who rushed after their battle flags,
Came on, breaking into the line
Where Walwain went about as leader
And Hoel with him, his companion;
No lords have ever been their equals.
Never after this time had passed
Has there been such a pair of lords
In goodness or in courtesy
Or in their fame for chivalry.
The men who came from Brittany
Followed Hoel, their own lord.
Their company was so fierce there
And was so hardy in its manner
That it feared neither press nor mob.
They went around; they pierced through all.
The men who formerly chased their men

And struck them down in massive crowds
Were made to turn around at once
As numbers of them fell to death.
With the great blows the two were giving
And with the people they were leading,
They went from there up to the standard
That had a golden eagle on it.
There they found the emperor
And the flower of his baronage.
With him there were the noble men
And the good knights who came from Rome.
You would have seen a mortal battle.
You'll never see the like, I think.
Kymar, the Count of Tréguier,
Was in the company of Hoel.
He was a very noble lord;
He did great damage to the Romans.
A Roman man on foot, however,
Stabbed him dead right with his spear.
Two thousand Britons died with him,
Outside of his three noble friends.
One of the three was named Jaguz,
Who had come up from Bodloän;
Richomarcus was the second;
And Sir Boclovius was the third.
There was no one within their ranks
Who had their valor or their worth.
They could have been both counts and kings;
Forever after, so I believe,
There has been talk about their prowess.
For their endurance they were great.
They made attack upon the Romans;
No one came among their hands
Whose life did not come to its end:
It was with lance; it was with sword.
Into the guard of the emperor
They fought their way ahead alone,
And Romans put a stop to them
And killed all three at the same time.

Full of anger and of rage
Were Hoel and his cousin Walwain

When they observed the massive slaughter
That Romans brought upon them there.
To bring harm to their enemies
And get revenge for their companions,
They went among them just like lions,
Just like beasts put into passion.
They killed and devastated Romans,
They split them up with blows and slashes.
The Romans strongly made resistance:
They got and gave a lot of blows;
Well they held and well were held;
Well they struck and well were struck;
Well they slugged and well were slugged;
Well they knocked and well were knocked.
Walwain was so very angry
He never stopped giving them blows.
His strength was always nice and fresh;
He never let his hand relax.
He fiercely flew, pursuing Romans;
He fiercely forced his way along
Until he found the emperor
And had a fight with him himself.
He went so far and did so much
And pushed and dragged himself so much
That he had found the emperor.
Each one recognized the other.
The emperor looked straight at Walwain,
And Walwain knew just who he was.
They hit each other with great strength;
They had great strength; they did not fall.
The emperor was big and strong,
Young and hardy, very forceful,
Ingenious and very skillful.
He had great joy and happiness
To have a fight with Walwain then,
Who had such great renown and fame.
If he emerged alive from this,
He thought he'd boast of it in Rome.
They raised their arms and lifted their shields;
With wondrous strokes, they grieved each other.
They often hurt and pushed each other

And touched each other many times.
Each one fiercely sought the other,
And each one fiercely struck the other.
Portions of the shields flew off,
And sparks were flying from the steel.
They struck above; they struck below.
In bravery the two were equal.
If they had held the field alone,
The end of one would soon have come.
The Romans were recovering
And drawing to the golden eagle.
They rescued then the emperor;
By just a bit they didn't lose him.
They pushed the Britons back from there
And took the field away from them.
Arthur saw his men retreat
And saw the Romans grow emboldened
And saw the field taken from him;
He could not and would not wait longer.
With his companions he came crying:
"What are you doing? Go ahead!
See me here; I'm your protection.
Do not let one escape alive.
I am Arthur who now leads you,
Who does not flee the field for man.
Follow me; I'll make the way.
Make sure that none admits defeat.
Be mindful of how good you are
And how you've conquered many reigns.
I will not flee this field alive:
Either I'll conquer or I'll die!"
    Then you'd have seen Arthur at war,
Killing men, knocking men down,
Breaking hauberks, cracking helmets,
Striking heads and arms and hands.
With very bloody Caliburn,
He slashed to death the man he reached.
I cannot put his blows in writing.
He killed a man each time he struck.
Just like a lion, pressed by hunger,
He killed whatever beast he touched.

The good monarch did all with speed;
He left no man or horse alive.
Whomever he could strike or slash
Could then have need for surgery.
No man recovered from his blows
Even if he barely grazed him.
They fled away from Arthur's path
Like goats that from a wolf made flight.
He recognized the King of Libya,
Sertor his name, a man of wealth.
He cut his head off from his body
And said to him: "May ill befall you,
You who come here bearing arms
To put your blood on Caliburn."
The dead man did not say a word.
Near him, Polidetes stood,
A rich king from Bithynia,
A country off in heathendom.
Arthur found him straight in front
And gave the man a wondrous blow:
He cut the head right off his shoulders;
The head fell down; the trunk remained.
With Arthur's blows and with his words,
The Britons charged upon the Romans,
And they got angry in response:
They drew their swords and shook their lances.
They brought great damage to the Britons;
They stood against their force with force.
Arthur saw them and advanced,
Giving great blows with Caliburn.
The emperor did not delay;
He killed the Britons one by one.
They could not have a proper meeting,
For one could not get to the other.
The press between them was quite great;
The battle was quite difficult.
These men did well; those men did well:

12914 Another anachronism, since in actual late antiquity Bithynia was part of the Christian East Roman Empire.

Soon you'd have seen a thousand dead.
They fiercely fought against each other
And fiercely made each other die.
It was not clear just who would win
Or who'd be dead or be defeated,
When Morvid with his men arrived,
Who'd been among the mountain woods
Where Arthur could have made retreat
If things got awful for his people.
Six thousand six hundred sixty-six
Knights in arms with battle horses,
With shiny helmets, white-hued hauberks,
Lances fixed, on savage mounts—
They came down from the mountaintop;
The Romans caught no sight of them.
They came and struck them from the rear.
The penetrated Roman lines
And split them into separate groups,
Knocking down enough of them.
They trampled on them with their horses
And slaughtered them with blades of steel.
The Romans could not hold their ground,
And they could not retreat then either.
They went off fleeing in great crowds,
Some of them pushing down the others.
The emperor was made to fall,
His body wounded by a lance.
I cannot say who knocked him down;
I cannot say who struck at him.
He had been taken in the press
And in the press he had been killed.
Dead he was found among the dead,
His body wounded by a lance.
The Romans and the Eastern men
And other men both one and all
Fled the field as they were able.
The Britons chased them and destroyed them.
They killed a lot and let them lie;
They had to ride across the dead.
You would have seen the streams of blood,
The slaughtered lying there in pieces,

Good palfreys and good battle mounts
Running loose around the fields.
 Arthur became joyous and happy
That he had curbed the pride of Rome.
He rendered thanks to the King of Glory
Through whom he had the victory.
He had the dead completely searched
To take his men and friends away.
He had some buried in that place
And had some taken to their lands.
Inside the abbeys in that land
He had the greater number buried.
He had the corpse of the emperor
Taken and guarded in great honor.
He sent it on a bier to Rome
And sent word to the Roman people
That from the Britain that he owned
To them he owed no other tribute
And to the man who asked for tribute
He'd send a similar kind of thing.
Kay, who had been mortally wounded,
Was carried to Chinon, his castle.
Sir Kay designed and built Chinon,
Which was named *Kynon* after Kay.
He did not live much longer then;
Quickly enough he passed away.
He was interred within a grove
Inside a hermitage near Chinon.
In Bayeux up in Normandy,
Where he had been the feudal lord,
They made the grave of Bedevere
Outside the southern city gates.
Holdin was carried up to Flanders
And was interred in Thérouanne.
Lygiers was carried to Boulogne.

12995–98 "Wace adds the fake origin of Chinon" (Weiss, *Roman de Brut*, 327, n. 1).

XIII. The Great Destruction

Arthur, who stayed in Burgundy,
Spent all the winter in that place.
He took the cities and made peace.
He wished to pass Montjoie in summer
And wanted to go down to Rome,
But Modred turned the king around.
God, how shameful! God, how vile!
He was King Arthur's sister's son,
His nephew, who was left as regent.
King Arthur gave him the whole realm
And ordered him to guard it all.
But Modred wished to take it all
And keep it all for his own use.
He got the homage of the barons
With hostages from all their castles.
After this great felony,
Modred did another evil,
For in the face of Christian law,
He took the king's wife to his bed;
The woman of his lord and uncle
He took just like a traitor would.
Arthur heard and knew the truth
That Modred did not bear him faith:
He had his land; he took his wife.
He could not thank him for such service.
He had his men take leave of Hoel
And left him France and Burgundy

13013–34 Wulf ("Wace's Guenevere") has pointed out that Wace devotes more space to Modred's treason than Geoffrey does: Geoffrey's concerns are political; Wace emphasizes Modred's lack of good faith. See also note to lines 11173–84.

And asked him to defend it all
And to make peace in every part.
He would return to Britain then;
He'd take his island men with him
And take his vengeance out on Modred,
Who had his kingdom and his wife.
He little valued all his conquests
If he lost Britain, his own fief.
He'd rather give up taking Rome
Than suffer the loss of his own land.
He would return in a short time,
And he would go to Rome, he said.
Thus Arthur came ashore at Sandwich,
Bemoaning Modred's perjury,
Which turned him from his greatest conquest.
He got his fleet to Sandwich quickly.
    Modred knew of Arthur's return.
He had no wishes to make peace.
From Saxony he summoned Childric,
A duke who brought along with him
Eight hundred well outfitted ships
Completely loaded up with knights.
And Modred made a grant to them
And put into their legacies—
Both for their help and for their force—
The land between the Humber and Scotland
And land in Kent that Hengist got
When Vortigern received his daughter.
When Modred had his men together,
It was a grand and handsome group.
With all the people who were heathen
And all the people who were Christian,
He had with hauberks and with horses
Sixty thousand fighting knights.
    Secure, he thought he'd wait on Arthur;
He thought he'd keep him from the ports.
He did not wish to quit his throne
Or seek the peace or make repentance;
He knew himself to be so guilty
That seeking peace would be quite stupid.
Arthur had his ships embark;

He led a number unknown to me.
At Richborough he wished to land
And asked his ships to turn that way,
But well before he came ashore,
Modred had come against him there
Without delay with all his men
Who were with him in battle lines.
The men on vessels tried to land;
The men on land forced them right back.
They often struggled on both sides:
They drew back arrows, launched off spears;
They pierced stomachs and chests and heads
And feared their eyes might get stuck through.
The men on ships had to attend
To guiding them onto the land.
They could not strike or seek protection;
Many a dead man lay in the sea.
They often fell; they often died;
"Traitors" they called the ones on land.
To get the ships unloaded there,
Arthur lost a lot of men:
Many a body was struck down.
His nephew Walwain was killed there.
Arthur sorrowed much for him,
For he loved no man quite so much.
Angusel was also killed,
Who was the leader of the Scots.
Many others were killed there
About whom Arthur moaned and sorrowed.
As soon as they were on the sand,
Arthur behaved like nothing happened;
And after they were on the land
And on the plain on equal footing,
Modred could not manage there
And neither could the horde he led.
Modred's men were cultivated,
Raised in times of peace and rest;
They knew not how to seek for cover
Or how to turn or how to strike
As Arthur's men knew how to do,
Who were raised up in times of war.

Arthur and his men struck there
And gave them service with their swords.
They killed by twenties and by hundreds;
They killed a lot; they caught a lot.
The great slaughter would have been greater
Had evening not prevented it.
The day failed and the night came on.
Arthur stopped and restrained his men.
Modred's people fled away.
Do you suppose one led the other?
None used another battle plan:
Each thought that he would save himself.
Modred fled away at night,
Seeking a fort where he'd be safe.
He thought he'd stay in London then,
But men there would not let him in.
He went beyond the Thames and London;
Winchester was the place he stopped.
He got some lodging in the city;
He got his men and friends together.
He got the pledges and the oaths
Of citizens, without consent,
To use their power to maintain him
And bear him peace and also faith.
Arthur had no care to rest
And had great hatred for this Modred.
He sorrowed much for Angusel
And Walwain, both of whom he lost.
Great was the sorrow for his nephew;
I don't know where he put the body.
He was so angry and worked up
At Modred he could kill the man.
He went to Winchester after him,
Summoning men from everywhere.
He wanted to besiege the city
And set his people all around it.
When Modred saw the host of Arthur,
Which closed the city in a siege,
He acted as if he would fight
And as if he desired to fight;
For if he was besieged for long,

He would be taken in the end;
And if he could be captured, then
He'd not escape alive from Arthur.
He had all of his men assemble
And take their weapons and their armor;
He had them put into formation
To go outside to join the fight.
When they had gone outside like this,
All of the host came running up.
At once a lot of blows were given,
Many killed and many wounded.
Misfortune fell upon this Modred;
His people were not adequate.
But he then thought he'd save himself;
He had done wrong and feared the king.
All of his private guards and cronies
And those whom Arthur hated most
He got together secretly
And let the others go on fighting.
To Southampton he took a path;
He did not stop till he reached sand.
He got a captain and some seamen
With promises and with some cash.
He had himself launched out to sea
So Arthur could not get to him.
To Cornwall they conducted him.
He feared the king and gladly fled.
Arthur put Winchester under siege;
He conquered the folk and took the town.
To Ywain, the son of Urien,
Who stood quite high within the court,
He gave the legacy of Scotland;
And Ywain did him homage for it.
He'd been the nephew of Angusel
And claimed it by inheritance,
For that man had no son or wife
Who'd have the realm instead of Ywain.
Ywain's valor was very great.
He got great honor and great fame
In the hard fights and in the war
That Modred started up in England.

The queen had learned and she had heard
That Modred had been fleeing often.
He could not hold against the king
And did not dare to stay the field.
She spent her time in Everwic;
She was in thought and was in sadness;
She thought about the villainy
And was ashamed of Modred then.
She had brought shame to the good king,
And she had loved his nephew Modred.
She'd married him despite the law,
And she was very vile to do so.
She much preferred to die than live.
She was quite sad; she was quite pensive.
She fled away to Kaerleon
And went into an abbey there.
She took the veil there as a nun
And was encloistered in the abbey.
She was not seen and was not heard
And was not found and was not followed,
For the great shame of her misdeeds
Or for the sin she had committed.
Modred still had Cornwall then;
He'd lost the other lands completely.
He sent off pleas by sea and land;
He called the pagans and the Christians;
He called the Irish and the Norse;
He called the Saxons and the Danes;
He called the men who hated Arthur
And who were frightened of his service.
He called the men who had no land,
Who wished to serve to get some land.
He gave and promised and he begged

13201–72 According to Wulf, Guinevere is less independent in Wace's version: she seems "indecisive"; emphasis is put on her emotions; she emerges as "a regretful, repentant sinner" ("Wace's Guenevere," 77). Weiss observes that Wace follows the Vulgate version of Geoffrey here; the change in the order of events is "important, because Guinevere reacts not, as in *HRB*, to Modret's advance on Winchester (i. e., she fears the usurper) but to his defeat and flight (i. e., she guiltily fears Arthur)" (*Roman de Brut*, 331, n. 1). "Wace adds the details of Modred's allies" (333, n. 1).

Just like a man who had to do so.
Arthur was sad and angry too
That he was not avenged on Modred.
He was depressed about this traitor
Who had his land without a fight,
Who drew his people now to Cornwall,
Who struggled to increase their number,
Working to keep these and get more.
Arthur knew and was depressed.
He called for men as far as the Humber;
Great was the host of unknown numbers;
Great were the men that the king had.
He knew just where to look for Modred.
He wished to kill him and destroy him,
This traitor and this perjurer.
Modred did not care to flee:
He thought it best to hazard risk
And open up himself to death
Than to flee from the field so much.
The battle took place close to Camblan
Within the Cornish territory.
It came together through great anger;
And through great anger it was joined;
The work was started through great anger.
Great were the hosts; great was the killing.
I cannot say who did the best
Or say who lost or say who won
Or say who fell or say who stood
Or say who killed or say who died.
The losses on both sides were great;
The plain was covered with the dead
And with the blood of bleeding dying.
The handsome young men perished then
Whom Arthur had raised up so great
And chosen from so many lands;
The Round Table men also died,
Who had such fame throughout the world.
Modred was killed there in the battle
And all his many people too
And all the flower of Arthur's men,
Both the strongest and the best.

Arthur, if the tale's no lie,
Was mortally wounded in the body
And borne away to Avalon
To have his wounds attended to.
Still the Britons wait for him,
And so they talk of him with hope:
From there he'll come; he's still alive.
Master Wace, who made this book,
Wants not to say more of his end
Than Merlin the prophet said of it.
Merlin said—and he was right—
That Arthur's death would be in doubt.
The prophet said the very truth.
It's always been in doubt since then
And will be every day, I think,
If Arthur's dead or if he's living.
He was borne away to Avalon,
In truth, five hundred forty-two
Years after Jesus' Incarnation.
It was a shame he had no children.
To Cador's son, to Constantine,
Who was his cousin out of Cornwall,
He gave his realm and said to him
That he'd be king when he returned.
Modred had two sons: quite large,
Quite proud, and quite presumptuous.
They saw that all the lords were dead;
They saw the massive armies gone;
They saw that Arthur had gone off;
They saw the newly raised-up king.
The Saxons who had been with Modred,
Who from the battle had escaped,
Made an alliance with these two.
They begged and blandished them so much
That they retained them as their soldiers,

13282–90 As part of his devotion to what he considered "historical accuracy," Wace shows some "reluctance to pass judgment on Arthur's expected return. . . . Wace has fulfilled his obligation as historian by revealing this controversy, thereby recording the 'facts' as well as they could be known" (Blacker, *Faces of Time*, 35).

13292 Note here again an explicit date (A.D. 542).

And so they gave them lots of land.
The Saxons took the land's best parts.
Some of the Saxons went to London;
Winchester was the others' choice.
They thus expected to be lords.
But Constantine pursued these men
And did his best to wipe them out.
In Winchester he found one brother;
He cut his head off in a church
Before St. Amphibalus' altar.
See if he sinned or he did wrong.
He then pursued the other brother,
Who learned and heard about his coming.
He went to hide within a church,
But he could get no service from it.
The king had him beheaded there
And had the head fly from the body.
He ruled three years and then was killed;
The sorrow of his friends was great.
To Stonehenge he was carried then
And buried there with all great honor.

Conan, his nephew, ruled thereafter.
Proud he was; he praised himself;
He could not make or maintain peace.
He let his people fight each other.
They fought each other in the cities;
The barons also went to war.
Between himself and his own people,
There was great discord many times.
He fought and captured his own uncle
And killed the two sons of his uncle
Because they were the rightful heirs
And should have therefore had the realm.
For more than four years he was king;
Vortiporus ruled after him.
The Saxons in his time came back
And thought they'd have all of the land.
Many harms they brought the people:
May God confound them for their deeds!
Things stood them well at the beginning;
They brought great troubles to the king,

But he reversed them at the end:
He drafted soldiers, increased his men,
And did not let a group alone
That did not give good hostages.
He then had peace until his death.
Malgo, his nephew, was then king,
A special fan of chivalry
Who spent his life in its pursuit.
He conquered the surrounding isles
And got the homage of the kings.
In beauty and in good behavior
He well surpassed all of his forebears.
He was extremely handsome and noble;
He loved his kinfolks very much
And had largesse to an excess:
He never worried over money.
Malgo held himself in disdain
And in dishonor and in shame
On any day he did not give,
For giving always gave him pleasure.
He had one evil quality,
The one that shames the Sodomites.
I know no other vice in him,
And he did not do other evil.
Cariz then was king of the land,
But lost it all by means of war.
This man was sad and irritable
And hateful to all of his people.
In his time came the great return
Of heathens and of enemies
Whom Gurmund led across the sea.
You well have heard some talk of them,
The men who brought the great destruction
That caused Britain to lose its name.
   Gurmund was rich and powerful
And very valiant physically.

13375 Wace adds the remark on Britain's loss of name (Weiss, *Roman de Brut*, 337, n. 1).

13385 Wace adds the details of Gurmund's history. For details on Wace's sources, see Arnold, *Roman de Brut*, 2:813, and Houck, *Sources*, 288–310.

Brave he was, with a noble heart,
And he was from a noble line.
He was from Africa, son of a king,
And also from the heathen law.
After his father, he could have ruled
And had the kingdom as he pleased,
But he did not desire to have it
And gave it to one of his brothers.
To one of his younger brothers then,
He gave away his land and throne.
He said that he would be no king
Unless he won a realm himself.
He said he'd go to sea to conquer
And be the king in another land.
Merlin prophesied of him
And said he'd be an ocean wolf.
He looked for sailors and for captains
And ships, barges, and flat-topped boats.
One hundred sixty thousand men,
All recognized by face and name,
Not counting mariners and captains,
Not counting servants and the archers,
Gurmund led into his fleet.
(I do not know the count of barges;
He had a lot of ships and people.)
He sailed around a lot of oceans,
Often took islands and beat kings,
And often took and captured lands.
He sailed a long time on the sea,
Conquering kings and conquering lands,
And safely came at last to Ireland:
He took that land without delay.
He was proclaimed the King of Ireland;
He wished to go to England then.
In England there were Saxon men
Who waged a war upon the Britons.
They often had engaged in fights
And often went to war to conquer

13421–28 "Wace adds these details of Saxon claims" (Weiss, *Roman de Brut*, 337, n. 2).

The shire of Kent and Thongchester, Lindsey,
Which Hengist had in earlier times,
And places held by his son Octa,
Who up near Scotland had once thrived.
They often had it all in hand;
They often lost it back again;
They often gave up hostages
And often had to render homage
And recognize the British right
And keep their treaties and their truces.
When they had promised everything,
Rendered homage with hostages,
Their faith was such an evil kind
That when they saw the time and place,
Like when some king would pass away
Or grow enfeebled in his body,
They always started up again
And turned to robbery and pillage.
In Northumberland they remained;
There they returned; there they would go.
Of Gurmund they had heard the talk,
Who was so powerful and brave.
They held the British peace and truce
And meanwhile sent off word to Gurmund.
They gave him much; they promised more;
And then they prayed and then they begged
That he would come to them in Britain
And that he'd free the land for them.
They'd hold it willingly from him
And serve him willingly for it.
They'd give him tribute every year
And recognize him as their lord.
He was heathen, and so were they;
The Britons, though, were Christian men.
They ought to help each other then
And level Christianity.
Since they possessed a common faith,
They ought to have a common king.

13447–62 "Wace invents these messages and emphasizes the paganism in the alliance" (Weiss, *Roman de Brut*, 339, n. 1).

When Gurmund heard what they requested,
With a flotilla he'd prepared
He passed into Northumberland
And had a talk with the Saxon men.
They sealed the covenant they made
With hostages and oaths they swore:
Gurmund would obtain the land
And then enfeoff it to the Saxons;
The Saxons would be loyal men
And pay their tribute every year.
They took the land then to destroy it.
God, what sorrow and what harm
Befell the noble land and people
From such a level of destruction!
The Africans were leading Saxons,
Burning houses, destroying towns.
The noble knights and peasants too,
The clergymen, the monks and nuns
They struck, they chased and put to death:
They went against the law of God.
You would have seen the land on fire,
The women shamed, the men struck through,
Infants gutted in their cradles,
Possessions seized, plunder taken,
Towers knocked down and towns on fire.
The king was powerless in this
And could not get up men enough
To dare to even look at Gurmund.
He dared not stay upon the plains,
For he could make no brave defense.
The heathen men took all by force;
No priest or cleric there was safe.
The noble bishop and the canons,
The noble abbots and the monks
Had no assurance of their lives.
They left their cells and left their abbeys;
They carried the remains of saints.
Some of them ran right over others.

13499 A sad version here of an earlier joyous procession (10359ff.)

They were in total fear and sorrow;
The one who could flee faster did so.
The poor men fled; the rich men fled;
The townsmen and the farmers fled;
The vassals and the peasants fled,
And a great portion of the lords.
A few put trust in the great towers
When they'd no hope of being rescued.
They emptied rooms, abandoned halls.
Some of them fled away to Wales.
The ones who could and who had ships
Then went across to Brittany.
In Cornwall some remained, the ones
Who could not get themselves a ship.
Gurmund looked for Cariz then,
And Cariz thus maintained his flight
Till he was locked in Cirencester
And Gurmund had besieged the place.
Ysembard came there with him;
He could not find another refuge.
He was the nephew of King Louis,
Who'd chased the man from France already.
He had ejected him from France
And stripped him of his legacy.
Ysembard had a talk with Gurmund.
He became his man, denying God;
He denied God and his belief
To get revenge on France's king.
This fallen man was so deceived
And was so foolish and agnostic,
He threw away the Maker's love
And then took up the heathen rites.
The heathens besieged Cirencester;
The ones inside wished not to be there.
The heathens put pavilions up,
Set up some tents, and built some shelters.
They put the countryside to waste;
They took the food and bore it off.
They closed the city off so tightly
That none of those inside dared leave.
They built rock throwers and siege towers

And made attacks on several occasions.
They dragged their engines to the walls,
But they could make no engine do
What those inside could not undo.
They put together boards and nails,
Redid the peepholes, fixed the gates.
They worked by day; they watched by night.
They fixed the shutters and the walls.
When some were sleeping, some were waking.
They dragged up stones in the defenses
And they were very scared, indeed,
For they had never known or seen
Anything that could protect them.
The ones outside assailed them often
And worked quite hard to capture them,
But these men struggled to resist.
Gurmund could not take them with force.

When he observed he could not take them
And thus would have to waste more time,
He built some castles around the town
With shutters and with peepholes too.
He gave Ysembard one of them,
Who watched the town in front of him.
He gave another to his barons,
Another to the Saxon princes.
For his own use he made a tower
Where he then spent all of his days.
He stayed in there; he lay in there;
He played in there; he slept in there.
The city's people were not cowards:
Often, when they saw occasion,
They made assaults on those outside
And put their lives into great risk.
There often were great shows of strength
And often massive skirmishes.
Often there were captured men,
Often dead and wounded men.

13558 "Wace adds all the details of the siege" (Weiss, *Roman de Brut*, 341, n. 1). See Houck for other examples of cities captured in the same way (*Sources*, 300–10).

But those outside, with their great numbers,
Made them go back into the town.
They chased them and pursued them there,
But they did little to the walls.
For a long time, they made resistance;
For a long time, they held together
And would have held together longer
Without their taking them with force,
If flames had not burned down the town.
They did great evil and great harm,
The ones outside; through a big trick
Not heard of after or before,
They set the city all aflame.
Listen to how they set the fire:
With nets and glue they caught some sparrows
And put some fire in shells of nuts.
They put inside them with the fire
Some wads of flax and tinder wood.
They hung them from the sparrows' feet.
They made thereby a wondrous trick.
At night, when evening had arrived,
They let the sparrows fly away.
They went back home to spend the night
Where they habitually nested
In heaps of wheat and stalks of hay
And underneath the eaves of houses.
The fire found fuel and got quite hot;
The town caught fire and burst into flames.
The Britons saw the town on fire,
With flames flying and houses falling.
They organized to stage a fight,
But their small numbers were defeated.
King Cariz then turned away and ran;
He took his leave in a big rush.
He made his way straight into Wales;
I cannot say what he did then.
In just this way the town was burned,
Totally wrecked and left in cinders.
Because the town was won with sparrows
And so was conquered with the sparrows,
It was the custom after that

And still the custom of the peasants
To name the town after the sparrows
To keep the memory of the marvel
That it was lost because of birds,
The town that had held out so long.
Gurmund destroyed a lot of towns
And lots of castles of great age,
Lots of churches, lots of clergy,
Lots of bishoprics, lots of abbeys,
Which were not afterwards restored
And were not lived in afterwards.
Still there one can see the ruins,
The deserted and the wasted things,
That Gurmund left in many places
To take the Britons' fiefs away.
When he had laid their land to waste,
Burned the towns and taken booty,
He gave the kingdom to the Saxons
As he had sworn that he would do
If he succeeded in its conquest.
He did so and did right by them.
The Saxons then received the land
That they had coveted so long.
For the tribal group to which the first
Ones who received the land belonged,
They called themselves *the English* then
To keep their origins in mind.
And *England* was the word they used
To name the land that they were given.
In French one calls it *Angleterre;*
In English one says *Engleland*:
"Land of the Angles" is what it means,
And that's the explanation for it.
After Brutus came from Troy,
Britain always bore his name
Until the time that I have told you

13643–62 The explanation of how and why names change has been added by Wace (Weiss, *Roman de Brut*, 343, n. 3).

13653 Arnold notes that Wace is mistaken about Brutus' coming from Troy (*Roman de Brut*, 2:814).

In which it lost its name through Gurmund
And got some new inhabitants
And some new kings and some new lords.
These men desired to keep their customs
And not to learn another language.
They changed the names of all the towns
And gave them names in their own language.

XIV. The Britons Lose Britain

The English wished to have a king,
But they could not give their consent
To have one king and only one
And make all subject to one king.
They never would agree on one,
And so they had, by common wish,
Many kings in many lands;
And so they left the land divided.
Many times they went to war,
And many times they came to peace.
And so the ones with greater strength
Would conquer those with lesser strength.
They were this way for a long time
Without a central monarchy.
The churches there were not restored,
And Christian ways were not maintained:
No holy altars dedicated,
No infants brought for christening.
One hundred years or more went by
Without the Christian law and faith.
St. Gregory heard talk of this;
He was the pope then in those days.
He sent St. Augustine to this place;
He loved this noble cleric much.
With him he had in company
Forty highly valued clerics.
He came first to the Isle of Thanet
And went from Thanet into Kent.

13685 For a detailed discussion of the sources for the stories about St. Augustine, see Houck, *Sources*, 261–87.

To Canterbury he went down,
And people there much honored him.
King Ethelbert, who ruled in Kent,
Was of the lineage of Hengist.
He gave an ear to St. Augustine,
Was baptized, and believed in God.
After the king, his company
Was born again and was baptized.
St. Augustine was overjoyed
About the people he converted.
Naming it Holy Trinity,
He built a church within the town.
He went around the land and preached,
Building churches, ordaining priests.
In places he found evil folks
Who wished to make things difficult.
St. Augustine tried really hard
And labored there for quite awhile
Before he could bring them to change
To serve the Lord and love the Lord.
When he had gone through all the land
And had been everywhere around it,
He wandered into Dorchester,
Announcing the law of God Almighty.
To people close to Dorchester
In a nearby place just to the south,
St. Augustine was giving sermons
And telling all about God's law.
They were of such an evil nature,
They did not care about his sermon.
There where the saint gave them the sermon
And spoke to them about their pride,
They hung behind him on his clothes
The tails of stingrays that they had.
They sent him packing with the tails
And followed him for quite awhile.

13693–701 Wace adds Ethelbert's lineage and the information about the building of the church (Weiss, *Roman de Brut*, 345, ns. 1 & 2).

13711ff For more information on the story of the tails, see Houck, *Sources*, 269–75.

And he petitioned our Lord God
To put some sign or souvenir
On them for this disgraceful deed
And for this awful vile behavior.
And so they got one, truthfully,
And so would have one for all time:
For all those men who gave him scorn
And who had hung the tails on him
Were tailed themselves and sported tails
And never could get rid of them.
From here on out, these folks had tails
If they had tailed folks as their parents.
They once were tailed and still are tailed;
They once had tails and still have tails.
They have the tails on their behinds
In memory of all the scorn
They heaped upon the friend of God
Whom they had uglied with the tails.
And when he had escaped from them,
He went into a valley there
Five leagues away from Dorchester
To the northwest between two valleys.
Beneath a mountain there he stopped
With his companions, all tired out.
They stopped themselves to take a rest;
They all were hot; they all were tired.
St. Augustine began to think
How he could not endure much more
The shame that people did to him.
He thought that he would go away.
But God appeared to him, however,
Speaking with clarity to him:
"Hold" he said, "to your objectives;
Conduct yourself with confidence.
You are my servant; you please me,
And what you do well pleases me.
You'll have my aid; I am with you.
What you will ask I'll grant to you.
Heaven's gates are open for you,
And you've been granted your admission.
You'll come upon an open heaven

Where he who serves me well goes in."
St. Augustine looked right at God,
And he received His comfort there.
He looked at Him as long as he could,
For just as long as it pleased God.
He went to where the Lord had been;
He prayed while crying in that place.
He lay down flat and kissed the ground
And genuflected many times.
He stuck a stick then straight into
The place where he had looked at God.
A stream of water rushed from it
And covered up the place completely.
The water surged and streamlets grew;
It made a channel and ran down.
This country from the olden days
Had not been occupied or farmed
Because there was no running water
Or springs that came forth in this place.
St. Augustine gave thanks to God,
And he gave comfort to his friends.
He therefore called the place *Cernel*
Where he had looked upon the Lord.
The name that I have said, *Cernel*,
Means that "I see or saw the Lord."
Scholars well can understand
That *cerno*, *cernis* means "to see"
And *El* in Hebrew means "the Lord."
Cernel is made from these two words.
Cerno and *El* are put together:
One means "I see"; the other "Lord."
One letter is cut off, however,
And taken from the end of *Cerno*;
And so by an abbreviation
The compound word was thus constructed.
The one part's Hebrew; the other's Latin.
St. Augustine observed the spring
And wished when naming it *Cernel*
That it would make us call to mind
That the Lord God was at that place
And that he'd seen Him in that place.

When we now hear this name *Cernel*,
We ought to know and call to mind
That the Lord God appeared right there
And deigned to be there and to speak there.
After the Angles and the Saxons—
First the king and then the lords—
Had been baptized both one and all,
Raised from the font and been anointed,
St. Augustine was full of joy,
For he desired to see them saved.
In lands that Britons still retained
And made defense against the Angles,
He found some monks and found some abbots;
He found some consecrated bishops
And found an archbishop there too,
Who had his see at Kaerleon.
At Bangor there had been an abbey
Established since the ancient times.
The abbot there was Dionot.
He had close to two thousand monks
Divided into seven groups.
In each one of the seven groups
He had close to three hundred monks.
And so they were in seven houses.
They made their living with their hands
And with their labor got their bread.
St. Augustine assembled then
The seven bishops, and he said
To them he was the Roman legate
And was the primate there in England,
And they should logically receive
Their benefices from his hands
And subjugate themselves to him.
They answered: "This we should not do;
We have our own archbishop, now,
Who has his see at Kaerleon
And has authority from Rome.
No one has ever altered this.
Furthermore, we should refuse
Because the Angles are our foes.
They threw us out of our own lands

And took away our fiefs from us.
We are right now and we have been
Christians born from Christian men,
And they are from the heathen people
And have converted recently.
It seems a vile and hateful thing,
And none of us would dare advise
That we be subjects of a man
Who tried to save the very men
Who chased us off our feudal lands
And still remain there on our fiefs.
And all to us are enemies
By whom the Angles are converted
And with whom they have company,
Community, and common bonds."
St. Augustine could get no more
And could not make them understand.
He told all this to Ethelbert,
Who got quite angry over this.
Ethelbert was King of Kent;
He called on Alfred, one of his kin,
Who was the King of Northumberland.
He got the Angles all together,
The friends and all the men they had,
Who were the strongest and the bravest.
They wished to violently destroy
Bangor and Abbot Dionot
And the monks too who came from there
And other clergy in addition
Who bore no reverence for them
And who did not desire to make
Obeisance or subject themselves
Beyond the see of Kaerleon.
They had rejected St. Augustine
To their great shame and villainy.
They ordered knights and peasantry;
In Leicester they assembled then.
They wished to travel through that place
And through that place to enter Wales.
Brochinal then ruled that town;
He was a count of British stock.

He got together what he could
And wished to stand against the Angles,
Who carried on with fierceness, though.
His men were few; he was defeated.
He had great losses in his men,
And so he fled into some woods.
The good hermits and good monks
And also the religious canons
And even those from Bangor too
Had come together as a group
To plead at Leicester with King Alfred
And with the ones who had the power
That on the people and the clergy
They might have and feel some pity.
The people of religious life,
Who did not fly away too well,
Hermits, monks, clerics, and farmers,
The poor folks and the urban folks,
Who'd gone away to hide themselves,
From many places came out front,
With some in bare feet, some in wool,
And sought some mercy from the others.
These men were very cruel and evil
And full of pride just like a lion.
On those on whom they had below them,
They did much worse than had been feared.
God, what suffering! God, what sin!
On them they had no greater pity
Than hungry wolves on flocks of sheep.
They slaughtered many of them there.
They took two thousand and two hundred
And cut their heads off, murdering them.
No monk or cleric made resistance;
They made confessors into martyrs.
They wished to go to Bangor then
To waste the town and kill the people.
The British and the Welsh who heard it
Assembled many men to fight them.
There were three barons in the land
Who were the British overlords.
They were the lords of other men,

For they were stronger and were better. 13932
Bledric of Cornwall was one lord,
Who had control of Devonshire.
There where the Esse's waters flow
From the spring where it surges up 13936
Down to the sea where it descends,
The Britons held on for a while.
But Athelstan when he was king
Pushed them back beyond the Thames. 13940
Cadwan was king of Northern Wales;
And Margadud, of Southern Wales.
All was theirs up to the Severn,
Which ran quite close to Malvern Hill. 13944
But Athelstan distressed them so
That he pushed them beyond the Wey.
They led both knights and peasantry,
The ones who were the lords of others. 13948
Bledric, Cadwan, and Margadud,
With lots of anger, lots of strength,
Attacked the Angles and the Saxons,
Who fiercely welcomed them in turn. 13952
But Alfred was soon wounded there
And turned to flee out of the field,
But wondrous numbers there were killed
Of his own people and his friends. 13956
Within this battle there was killed
Bledric of Cornwall, who was count.
The Britons were assembled then;
Away to Leicester they did go. 13960
Cadwan, who was both wise and brave,
Was made the king by common choice.
He called on all and summoned all
The servants, knights, and barons too. 13964
The Angles whom the counts retained
And who acknowledged Cadwan king,
Completely came beneath his mercy,
And so they came to be his men. 13968
He said that he would cross the Humber
If fiercer folks did not prevent him.
He would destroy Northumberland
And chase the people all away. 13972

If Alfred the king waited for him
And did not keep him back with force,
He'd take him in the field or kill him
Or take his land while he was living.
Alfred heard that he was coming
And that he menaced him with threats.
He called his friends; he called his kin;
He called his people and his nobles;
He called the Angles, called the Saxons
To wage a war against the Britons.
Great were the numbers on both sides,
Both the brave ones and the cowards.
The noble people of the land,
Who had good friends on either side,
Observed the evil that would come
And the great loss that there would be
If these two kings engaged in war,
Who were in grievous mutual hate.
They went to one king, then the other,
And gave advice and spoke so much
They made the kings come to agreement
And seal the peace with hostages.
They made a deal about the land,
And each one had his part of it
And each one bore the other trust.
Alfred's part was north of the Humber;
Cadwan's part was south of the Humber.
And so the land was held by both,
And they had then such mutual love
That there could never be a greater.
They put the things they owned in common:
All would be for two or one.
They could not have a greater love.
They married and they had some children;
They had two children at one time;
The son of Alfred was called Edwin;
And Cadwan's was called Chadwalein.
The two were born within one year.
To keep the fathers' love maintained
And make the sons have mutual love,
The sons were always kept together,

Nursed together, taught together.
The shoes they wore were just alike;
The clothes they wore were just alike;
When they could ride their horses well,
Bear their shields, control their lances,
Spur and hold their horses well,
Draw their swords and swing them down,
They were together dubbed as knights,
In Armorica, it seems to me.
Cadwan had them taken there
And had them given weapons there.
The relatives who lived down there
Were Britons who were born in Britain.
After the fathers met their ends
And passed beyond the earthly veil,
Each son then ruled his legacy.
They were then friends for two whole years,
And for two years they kept the love
That their two fathers had once had.
Edwin ruled from the Humber north;
Chadwalein, from the Humber south.
But Chadwalein had many more
Fortresses and towns and cities
Than Edwin had as king up there.
He had himself crowned when he wished.
He held great feasts and held great courts
And acted with nobility.
Edwin asked him and requested
That he consent and authorize
That he be able to be blessed,
Be consecrated, and be crowned
North of the Humber where he lived
Just as he was south of the Humber.
The Briton said he'd take advice
And speak of it among his men,
And he would quickly answer him
With what advice his people gave.
Beside the waters of the Douglas
They'd meet together at a ford
To make provisions for this thing
So that it could come off more nicely.

They were on the two riverbanks
And had to talk through messengers.
All through this the messengers,
The oldest and the wisest men,
Passed from one king to the other
And bore the counsels back and forth.
King Chadwalein then settled down;
He was quite tired and fell asleep.
His nephew Brian held his head,
Who was enraged and feeling sad
That Edwin had requested something
That never had occurred before.
From anxiousness and bitterness
He sighed from deep within himself.
He often sighed and puffed in anger;
The tears ran from his eyes in streams.
The head of the king got wet this way;
And so the king awakened then.
He raised his hand up to his head;
He found his face sprinkled with water.
He then began to look at Brian,
And Brian burst right out in sobs.
"Brian," said the king, "what's wrong?
Why do you cry? What's wrong with you?"
"Sire," he said, "I'll tell you now:
I am enraged and have great pain
That in our time and through ourselves—
And this is why I'm sad and angry—
This land of ours has lost its honor.
Great shame has now come down on us.
You wish to have two kings with crowns.
You could come to an evil end
Because a single king could rule,
And then a man would serve one king."
Because of that which Brian said,
The king agreed that he'd done wrong.
He fiercely sent to Edwin the king
Word he would do no such thing,
Because the lords advised against it.
They said it was not logical,
Not rightful and not legal for

What should belong to just one king
To be split up as gifts for two
So each of them should wear a crown.
He did not wish to split the realm
And lower thus his dignity.
Edwin, who was full of pride,
Angrily replied to him
That he would never seek permission:
Without permission he'd be crowned
And have the franchise in his realm
Just like the one he had in his.
King Chadwalein said in this case
That he'd remove that very crown
And with it beat him on the head.
The other said he had no fear.
And so they were split up by evil,
And each one then despised the other.
Each found displeasure in the other;
Each one defied the other one.
Edwin was furious and angry;
He was quite puffed up in his pride.
He said that what he asked for once
Would be removed as pillage shortly.
One saw the war develop then
And saw the land then laid to waste.
They fought together very often;
They captured lands; they pillaged towns.
King Chadwalein raised a great force.
He came to the Humber and he crossed it;
He wished to waste Northumberland
And disinherit Edwin there.
Edwin was a man of courage;
He had no will to flee from harm.
He wished to guard his land and person.
He did not want a truce or peace.
He rode against King Chadwalein,
And so he won and made him flee.
King Chadwalein desired to leave
And wished to go back to his lands,
But Edwin came in front of him,
Cut off his route, and held it then;

So Chadwalein fled somewhere else.
Through forests and up winding roads,
He went to Scotland in his flight.
Edwin sought him from behind.
Great pain and trouble grew for him;
He had to cross to Ireland then.
The King of Ireland welcomed him
And honored him just as he should have.
And Edwin, who was left behind,
When he could not get to the ships,
Then seized the realm of Chadwalein,
Destroyed the castles, knocked down towers,
Captured lands and wasted cities,
Held men for ransom, pillaged towns.
Brian's sister was shown to him;
In Worcester he discovered her
And had her brought to Everwic
And guarded in his chamber there.
I do not know who brought to him
Pellis, a scholar born in Spain,
Who was a very learned man,
An expert in astronomy.
Through the course of shining stars
And through the flights of flying birds,
He could foresee coming events
Of things in which he was involved.
King Chadwalein could do no thing—
Assemble ships or call up men—
That the diviner could not see
And Edwin would not therefore know.
He often got a fleet prepared
And often had a lot of men;
He often put to sea by sail;
He often wished to come to port;
But Edwin always got there first
And kept the other off the land.
For the diviner saw it all;
He knew just where and when he'd come.
King Chadwalein felt bitterness
Because he was turned back so much.
Out of his land there followed him

Servants, relatives, and friends.
Most of them had left behind
Their legacies for love of him.
He said he'd go to Brittany
And speak to Solomon the King.
They both were from one family,
And often he'd invited him,
And he was very powerful.
Night and day, morning and evening,
They ran so much and sailed so much
That they came to the Isle of Guernsey,
An island lying toward the south.
The reason was that in that place
There was no other land with people
Between Cornwall and Brittany.
They had just gotten to the island
When Chadwalein became quite sick.
He suffered from an ague fever
That made him sweat with frequency.
He had cravings for venison;
He could not eat another meat.
The king appealed to Brian then;
He begged him and commanded him
To find him flesh of venison—
He did not care just how he got it.
He'd never make it to recovery
If he did not have venison.
Brian was anxious for the king
And was desirous of his cure.
He called for soldiers and for squires;
He had them lead out hounds and brachets.
They sought the valleys and the plains;
They sought the cliffs and mountains too.
All around the land they went;
They did not find a buck or doe
Or fallow deer or hare or roe.
Thus Brian felt a lot of sorrow.
When he saw that his uncle'd die
Because he had no venison
(And he did not know where to find some),
He cut a steak out of his thigh

And had it charred and roasted well.
He had it offered to his uncle.
I don't know if the king enjoyed it,
But he was cured and passed the crisis.
And when he could get out of bed,
He had his ships put out to sea
And came ashore at Kidaleta,
Which was located at that time
Between the seashore and Dinan.
The ruins there can still be observed.
One king received the other king
With all the honor that could be.
He made his lodging and his stay
With him an honor of some greatness;
And to recover all his lands—
If he desired to go at Edwin—
He'd help his cause quite readily
With his possessions and his men.
They were together all the winter;
All the winter they passed the time.
In the meantime they got some ships,
Requested help, accepted help.
They sent off Brian into England
Dressed up in clothes that would disguise him
So that he could kill the diviner,
Who could predict where they would be.
They held counsel and were advised
That while the wizard was alive
They'd never make it into England
Or come ashore within the land.
He could predict the time and port
To which the mariners would go
If he desired to take the trouble.
Brian took on this great adventure.
At Barfleur Brian went to sea
And at Southampton came ashore.
He changed his clothes for very bad ones
And dressed himself in ragged clothes.

14221–22 "Wace's doubts reduce the impact of this distasteful incident" (Weiss, *Roman de Brut*, 357, n. 2).

He made himself an iron pike
Just like a pilgrim's walking stick;
The iron was quite long and sharp.
It was quite cutting and well honed.
Brian adopted the disguise
Of someone on a pilgrimage.
In view of folks he went disguised;
He looked like a poor penitent.
He walked while leaning on the staff,
From one time to the other limping.
He sought the court and asked around
And found the king at Everwic.
Among the poor he made his way;
Among the poor he hid himself.
Among the burdened he was burdened
Just like a needy beggar man.
His sister came out of a room,
And Brian recognized her well.
He held a basin in his hands;
He asked for water from the queen.
Brian moved along his way
So she would see and recognize him.
She recognized her brother well,
But with his eyes he gave her signs
That she should not make any semblance
That he belonged to her at all.
He kissed her and she kissed him back;
The two of them cried quite enough.
They drew themselves outside the crowd
So that no man or woman watched them.
She told him all the situation
And pointed Pellis out to him,
Pellis, the wizard, just arriving;
By chance he had just come outside.
He often came; he often went;
He passed among the groups of poor.
Brian parted from his sister,
Who was quite frightened for his sake.
He moved into the wizard's path,
Which passed among the begging people.
He bade his time and waited till

The wizard passed right next to him.
With the great staff of iron he held,
He gave him such a heavy stab
He pierced him there right through the body.
He hurt him badly, and he fell:
He never said a yes or no.
Brian left his staff right there.
Without the staff, all secretly,
He drew himself among the poor,
And so he was not given notice,
Recognition or suspicion.
He stayed in hiding for the day,
Moving around among the poor.
He left the city in the night
All quietly and privily.
He went some distance from the land.
He traveled both by night and day
And came to Exeter on the Esse.
One saw a massive crowd around him
Of Britons and of Cornish men,
Of noble knights and burgesses.
They asked where he was from and bound,
What he desired, sought, said, and did.
They asked where Chadwalein was now
And why he made such long delay
And if he would return in truth
And ever rule the land again.
"Yes," said Brian, "soon enough
You'll see him come with such a host
That Edwin will not wait for him
And won't remain within the realm.
Often for our love of the king,
He has destroyed and damaged us.
Construct castles and ready towers,
For shortly help will come to you."
Brian made his speech to Britons;
He got consent from many men.
He took and captured Exeter;
He wished to hold and make it ready.
By letter he informed his uncle
What he had done and how he'd done it.

He sent him all the news of this
And asked the king for ships and vessels.
King Solomon, his relative,
Gave him two thousand knights in arms,
(Both of his own and of his neighbors),
Not counting captains and their sailors.
They went to Totnes under sail;
The peasants thus were overjoyed.
King Edwin, though, was sorrowful
About the wizard he had lost
And Exeter that Brian had
Captured and now was there inside it.
He sent Penda, the King of Mercia,
Which was a part of England then,
With massive military forces
To guard the country and the ports
And lay a siege on Exeter
If he could do nothing else.
Penda laid siege on Exeter;
He wished to go inside but couldn't.
Inside was Brian, who kept it till
King Chadwalein made his arrival.
To Totnes he'd already come,
And he had left his ships for land.
The king inquired about the news,
And he was told the news about
The siege on Brian, his own nephew,
Who would be hanged if he were taken.
The king was anxious over Brian,
And he was eager for his rescue;
So with his vassals he rode through
The woods, the plains, the hills, and vales
And came quite quickly to the siege.
God, what joy was Brian's then!
The men of Chadwalein were rich
And were outfitted richly too.
He put his men into four groups
And then attacked the men in siege.
Many there were seized or killed,
Among the richest and the strongest.
Penda himself was captured there:

He was not wounded, was not killed.
He was held well and guarded well;
He could not be delivered till
He rendered homage to the king
And took his legacy from him.
He made his feudal ties with him;
And to make ties between them firm
And to make love between them firm,
King Chadwalein received a sister
Whom Penda had, a very pretty,
Noble, and courteous young woman.
Chadwalein called the Britons there;
He praised them much and thanked them much
For the travail and for the hate
That they had suffered for his love.
He then went wasting through the land
There where he knew his enemies were.
He crossed the waters of the Humber,
Wasted castles and pillaged towns.
Edwin called on all the kings—
The Saxon and the English kings
(Many who claimed to be a king
Regarded counties as their kingdoms).
Edwin had them all with him
Both through homage and through faith.
He rode against King Chadwalein,
Who did not fear him in the least.
There in a field that one called Hedfield
The battle and the fight ensued
Between Edwin and Chadwalein.
There was much mortal hate between them.
Edwin died and his son did too;
Offrid was the name of the son.
The King of Orkney also died,
Who had come there to give them help.
Enough of the others there were taken;
Many were killed; many were wounded.
Great was the killing and the taking,
And thereby Chadwalein got vengeance.

14390 Detail added by Wace (Weiss, *Roman de Brut*, 361, n. 2).

He wiped out those and all their kin
Who'd been against him in this thing.
He had the women and children killed,
Even the little nursing ones.
He could not make a special case
For age or worth, beauty or birth.
From Edwin there remained an heir
Who ruled his realm and his estates.
He was called Offric at his baptism.
But Chadwalein got his domain:
He took up war and strife with him
And killed him and a pair of nephews
Because they held a part of the realm
And they would be his heirs thereafter.
He did not stop when he could find
One who could claim inheritance.
Oswald then, a noble good
At guarding Christianity,
A noble man with generous heart,
Inherited the realm thereafter.
But Chadwalein brought war on him
And up to Scotland gave him chase.
When he observed he fled so far
And he could not get close to him,
He did not wish to chase him further
And to work all his men so hard.
He gave a portion of his men
To Penda and he asked that he
Chase Oswald and pursue him till
He captured him or got to kill him.
When Oswald learned about this plan,
It pleased him much; he was advised
That he should not take flight from Penda
But should await him if he followed.
He stopped his flight within a field
That has the name of *Heavenfield*.
Heavenfield, an English name,
In French is *Champ Celestiel*.

14435–38 Praise of Oswald added by Wace, "possibly influenced by Bede" (Weiss, *Roman de Brut*, 363, n. 4).

He had a cross raised in the field
And had his people pray to it.
"Adore the Holy Cross," he said.
"Confess your sins and beg forgiveness.
Make repentance for your sins
And seek pardon for your misdeeds.
Make yourself a humble confession
For what might happen afterward.
The men can feel thus more assured,
Both those who'll live and those who'll die."
They did what he commanded them:
Quite humbly on their bended knees
They prayed to God and to His Cross
With humble hearts and simple voices:
They asked Almighty God's forgiveness;
They took their discipline and penance.
They then got ready for a fight,
If anyone might choose to charge them.
Penda came and charged upon them,
But he fared badly in this thing:
He lost the best ones of his people,
And he himself was put to flight.
His heart was proud and full of anger.
He made complaints to Chadwalein.
He said he'd never show him love
And never hold his land from him
Unless he got revenge on Oswald,
Who brought great misery on him.
They called their army when it pleased them
And passed into Northumberland.
They had a fight with Oswald there;
Many were lost on either side.
And Penda came across King Oswald;
He hated him and cut his head off.
Great was the sorrow, great were the losses,
The people killed, the land deserted,
The women widowed, the cities wasted,
The houses emptied, the plunder taken.

Oswi, one of Oswald's brothers,
Took the kingdom of his brother.
The lords accepted him as king

Since they had lost the lord they had.
He saw the people very weakened,
The country very impoverished.
He looked at Chadwalein's great force;
He looked at Chadwalein's great strength;
He saw that he could not resist
If Chadwalein the King invaded.
He'd rather lose his dignity
And gladly take humility
Than take on war with such a man
From whom he could make no defense.
He had a talk with Chadwalein:
He gave him lots of gold and silver;
He put himself into his power,
Became his man, swore oaths to him,
And took his kingdom from his hands;
King Chadwalein increased his fief.
Peace was granted in this fashion
And was protected long this way.
    Oswi had relatives and nephews
Who were quite valiant and quite brave;
And just to get a piece of land,
They started fighting with each other.
But Oswi staged a good defense,
And no one took his land away.
He chased them down across the Humber.
Those relatives went straight to Penda,
A man of strength, and so they asked
And promised him both things and land
If he would keep them and advise them
And go to war for them with Oswi.
Penda said that he dared not
Unless the king gave him permission.
He would not dare commence a war
Or be the first to break the peace,
But if he could then he would ask
King Chadwalein to let him do so.
It happened that one Pentecost

14535–36 A parallel to Arthur's coronation feast at Pentecost (10200ff.)

King Chadwalein held court and feasted.
In London he was crowned the king
And had his barons all attend.
Oswi was not seen at all,
For he had not come to that place.
I don't know if he couldn't or wouldn't
Or if the king had even asked him.
Penda stood up on his feet.
He then inquired of Chadwalein
How it could be or it should be
That Oswi did not come to court.
All the noble lords were there,
Both the English and the British.
Oswi alone deigned not to serve,
And he deigned not to come to court.
"He has permission," said the king.
"He ought to have it; he lies sick."
Penda said, "That is not so.
You must not know Oswi at all.
He has sent off to Saxony
For men on horseback and on foot.
He asks for men and asks for soldiers.
When he is able and in place,
He wants to wage a massive war.
He can and will not keep the peace.
But if it does not bother you,
I'd like to go and crush his pride.
If I have your permission then,
I'll give him to you dead or alive.
I'll chase him right out of the land."
The king replied, "I'll talk about it."
He then made Penda go outside
And all the English go away.
He kept behind the oldest Britons,
The richest ones and oldest ones.
He then explained the request to them,
The one that Penda had just made.
Near Chadwalein sat Margadud;
He was the Lord of Southern Wales.
"Who cares," he said, "if there begins
And, as I see it, there continues

Deadly ire and deadly hate
(Although it might come to an end)
Between us Britons and the Saxons?
They're always hot to bring us harm.
They'll never love us for one day
Or keep their word or peace with us.
Remember all their felonies;
Remember all their trickery;
Remember all their cruelties;
Remember how they've damaged us.
You often have both sworn and said—
But you have all just let things pass—
That you could always conquer them
And not allow them in this realm.
When you don't dare to wipe them out—
Or you cannot or you will not—
Let one bring harm upon the other
And let them handle the details.
Penda was born among the English,
And all his relatives are English.
Oswi is English just like them.
You'll never have a bit of harm
If one dog skins the other dog,
If one crook brings the other evil.
Let the one strangle the other
And let the one oppress the other."
With Margadud's suggested plan,
All the Britons were at one.
Penda then was called back in;
He was then given full permission
To hurt this Oswi if he could;
King Chadwalein would not complain.
Penda turned away from court,
Very proud and arrogant,
And fought a fearful war with Oswi
And very often damaged him.
And Oswi asked him many times
And begged him from his very heart
To have a truce and peace with him
And not to do him any damage.
Gold and silver, if it pleased him,

And other treasures he would give him.
Penda said that he would not
And that he'd never give him peace.
Oswi was not bad at all:
When he observed that he could not
Get peace or concord or a truce,
He struggled to defend himself.
The anger mounted and increased;
The war increased and got much greater.
One day they came against each other
And fought each other in their ire.
Oswi had great faith in God,
And his belief in him was firm;
And Penda was quite full of pride
And trusted in his massive armies.
But he was crushed and met his death
Along with many of his friends.
Ozfriz, who was his first-born son,
Brought up in Chadwalein's own court,
Asked for and got his legacy,
And so gave Chadwalein his homage.
Chadwalein was an able ruler;
He was a true and righteous king.
Forty-eight years he ruled the land,
Often at peace, often at war.
At London he lay down in sickness.
He ended there; he met death there.
The Britons had great dole for him,
But he could not escape his death.
To keep him long in memory,
They had a copper statue cast:
A noble knight upon a horse
In regal arms and regal clothes.
The royal corpse was put inside it,
And it was placed above a port
In London, facing to the west.
For a long time, it stood right there.

14648ff Late antique legends of metal equestrian statues with bodies inside? cf. Tatlock, *Legendary History of Britain*, 374–75; A. Cameron and J. Herrin, *Constantinople in the Early Eighth Century: The Parastaseis Syntomoi Chronikai* (Leiden: Brill, 1984).

They made a chapel next to it
For St. Martin, quite rich and pretty.
    Chadwalader ruled afterwards,
The dead king's son and Penda's nephew.
Penda's nephew, his sister's son,
He was a king who was well loved.
The wheat crop failed when he was king,
And failure led to shortages,
And shortages brought famine on.
Need was in the town and city.
You well could travel three whole days
And would not find for sale a bit
Of bread or wheat or other food.
The shortages were everywhere.
On fish and on the meat of game,
On venison and roots and tubers,
On leaves and grass the people lived;
They had no other things to eat.
And with these most unfortunate things,
Another just as hard appeared.
There was a plague among the people
From rotten air and rotten wind.
In houses and fields and in the roads
And in the markets and the highways,
They fell while eating, walking, talking;
They died before they could lie down.
The fathers died; the infants died;
The barons died; the servants died.
The husbands died; the women died;
The peasants and the nobles died.
There was no need to mourn a father.
You would have seen a few alive
In hidden places in the wilds.
You've never seen such pain as this.
The insufficient numbers alive
Were not able to bury the dead.
The ones who should have buried the dead

14661ff Expanded details of the plague are added by Wace (Weiss, *Roman de Brut*, 369, n. 3).

Had need of burial with the dead.
Those who could flee then fled away
And threw away their fiefs and houses
As much as for the lack of wheat
As for the great mortality.
He had despair for his own house
Who saw his neighbor's house on fire.
Chadwalader, who was the king,
Who should have stayed to guard the land,
Went to Rennes in Brittany
To King Alain, who loved him much.
He'd been the nephew of Solomon,
Who loved his father very much.
He welcomed him with joyousness
And gave him rich accommodations.

England was impoverished then.
The wheat crop failed; the people died.
Most of the land was left deserted,
For there was no one there to work it.
Eleven years and more it lay
In waste devoid of laborers.
Whatever Britons that there were
Stayed in the mountains and the forests.
The Englishmen who were still there,
The ones who had escaped the famine
And many who were born much later,
Survived the best way that they knew.
Both to fix the cities up
And to do labor on the land,
They sent word off to Saxony,
There where their ancestors were born,
That with their wives and with their children,
That with their households and their servants
They all should come as an armed force.
They would have land as they desired.
They would have good arable land.
They needed nothing more than men.
These men then came in massive numbers,
In massive hordes, at many times.
They set up camps throughout the land.
They grew and multiplied a lot.

They found no one who would disturb them
Or who'd refuse the land to them.
They often came in massive groups.
They held the customs and the laws
Their forefathers had held before
There in the land from which they'd come.
The names, the language, and the laws
They wished to keep as they received them.
They said *chester* instead of *kaer*;
And they said *shire* instead of *suiz*;
And they said *town* instead of *tref*.
Map is Welsh; English is *son*.
In French the Welsh *kaer* is "city,"
Map, "fiz"; *tref*, "vile"; *suiz*, "cunté."
But some say French *cuntrée*
Means just what *suiz* does in Welsh;
And some folks say a *shire* in English
Can mean what *suiz* does in Welsh.
Among the Welsh there still endures
The language coming straight from British.
The counties and the baronies,
The countries and the earldoms—
They keep them there in their divisions
Just as the Britons drew them out.
Athelstan was then the king.
He was the first one of the English
Who had all England in his power
Except for just Cornwall and Wales.
He was anointed first and blessed,
And he was crowned the very first.
Many say he was a bastard.
His father was Edward the King,
Who went to Rome to say his prayers
And granted at St. Peter's there
And made his offering at the altar

14739–52 The explanation of words from Welsh and English is one of Wace's "characteristic comments" (Weiss, *Roman de Brut*, 371, n. 1).

14757ff Wace is responsible for the notes about "Edward's gift of the silver penny" and Yne as the "original institutor of Peter's Pence" (Weiss, *Roman de Brut*, 371, n. 4). See also Houck, *Sources*, 252–53.

Of a silver penny every year
From every man who had a house
And lived within his royal sway.
The first to ever make this gift
Was his forebear, a man called Yng.
The later heirs maintained the gift;
They rendered it unto the pope.

Chadwalader wished to return
And wanted to maintain his land.
When he learned it was populated
And the plague now had gone away,
He wished to go back to his land.
He made his travel preparations;
He then asked God with all his heart
To make it very clear to him
If his return might give Him pleasure,
For he desired to do His pleasure.
A voice that was divine then told him
To leave this trip and take another.
He should not go to England then;
He should go to the Pope of Rome.
With sins of his forgiven there,
He would then go among the blessed.
The English should own Britain now;
Britain would never be recovered
Until the time of prophecy
That Merlin said would come to pass.
These things could never happen, though,
Until that certain time would come
When relics of his very corpse,
Drawn outside of his sepulcher,
Would be transported out of Rome
And be presented there in Britain.
Chadwalader was quite amazed,
And in amazement he was troubled
By this divine announcement that
He heard so openly like this.
To King Alain, who was his friend,
He told what he had heard just then.
Alain then had the closets opened
And had the learned clerks appear.

He had the histories brought out
And had men search and find the proof
That what Chadwalader had said
About the vision that he had
Accorded with the dicts of Merlin
And of Aquilus the good divine
And with what Sybil had recorded.
Chadwalader did nothing then;
He left his navy and his men.
He called to Yvor and to Yni.
Yvor was his legal son;
Yni, his nephew, his sister's son.
"To Wales," he said, "you will now go,
And you will be the lords of Britons
So that through lack of noble lords
The Britons don't become dishonored."
They did what he commanded them,
And he made travel preparations.
He went to St. Sergius, the pope,
Who cherished him and honored him.
He made confession of his sins
And did his penance afterwards.
He hardly had arrived in Rome
When he fell into sickness there.
He was quite sick; he had to die.
Eleven days before May came,
He died the nineteenth day of April,
Freed from his earthly exile here,
One less than seven hundred years
Since Christ took flesh in Holy Mary.
The corpse was laid out very nicely
And put among the bodies of saints.
His soul flew up to Paradise,
Where we with him may someday sit.

14814 In reference to the Auguries of the Eagle in Geoffrey, Tatlock, *Legendary History of Britain*, 44, claims that "here is the first appearance anywhere of this gifted bird at Shaftesbury." Tatlock says that Wace and others misunderstood the Latin *aquila* to be the name of a man (*Aquile* in Wace rendered here as *Aquilus*). For more discussion, see Tatlock, 44–45.

14827 Pope Sergius (A.D. 687–701) fits with the date of 699 given in line 14837.

Yvor and Yni crossed the sea
With great numbers of ships and people.
The remnants of the British people,
Whom we refer to as the Welsh,
Who are a way off in the west,
Became the subjects of these men.
They never later had the strength
It took to hold the realm of Logres.
All had moved; all was changed.
All was different and all lacked
The honor, customs, nobleness
And life of those who'd lived before.
Wales had come to be its name
From Duke Gualon, who ruled in Wales,
Or from Galaes, who was the queen
To whom the land was once subjected.
So ends the book of British deeds
And ends the line of noble lords
Who as descendants of King Brutus
Ruled over England a long time.
Master Wacë wrote this book
One thousand one hundred fifty-five
Years after God assumed our flesh
To gain our souls' redemption.

Works Cited

The Arthurian Portion of the Roman de Brut. Trans. Eugene Mason. Toronto: University of Toronto Press, 1996. Available at <http://www.yorku.ca/inpar/Arthurian.html>.

Barron, W. R. J., ed. *The Arthur of the English*. Cardiff: University of Wales Press, 1999.

—. "Geoffrey of Monmouth's *Historia Regum Britanniae*." In *The Arthur of the English*, ed. idem, 11–18.

Baswell, Christopher. *Virgil in Medieval England: Figuring the* Aeneid *from the Twelfth Century to Chaucer*. Cambridge: Cambridge University Press, 1995.

Bennett, Matthew. "Poetry as History? The 'Roman de Rou' of Wace as a Source for the Norman Conquest." In *Proceedings of the Battle Conference 1982*, ed. R. Allen Brown, 21–39. Anglo-Norman Studies 5. Woodbridge: Boydell Press, 1983.

Blacker, Jean. *Faces of Time: Portrayal of the Past in Old French and Latin Historical Narrative of the Anglo-Norman* Regnum. Austin: University of Texas Press, 1994.

—. "'La geste est grande, longue et grieve a translater': History for Henry II." *Romance Quarterly* 37 (1990): 387–96.

—. "History or Romance? Wace's *Roman de Brut* in Insular and Continental Manuscripts." Paper presented at the Annual Meeting of the MLA, Toronto, 27–30 December 1993.

—. "'Ne vuil sun livre translater': Wace's Omission of Merlin's Prophecies from the *Roman de Brut*." In *Anglo-Norman Anniversary Essays*, ed. Ian Short, 49–59. Anglo-Norman Text Society Occasional Publications 2. London: Anglo-Norman Text Society, 1993.

—. "Where Wace Feared to Tread: Latin Commentaries on Merlin's Prophecies in the Reign of Henry II." *Arthuriana* 6 (1996): 36–52.

Blacker-Knight, Jean. "Transformations of a Theme: The Depoliticization of the Arthurian World in the *Roman de Brut*." In *The Arthurian Tradition: Essays in Convergence*, ed. Mary Flowers Braswell and John Bugge, 54–74. Tuscaloosa: University of Alabama Press, 1988.

—. "Wace's Craft and His Audience: Historical Truth, Bias, and Patronage in the *Roman de Rou*." *Kentucky Romance Quarterly* 31 (1984): 355–62.

Blanchet, Marie-Claude. "Arthur chez Wace et Lawman." *Bibliographical Bulletin of the International Arthurian Society* 6 (1954): 108.

Blenner-Hassett, Roland, and F. P. Magoun. "The Italian Campaign of Belin and Brenne in the Bruts of Wace and Lawman." *Philological Quarterly* 21 (1942): 385–90.

Boethius. *The Consolation of Philosophy*. London: Penguin Books, 1969.

Box, J. B. H., and A. D. Deyermond. "Mestre Baqua and the Grail Story." *Revue de Littérature Comparée* 51 (1977): 366–70.

Boutet, Dominique. "La fin des temps arthuriens, du *Roman de Brut* au *Lancelot-Graal*: critique esthétique et critique historique." In *Lancelot-Lanzelet: hier et aujourd'hui*, ed. Danielle Buschinger and Michel Zink, 39–52. Greifswalder Beiträge zum Mittelalter 51; Ser. 3, Tagungsbände und Sammelschriften 29. Greifswald: Reineke, 1995.

Brayer, Edith. "Deux manuscrits du *Roman de Brut* de Wace." In *Studi in onore di Angelo Monteverdi*, ed. Giuseppa Gerardi Marcuzzo, 2 vols., 1: 100–8. Modena: Società Tipografica Editrice Modenese, 1959.

Brewer, Derek. "The Paradox of the Archaic and the Modern in Laȝamon's *Brut*." In *From Anglo-Saxon to Early Middle English: Studies Presented to E. G. Stanley*, ed. Malcolm Godden, Douglas Gray, and Terry Hoad, 188–205. Oxford: Clarendon Press, 1994.

Brosnahan, Leger. "Wace's Use of Proverbs." *Speculum* 39 (1964): 444–73.

Buttry, Dolores. "Contempt or Empathy? Master Wace's Depiction of a Peasant Revolt." *Romance Notes* 37 (1996): 31–38.

Caldwell, Robert. "Geoffrey of Monmouth, Wace, and the Stour." *Modern Language Notes* 69 (1954): 237–39.

—. "Wace's *Brut* and the *Variant Version* of Geoffrey of Monmouth's *Historia Regum Britanniae*." *Bibliographical Bulletin of the International Arthurian Society* 6 (1954): 109.

—. "Wace's *Roman de Brut* and the *Variant Version* of Geoffrey of Monmouth's *Historia Regum Britanniae*." *Speculum* 31 (1956): 675–82.

Cameron, A., and J. Herrin. *Constantinople in the Early Eighth Century: The Parastaseis Syntomoi Chronikai*. Leiden: Brill, 1984.

Carr, Gerald F. "The Prologue to Wace's *Vie de Saint Nicholas*: A Structural Analysis." *Philological Quarterly* 47 (1968): 1–7.

D'Alessandro, Domenico. "*Historia Regum Britanniae* et *Roman de Brut*: Une comparaison formelle." *Medioevo romanzo* 21 (1994): 37–52.

Dean, Ruth J. "*Roman de Brut*," "*Roman de Rou*," "Verse Epitome of Wace's *Brut*," "*La Conception Notre Dame*," "The *Life* of St. Margaret," "The *Life* and *Miracles* of St. Nicholas," in eadem, *Anglo-Norman Literature: A Guide to Texts and Manuscripts*, 2–4, 35, 269–70, 315, 297–98. London: Anglo-Norman Text Society, 1999.

Duchesne, L., ed. *Le* Liber Pontificalis: *Texte, introduction et commentaire*. 3 vols. Bibliothèque des Écoles françaises d'Athènes et de Rome. 2e série. Paris: E. Thorin, 1886–1957.

Durling, Nancy Vine. "Translation and Innovation in the *Roman de Brut*." In *Medieval Translators and Their Craft*, ed. Jeanette Beer, 9–39. Studies in Medieval Culture 25. Kalamazoo: Medieval Institute Publications, 1989.

Faral, Edmond. *La légende arthurienne, études et documents. Première partie: Les plus anciens textes*. 2 vols. Paris: Champion, 1929; repr. New York: AMS Press, 1973.

Finke, Laurie, and Martin B. Shichtman. "The Mont St. Michel Giant: Sexual Violence and Imperialism in the Chronicles of Wace and Layamon." In *Violence Against Women in Medieval Texts*, ed. Anna Roberts, 56–74. Gainesville: University Press of Florida, 1998.

Foulon, Charles. "De quelques additions de Wace." *Annales de Bretagne* 80 (1973): 627–37.

—. "Wace." In *Arthurian Literature in the Middle Ages: A Collaborative History*, ed. Roger Sherman Loomis, 94–103. Oxford: Clarendon Press, 1959.

Gabiger, Laura. "The Middle English 'History of the Kings of Britain' in College of Arms Manuscript Arundel 22." Ph. D. Diss., University of North Carolina-Chapel Hill, 1993.

Gallais, Pierre. "La *Variant Version* de l'*Historia Regum Britanniae* et le *Brut* de Wace." *Romania* 87 (1966): 1–32.

Geoffrey of Monmouth. *The* Historia Regum Britannie *of Geoffrey of Monmouth I. Bern, Bürgerbibliothek, MS. 568*. Ed. Neil Wright. Cambridge: D.S. Brewer, 1984.

—. *The* Historia Regum Britannie *of Geoffrey of Monmouth II: The First Variant Version: A Critical Edition.* Ed. Neil Wright. Cambridge: D.S. Brewer, 1988.

—. *Historia Regum Britanniae.* In Faral, *La légende arthurienne,* 2:71–305.

—. *Historia Regum Britanniae: A Variant Version Edited from Manuscripts.* Ed. Jacob Hammer. Cambridge, MA: Mediaeval Academy of America, 1951.

—. *The* Historia Regum Britanniæ *of Geoffrey of Monmouth with Contributions to the Study of Its Place in Early British History.* Ed. Acton Griscom. London: Longmans, Green, 1929.

—. *The History of the Kings of Britain.* Trans. Lewis Thorpe. Harmondsworth: Penguin, 1979.

Glowka, Arthur Wayne. "Laȝamon's Heathens and the Medieval Grapevine." In *Orality and Literacy in Early Middle English,* ed. Herbert Pilch, 113–45. ScriptOralia 83. Tübingen: Gunter Narr, 1996.

—. "Masculinity, Male Sexuality, and Kinship in Wace's *Roman de Brut.*" In *Laȝamon: Contexts Language and Interpretation,* ed. Rosamund Allen, Lucy Perry, and Jane Roberts, 413–31. King's College London Medieval Studies 19. London: King's College London Centre for Late Antique and Medieval Studies, 2002.

Gouttebroze, Jean-Guy. "Henry II Plantagenêt: Patron des historiographes Anglo-Normands de Langue d'Oil." In *La littérature angevine médiévale: Actes du colloque du samedi 22 mars 1980,* 91–105. Paris: Champion, 1981.

—. "Pourquoi congédier un historiographe: Henri II Plantagenêt et Wace." *Romania* 112 (1991): 289–311.

Gransden, Antonia. *Historical Writing in England c. 550 to 1307.* Ithaca: Cornell University Press, 1974.

Greimas, Algirdas Julien. *Dictionnaire de l'ancien français: Le moyen âge.* Paris: Larousse, 1994.

Grisward, Joël. "A propos du thème descriptif de la tempête chez Wace et chez Thomas d'Angleterre." In *Mélanges de langue et de littérature du moyen âge et de la renaissance offerts à Jean Frappier,* 2 vols., 1:375–89. Publications Romanes et Françaises 112. Geneva: Droz, 1970.

Homer. *The Iliad.* Trans. Robert Fitzgerald. Garden City, NY: Anchor Books, 1975.

Houck, Margaret. *Sources of the* Roman de Brut *of Wace.* University of California Publications in English 5.2. Berkeley: University of California Press, 1941.

Keller, Hans-Erich. "Les conquêtes du roi Artur en Thulé." *Cahiers de civilisation médiévale* 23 (1980): 29–35.

—. "De l'amour dans le *Roman de Brut*." In *Continuations: Essays on Medieval French Literature and Language in Honor of John L. Grigsby*, ed. Norris J. Lacy and Gloria Torrini-Roblin, 63–81. Birmingham: Summa, 1989.

—. "The Intellectual Journey of Wace." *Fifteenth-Century Studies* 17 (1990): 185–207.

—. "Le mirage *Robert Wace*." *Zeitschrift für Romanische Philologie* 106 (1990): 465–66.

—. "Two Toponymical Problems in Geoffrey of Monmouth and Wace: *Estrusia* and *Siesia*." *Speculum* 49 (1974): 687–98.

—. "Vers une nouvelle édition de la 'Vie de Sainte Marguerite' de Wace." *Critique et édition de textes* 9 (1986): 85–97.

—. "Wace." In *Medieval France: An Encyclopedia*, ed. William W. Kibler, Grover A. Zinn et al., 969–70. New York: Garland, 1995.

—. "Wace et Geoffrey de Monmouth: Problème de la chronologie des sources." *Romania* 98 (1977): 1–14.

—. "Wace et les Bretons." In *Actes du 14e Congrès International Arthurien*, 2 vols., 1:354–70. Rennes: Presses Universitaires de Rennes, 1984.

Kennedy, Edward Donald. *Chronicles and Other Historical Writing*. Vol. 8 of *A Manual of the Writings in Middle English 1050–1500*, ed. Albert E. Hartung. New Haven: Connecticut Academy of Arts and Sciences, 1989.

Kibler, William W. "Wace." In *The New Arthurian Encyclopedia*, ed. Norris J. Lacy, 501. New York: Garland, 1996.

Lacy, Norris J. "The Form of the *Brut*'s Arthurian Sequence." In *Jean Misrahi Memorial Volume: Studies in Medieval Literature*, ed. Hans R. Runte, Henri Niedzielski, and William L. Hendrickson, 150–58. Columbia, SC: French Literature Publications Company, 1977.

—. "Round Tables." In *The New Arthurian Encyclopedia*, ed. idem, 391.

—, Geoffrey Ashe, and Debra N. Maucoff. *Arthurian Handbook*. 2nd ed. New York: Garland, 1997.

Langille, Édouard. "'Mençunge ou folie?': commentaire sur la mise en 'romanz' de Wace." *Dalhousie French Studies* 39–40 (1997): 19–32.

Laȝamon. *Brut, or Hystoria Brutonum*. Ed. W. R. J. Barron and S. C. Weinberg. New York: Longman, 1995.

—. *Laȝamon:* Brut. Ed. G. L. Brook and R. F. Leslie. 2 vols. EETS 250, 277. London: Oxford University Press, 1963, 1978.

Lawman. *Brut*. Trans. Rosamund Allen. London: Dent, 1992.

Layamon. *Layamons* Brut, *or the Chronicle of Britain*. Ed. F. Madden. 3 vols. London: Society of Antiquaries, 1847; repr. New York: AMS Press, 1970.

Lecoy, Félix. "*Meain* et *forain* dans *Le Roman de Brut*." *Romania* 86 (1965): 118–22.

Le Saux, Françoise H. M. *Laȝamon's* Brut: *The Poem and Its Sources*. Cambridge: Brewer, 1989.

—. "Wace's *Roman de Brut*." In *The Arthur of the English*, ed. Barron, 18–22.

Lewis, C. S. "The Genesis of a Medieval Book." In idem, *Studies in Medieval and Renaissance Literature*, ed. Walter Hooper, 18–40. Cambridge: Cambridge University Press, 1966.

Light, David Anthony. "The Arthurian Portion of the *Roman de Brut* of Wace: A Modern English Translation with Introduction and Notes." Ph. D. Diss., New York University, 1970.

Lim, Ilkyung Chung. "Authorial Interventions in Wace's *Roman de Rou*." Ph. D. Diss., Purdue University, 1996.

Loomis, Laura Hibbard. "Arthur's Round Table." *PMLA* 41 (1926): 771–84.

Mannyng, Robert, of Brunne. *The Chronicle*. Ed. Idelle Sullens. MRTS 153. Binghamton: Medieval & Renaissance Texts & Studies, 1996.

—. *The Story of England by Robert Mannyng of Brunne*. Ed. Frederick J. Furnivall. 2 vols. London: HMSO Rolls Series, 1897.

Marx, Jean. "Wace et la matière de Bretagne." In *Mélanges de langue et de littérature du moyen âge et de la renaissance offerts à Jean Frappier*, 2:771–74.

Mathey, Laurence. "De l'*Historia Regum Britanniae* de Geoffroy de Monmouth au *Roman de Brut* de Wace: Étude d'un écart à valeur idéologique." In *Et c'est la fin pour quoy sommes ensemble: Hommage à Jean Dufournet*, ed. Jean-Claude Aubailly et al., 2:941–48. Paris: Champion, 1993.

Matthews, William. "Where Was Siesia-Sessoyne?" *Speculum* 49 (1974): 680–86.

Ménard, Philippe. "La déclaration amoureuse dans la littérature arthurienne au xiie siècle." *Cahiers de civilisation médiévale* 13 (1970): 33–42.

Montgomery, Edward. "Structure and Symbol in Wace's 'Vie de Sainte Marguerite'." *Kentucky Romance Quarterly* 24 (1977): 301–9.

Morford, Mark P. O., and Robert J. Lenardon. *Classical Mythology*. 4th ed. New York: Longman, 1991.

Nezirovic, Muhamed. "Les fragments de Zadar du *Roman de Brut* de Wace." *Romania* 98 (1977): 379–89.

Noble, James. "Patronage, Politics, and the Figure of Arthur in Geoffrey of Monmouth, Wace, and Layamon." In *Arthurian Yearbook II*, ed. Keith Busby, 159–78. New York: Garland, 1992.

Noble, Peter. "Wace and Renaut de Beaujeu." *French Studies* 47 (1993): 1–5.

Panunzio, Saverio. "Una redazione del *Trespassement Nostre Dame* di Wace e altri testi inediti da un codice in antico francese della Biblioteca Nazionale di Torino." *Studi mediolatini e volgari* 21 (1973): 39–85.

Pelan, Margaret. *L'influence du* Brut *de Wace sur les romanciers français de son temps*. Paris: Droz, 1931.

Pickens, Rupert T. "Arthur's Channel Crossing: Courtesy and the Demonic in Geoffrey of Monmouth and Wace's *Brut*." *Arthuriana* 7 (1997): 3–19.

—. "*Vasselage* épique et courtoisie romanesque dans le *Roman de Brut*." In *De l'aventure épique à l'aventure romanesque: Mélanges offerts à André de Mandach par ses amis, collègues et élèves*, ed. Jacques Chocheyras, 165–200. Bern and New York: Peter Lang, 1997.

Postlewate, Laurie. "Vernacular Hagiography and Lay Piety: Two Old French Adaptations of the Life of Saint Margaret of Antioch." In *Saints: Studies in Hagiography*, ed. Sandro Sticca, 115–30. MRTS 141. Binghamton: MRTS, 1996.

Sargent-Baur, Barbara N. "'Veraces historiae aut fallaces fabulae'?" In *Text and Intertext in Medieval Arthurian Literature*, ed. Norris J. Lacy, 25–39. New York: Garland, 1996.

Shichtman, Martin B. "Gawain in Wace and Laȝamon: A Case of Metahistorical Evolution." In *Medieval Texts & Contemporary Readers*, ed. Laurie A. Finke and idem, 103–119. Ithaca: Cornell University Press, 1987.

Summerfield, Thea. *The Matter of Kings' Lives: The Design of Past and Present in the Early Fourteenth-Century Verse Chronicles by Pierre de Langtoft and Robert Mannyng*. Costerus New Series 113. Amsterdam and Atlanta: Rodopi: 1998.

Tatlock, J. S. P. *The Legendary History of Britain: Geoffrey of Monmouth's* Historia Regum Britanniae *and Its Early Vernacular Versions*. Berkeley: University of California Press, 1950.

Van Houts, Elisabeth. "Wace as Historian." In *Family Trees and the Roots of Politics: The Prosopography of Britain and France from the Tenth to the Twelfth Century*, ed. K. S. B. Keats-Rohan, 103–32. Woodbridge: Boydell & Brewer, 1997.

Vergil. *The Aeneid*. Trans. Patric Dickinson. New York: NAL, 1961.

Wace. "*La conception Nostre Dame* of Wace." Ed. William R. Ashford. Ph. D. Diss., University of Chicago, 1933.

—. *The History of the Norman People: Wace's* Roman de Rou. Trans. Glyn S. Burgess. Woodbridge: Boydell, 2004.

—. "*Life of St. Nicholas*." Ed. Mary Sinclair Crawford. Ph. D. Diss., University of Pennsylvania, 1923.

—. *La partie arthurienne du* Roman de Brut (*Extrait du manuscrit B.N. fr. 794)*. Ed. I. D. O. Arnold and M. M. Pelan. Paris: Klincksieck, 1962.

—. *Le Roman de Brut de Wace*. Ed. Ivor Arnold. 2 vols. Paris: Société des Anciens Textes Français, 1938–1940.

—. *Le Roman de Rou de Wace*. Ed. A. J. Holden. 2 vols. Société des Anciens Textes Français. Paris: Picard, 1970–1971.

—. *La vie de Sainte Marguerite*. Ed. Elizabeth A. Francis. Paris: Champion, 1932.

—. *La vie de Saint Nicholas par Wace: Poème religieux du xiie siècle publié d'après tous les manuscrits*. Ed. Einar Ronsjö. Lund: Gleerup, 1942.

Wace and Layamon: Arthurian Chronicles. Trans. Eugene Mason. Intro. Gwyn Jones. London: Dent, 1962.

Weiss, Judith. "Two Fragments from a Newly Discovered Manuscript of Wace's *Brut*." *Medium Ævum* 68 (1999): 268–77.

—, ed. and trans. *Wace's* Roman de Brut, *A History of the British: Text and Translation*. Exeter Medieval English Texts and Studies. Exeter: University of Exeter Press, 1999.

—, and Rosamund Allen, trans. *The Life of King Arthur*. By Wace and Lawman. Everyman Paperback Classics. Boston: Tuttleman, 1997.

Wilhelm, James J. "Wace: *Roman de Brut* (Merlin Episodes and 'The Birth and Rise of Arthur')." In *The Romance of Arthur II*, ed. idem, 5–17. New York: Garland, 1986.

Woledge, B. "Un scribe champenois devant un texte normand: Guiot copiste de Wace." In *Mélanges de langue et de littérature du moyen âge et de la renaissance offerts à Jean Frappier*, 2:1139–54.

Wulf, Charlotte A. T. "A Comparative Study of Wace's Guenevere in the Twelfth Century." In *Arthurian Romance and Gender; Masculin/Féminin dans le roman arthurien médiéval/Geschlechterrollen im mittelalterlichen Artusroman (Selected Proceedings of the XVIIth International Arthurian Congress)*, ed. Friedrich Wolfzettel, 66–68. Internationale Forschungen zur Allgemeinen und Vergleichenden Literaturwissenschaft 10. Amsterdam: Rodopi, 1995.

Yeo, Elspeth. "Wace's *Roman de Brut*: A Newly Discovered Fragment." *Manuscripta* 7 (1964): 101–4.

York, Ernest C. "Wace's *Wenelande*: Identification and Speculation." *Romance Notes* 22 (1981): 112–18.

Zatta, Jane. "Translating the *Historia*: The Ideological Transformation of the *Historia Regum Britanniae* in Twelfth-Century Vernacular Chronicles." *Arthuriana* 8 (1998): 148–61.

Line Index of Characters, Weapons, and Places

ANDROGEUS, son of Lud, 3793; receives London and Kent 3807–10, 3991–93, 4043; aids Nennius 4074–75; uncle of Evelin 4353; dispute with Cassibelan over death of Hirelgas 4363–402; becomes Caesar's ally 4403–558; ambushes Cassibelan 4573–682, 4699; responds to Cassibelan 4723–66; begs mercy from Caesar for Cassibelan 4767–806; leaves with Caesar as hostage 4632–34, 4844.

ANGARAD, daughter of Ebrauc, 1554.

ANGERS 10155, 10318.

ANGLETERRE (England), 13649.

ANGUES, daughter of Ebrauc, 1559.

ANGUSEL, brother of Urien and Lot, 9619, 9617–20, 10956–57; lands restored 9617–26, 9633–34; called to Arthur's coronation 10249; at the feast 10371–78; urges war against Rome 10955–11040; pledges knights for Roman expedition 11154–88; at Saussy 12359.

ANJOU 10109, 10155.

ANNA, Uther's daughter, 8339–44; marries Lot, gives birth to lords 8819–22.

ANOR, daughter of Ebrauc, 1559; named as the courtliest daughter 1567–68.

ANTENOR, Trojan lord 776.

ANTIGONUS, brother of Greek king (Pandrasus), rallies Greeks, 289–92; attacks Brutus 294–99; captured by Brutus 303–04.

ANTIOCH 5095.

APO, father of Donaud, 10271.

APOLLIN, TEMPLE OF, where Bladud crashed, 1652.

AQUILUS, prophet, 14814.

ARAVIA, MOUNT, 11588.

ARCHINAL, brother of Blegabret, 3711.

ARMORICA (Brittany), 796, 5900, 5950, 6331–34, 7551, 14022.

ARGAL, son of Morpidus, 3467; evil king, exiled 3481–96; wanders seeking help 3501–09; receives brother's pity, is restored to throne 3510–60; dies 3569–72; son takes throne 3612.

ARGHAL, count of Warwick, 10267; called to Arthur's coronation 10267.

ARNAUD, lord of Salisbury, 10263; called to Arthur's coronation 10263.

ARTHUR, prophesied by Merlin as boar 7577–82; future foretold 8336; his conception 8733–36 (named 8736), 8815–18; elected king 9009–12; qualities 9013–32; pursues the Saxons, besieges Colgrim 9033–58; counters the ambush of Baldulf 9075–96; retreats upon Childric's arrival 9117–36; attacks Childric at Lincoln 9166–88; defeats Childric in Calidon 9187–218; frees Childric, is attacked again 9219–54; leaves Scotland to fight Childric at Bath 9255–74; his weapons and armor 9274–300; puts Childric to flight 9301–60; turns toward Scotland 9369–72; causes Scots to flee to Moray 9409–18; forces Scots into Loch Lomond 9419–26; pursues Scots in islands 9447–54; defeats Gillomarus in Scotland 9455–62; grants mercy to the Scots 9465–526; explains strange pools to Hoel 9537–86; restores kingdom, marries Guinevere 9587–655; childlessness noted 9656–58; decides to conquer Ireland 9659–702; conquers Iceland 9703–07; gains the Orkneys, Gotland, and Wendland without a fight 9708–30; lives in glory and peace for twelve years 9731–46; constructs the Round Table 9747–60; his ideal, cosmopolitan kingdom 9761–84; marvels reported but not confirmed 9785–98; conquers France 9799–804; makes Lot king of Norway 9805–52; gains Denmark without a fight 9863–86; conquers Flanders and Boulogne on the way to France 9887–904; puts Frollo to flight 9914–32; his enlistment of foreigners as soldiers 9933–54; feared by Frollo 9955–72; besieges Frollo 9973–98; challenged to single combat by Frollo 9999–10016; defeats Frollo and takes Paris 10017–104; divides France among his men 10105–32; conquers the remainder of France 10131–32; stays in France for nine years 10133–46; divides France among his men 10134–70; returns to England 10171–96; rewards men 10197–98; chooses Kaerleon as site for coronation 10199–248; summons men for feast 10238–336; preparations for his coronation 10337–58; his coronation 10359–436; changes clothes 10437–44; at the feast 10445–520; fashions and customs in his kingdom 10493–520; after-dinner games and entertainment 10521–88; gives out gifts 10589–620; receives and hears the Roman ambassadors 10621–710, protects ambassadors 10711–24; consults with men and chooses war with Rome 10725–1058; described by Roman ambassadors 11059–84; 11090; summons army 11125–72; leaves Modred and Guinevere in charge of kingdom 11173–89; sails from Southampton 11190–238; dreams while on the Channel 11239–78; upon arrival in Brittany, hears about the Giant of Mont St. Michel 11279–318; fights with the giant 11319–598; remembers his fight with Rithon 11570–92; moves south through France 11609–20; hears reports of the emperor's strength and position 11623–36; sets up fortress on the Aube 11637–46; sends messengers to the emperor 11647–77, 11703–04; message relayed by Walwain 11709–33, 11880; sends knights to look for messengers 11881–86; sends reinforcements 11927–34; mentioned in Bos' speech 11981–98; disposes of captured Romans 12077–100, 12128; thought to be in battle 12221–22, 12251–52, 12274; shown new prisoners 12255–62; sets ambush for emperor at Saussy 12287–450; ambush discovered 12463–66; defeats Lucius at Saussy 12519–976; joins melee 12871–926, 12941; rejoices over victory, cleans up battlefield 12977–86; sends emperor's corpse to Rome as tribute 12987–94; winters in Burgundy with plans to go to Rome 13010–15; learns of Modred's perfidy 13015–34; leaves France 13035–52; prevented from landing in Britain 13071–96; loses men in the landing 13097–106; forces Modred to flee to Winchester 13107–178; takes Winchester 13187–88; fights Modred at Camblan 13235–73; mortally wounded, borne to Avalon 13275–92.

ARVIRAGUS, son of Kimbelin, 4884; helps Wider 4917; wears dead king's armor, routs Romans 4957–78; chases down and kills Hamun 4981–5006; besieged by Claudius, sues for peace 5019–50; helps Claudius take the Orkneys 5051–58; marries Genois 5063–92; refuses to pay tribute 5099–106; attacked by Vespasian 5106–32; accepts peace made by wife 5134–52.

ASCANIUS, son of Eneas, 17; raises Silvius Postumus 81–82; takes the throne of Italy 89; founds Albalonga 92; problem with the gods of Troy 97–104; dies 105–08; has soothsayers foretell future of unborn Brutus 118–28.

ASCHIL, king of Denmark, 9873; gives Denmark to Arthur without a fight 9873–86; called to Arthur's coronation 10307; at Saussy 12365.

ASCLEPIODOT, Cornish baron, 5494; elected king 5493–96; defeats Allec 5497–5512; defeats Gallus 5513–62; king in deed 5569–74; killed by Choel 5594–5602; 5616.

ASSARAC, son of Ebrauc, 1548; leads brothers in war against Germany 1583–90.

assault on Rome 3027–52; hangs Roman hostages 3053–66; final victory over Romans 3073–152; rules Italy cruelly 3153–58, 3878; deeds recounted 10855–65.

BRETEL, retainer of Gorlois, 8714.

BRIAN, nephew of Chadwalein, 14063; convinces Chadwalein to deny Edwin a crown 14061–90; sister taken by Edwin 14151–54; feeds his own flesh to Chadwalein 14175–222; goes to England in disguise 14241–72; sees sister, kills Pellis 14273–303; escapes, raises army, and takes Exeter 14304–36; summons Chadwalein to return 14337–40; besieged by Penda 14357–59; saved by Chadwalein 14363–80.

BRITAEL, king of North Wales, 4003.

BRITAIN (from *Brutus*), 1177, 2034, 3865, 3877, 4200, 4532, 4776, 4789, 4794, 4855, 5144, 5255, 5276, 5373, 5437, 5529, 5627, 5736, 5852, 7567, 7941, 8183, 8187, 8315, 8332, 9595, 10677, 10700, 10823, 10849, 10855, 10857, 10867, 10869, 10877, 10882, 11052, 11155, 12404, 12991, 13039, 13044, 13384, 13451; how it lost its name 13553–662, 14791–92.

BRITTANY (Armorica), 794–96, 3851, 5951, 5953, 6333, 6681, 7139, 9142, 10322, 12767, 13512, 14181, 14192, 14701.

BROCHINAL, British count, 13889; defeated by Ethelbert 13889–96.

BRUSSELS 12736.

BRUTUS, grandson of Ascanius, founder of Britain, 135; illegitimate conception 115–17; future foretold 118–28; mother dies in childbirth 132–34; kills his father 136–44; exiled 147–48; goes to Greece and finds relatives 149–60; gains fame in Greece 161–64; offered leadership of the Trojan rebellion 167–85; made general by the Trojans 210–12; prepares for war with the Greeks 213–23; letter to Pandrasus 224–52; prepares for the Greek attack 269–73; ambushes Greeks 274–88; devises a means to save Sparatin 357–66; threatens Anacletus to gain his help 369–436; defeats Pandrasus 441–88; takes advice on the fate of the Greeks 493–60; makes a deal with Pandrasus 561–610; leaves Greece 611; stops at Leogice 620–702; hears prophecy of Diane 635–702; encounters pirates 713–18; lays waste to Mauritania 720–26; meets Corineus in Spain 788–920; founds Tours 931–1026; defeats Goffars 1027–46; lands in Britain 1051–62; arranges match between Corineus and Gogmagog 1100–10; names Britain after himself 1176–86; keeps most of Britain for himself 1202; founds New Troy 1209–24; gives laws 1253–56; fathers three sons (Locrin, Camber, Albanactus), 1259–60; dies, is buried 1257–63, 3865, 3871, 14861.

BRUTUS GREENSHIELD, son of Ebrauc, 1543; takes throne after father 1593–94.

BUDIZ, king of Brittany, 6681; raises Aurelius and Uther 6680–86.

BUEL, son of Ebrauc 1548.

BURGUNDY 2655, 2691, 2786, 2790, 3849, 10111, 10856, 10916, 11082, 11616, 13010, 13036.

CADOR, count of Cornwall, 9078; foils Badulf's ambush 9077–96; ambushes the fleeing Childric 9361–94; finishes off remaining Saxons 9395–408; joins Arthur in Scotland 9407–11; foster parent of Guinevere 9649–51; called to Arthur's coronation 10255; at the coronation 10371–78; urges war against Rome 10735–64; commissioned to take Roman prisoners to Paris 12091–100; ambushed by Romans 12127–202.

assumes throne after father's death 14027–34; crowns himself without regard to Edwin 14035–40; considers Edwin's request for a crown 14047–60; convinced by Brian to deny Edwin a crown 14061–90; his denial enrages Edwin 14091–118; chased out of Britain by Edwin 14119–44; loses lands 14145–50; tracked by necromancer 14155–74; sick for lack of venison on the trip to Brittany, eats Brian's flesh 14175–222; received in Brittany with promise of help 14223–38; his location sought by Britons 14321–24; returns with army 14341–46, 14360–62; saves Brian at Exeter 14363–80; marries Penda's sister 14380–92; lays waste to England 14391–98; defeats Edwin at Hedfield 14399–424; takes Offric's domain 14425–34; chases Oswald into Scotland 14435–40; commissions Penda to pursue Oswald 14441–48; hears Penda's complaint 14479–84; accepts peace with Oswi 14459–516; allows Penda to war with Oswi 14529–608; grants Oswi Penda's legacy 14635–38; rules for forty-eight years, dies, is buried in a statue 14639–56; succeeded by Chadwalader 14657–58.

CHAMP CELESTIEL (Heavenfield) 14454–56.

CHARTRES 10314, 11149, 12362.

CHASTEL DE CUREIE (Thongchester), 6921.

CHAUZ, port in France, 1976.

CHENEUS, son of Coil, 10273; called to Arthur's coronation 10273.

CHERIM 3651; given to drink, rules in peace 3652–58; fathers three sons 3659–60.

CHESTER 10261, 12383.

CHESTERBURY, founded by Ruhundibras 1614; site of talking eagle 1617.

CHICHESTER 7286.

CHINON (Kynon) 12997, 13002.

CHILDRIC, king of Germany, 9061; 9067; arrives in Britain with Arthur in retreat 9117–36; routed by Arthur at Lincoln 9166–88; surrenders to Arthur in Calidon 9187–218; freed, attacks Britons again 9219–54; fights Arthur, flees 9301–60; ambushed by Cador 9361–94; allies himself with Modred 13053–70.

CHOEL, count of Gloucester, 5594; defeats, kills Asclepiodot 5594–5602; has daughter Eleine educated 5605–14; offers peace to Constance, dies 5630.

CHRISTCHURCH 1440.

CIRENCESTER 13517, 13533; burned by Gurmund with sparrows 13589–608; town renamed by peasants because of sparrows 13615–24.

CLAUDIUS, Roman emperor, 4895; attacks Britain, forced to return to ships 4895–80; returns to Britain and accepts Arviragus as vassal 5008–50; takes Orkneys with Arviragus 5051–58; fathers Glois 5075–88; returns to Rome 5090–92.

CLEDAUC, father of Edelin, 10275.

CLEDAUCUS, 3673.

CLOART, MOUNT, 7607.

CLOTEN, king of Cornwall, 2206–11.

COCTA, senator of Rome, 11116; summoned by Lucius 11116.

COIL, father of Cheneus, 10273.

COIL, son of Maurus, 5201; brought up by Romans 5202–06; noble king 5207–08.

COILUS 3650.

COLGRIM, lord of Saxons, 8915; becomes leader after Octa 8913–16; attacks Arthur, flees 9043–54; besieged at Everwic 9055–122; killed by Arthur 9358.

COLOGNE 6074.

COMPERT, king of Norway, 5778.

CONAN, nephew of Constantine, son of Cador, 1331; fails to keep peace in his kingdom 13331–42.

PIERRES PENDUES, LES (See **STONEHENGE**).
PINNER, king of Logres, 2204.
PIR, the attractive, 3726–28.
PIRAM, metropolitan, 9605; restores monasteries for Arthur 9605–10.
POITIERS 10317, 12204, 12727.
POITOU 797, 3851, 10109, 11142.
POLIDETES, lord of Bithynia, 11107; summoned by Lucius 11107; killed by Arthur at Saussy 12912–918.
PORCHESTER 5745.
PORLUD 3788.
PORREUS, son of Gorbodiagnes, brother of Ferreus, 2142; desires to kill his brother 2151–53; defeats brother 2160–62.
PORREUS, successor of Coilus, 3651.
PORSENNA, count of Rome, 2883; offers peace to Britons 2885–918; looks for help against the Britons 3067–72; final battle with Britons and capture 3073–148.
PORTCHESTER 4903–06; leveled by Claudius 5010–17.
PRIAM, king of Troy, 85; father of Helenus 151.
PRIDWEN, Arthur's shield, 9291–96.
PULLY 3072.
PUNTIF 10166.
QUINTILLIAN, nephew of Lucius Hiberius, 11741; responds insultingly to Walwain 11741–48; loses head to Walwain's sword 11749–53; recipient of Marcellus' message in hell 11833–38.
RADAN, daughter of Ebrauc, 1553.
RAGAU, daughter of Leir, 1673; lies to father 1705–12; marries the Duke of Cornwall 1780.
REDERCH 3724.
REDION 3723.
REGEIM, son of Elaud, 10272; called to Arthur's coronation 10272.
REGIN, son of Ebrauc, 1544.
REMUS, founder of Rome, 2108.
RENNES 5953, 14701.
RHINE 10328.
RICHBOROUGH 13079.
RICHIER 10166; commissioned to take Roman prisoners to Paris 12091–100; ambushed by Romans 12127–202.
RICHOMARCUS, friend of Kymar, 12797; dies at Saussy 12793–812.
RICULF, king of Norway, 9830; loses Norway to Lot through Arthur's intervention 9829–48.
RITHON, giant, 11563; constructs coat with beards of kings 11565–69; defeated by Arthur 11570–92.
RIVAL, son of Cunedages, 2123–33; plagues during his reign 2125–32.
RODRIC, king of Picts, 5163; invades Scotland, is killed 5164–84.
ROMANUS, saint, pope, 7140.
ROME 26, 27, 36, 2108, 2859, 2876–918, 3073, 3094, 3149, 3156, 3830, 3879, 3882, 3884, 3886, 3893, 5042, 5044, 5053, 5092, 5097, 5145, 5158, 5624, 5709, 5739, 5825, 5853, 5855, 7142, 9915, 9920, 9922, 10210, 10633, 10637, 10639, 10646, 10649, 10658, 10692, 10709, 10853, 10859, 10864, 10868, 10872, 10874, 10876, 10882, 10898, 10962, 11025–28, 11051, 11056, 11060, 11072–73, 11114, 11115, 11116, 11654, 12989, 13014, 13045, 13048, 13845, 14831, 14765, 14788.
ROMULUS, founder of Rome, 2107.
RON, Arthur's lance, 9297–9300.
ROWENA, daughter of Hengist, 6931; introduced to Vortigern 6925–96; married to Vortigern 6997–7018; poisons Vortimer 7156–60; 13064.
RUCIKADAM 711.
RUD, son of Ebrauc, 1548.
RUDAC, king of Wales, 2205; faces Dumwallo 2229; killed by ruse of Dumwallo 2255–64.
RUHUNDIBRAS, son of Leil, 1608–27; brings peace 1609–12; builds